ARMING THE FLEET

Arming the Fleet

The Development of
The Royal Ordnance Yards
1770–1945

David Evans

ENGLISH HERITAGE

Previous pages: 'The Straight' at Priddy's Hard; the fuzing room and shell filling rooms looking west. See also figures 6.4 and 6.5, page 102. *(Explosion! Museum of Naval Firepower)*

Front cover: Interior (2004) of one of the shell filling rooms of 1886–7 at Priddy's Hard. See also figures 6.4 and 6.5, page 102. *(Explosion! Museum of Naval Firepower)*

Back cover:
Main image: Cartridge Filling Rooms (c.1914) of A and B Sections on 'The Common' at Priddy's Hard, looking south, in about 1950. To the left is the narrow gauge railway and the steam pipes used for heating the buildings, while to the right can be seen the outer casing of an old mine filled with water or sand for use in the event of fire. *(Priddys Hard Archive, 1998.4.187).*
Insets, top to bottom: Colour-coded shells. *(from Treatise on Ammunition, 10th ed. [London, 1915]);* The gable end of A Magazine of 1770–6 at Priddy's Hard *(Stephen Dent);* One of the magazines of 1851–7 at Bull Point *(Jeremy Lake);* HMS *Exeter,* a Type–42 guided missile destroyer, passing the Camber at Priddy's Hard after leaving RNAD Bedenham, March 2004 *(Stephen Dent).*

First published in Great Britain in 2006 by Explosion! Museum of Naval Firepower in association with English Heritage

Explosion! Museum
Priddy's Hard
Gosport
Hampshire
PO12 4LE

www.explosion.org.uk
www.english-heritage.org.uk

British Library Cataloguing in Publication Data
A record of this title is available on request from the British Library.

ISBN 10: 0-9553632-0-9
ISBN 13: 9-780955-363207

Design management and layout by Stephen Dent
Editorial management by Nicki Marshall of Biscuitbox Ltd

Printed by Hobbs the Printers Limited, Hampshire

Contents

Acknowledgements

The publication of this book could not have been undertaken without the support and help of a great number of people and organisations. The book is in every respect a collaborative venture. Jeremy Lake of English Heritage developed the concept of the book and would like to express his thanks to Steve Dent and Nicki Marshall for their assiduous picture research and bringing the book to its final publication stage. Thanks are firstly due to Rob Harper, the Head of Conservation and Urban Design at Gosport Borough Council, who encouraged and supported this project in its early stages. David Hopkins, the Head Archaeologist at Hampshire County Council, is also to be thanked for his role in securing a grant from the County Council towards the cost of publication.

The author and production team are most grateful to the staff and volunteers of Explosion! Museum of Naval Firepower – in particular Marc Farrance, Jo Lawler, Bill Mansfield, Ian Proctor, Mike Hockin and former director Chris Henry – for their invaluable assistance in enhancing the captions, checking the text and assisting with the picture research.

Many thanks also go to: Paul Burkhalter, Gerry Rendle, Cdr. Charles Crichton, Graham Lang, LRO Payne, WO Peter Hooson and Allan Berry, Devonport Management Ltd and Plymouth Naval Base Museum; Faye Glover and Frances Griffith, Devon County Council Archaeology Unit; Derek Gurney, formerly of Priddy's Hard; Peter Lambert, Fort Blockhouse; Vicki Ingles, Portsmouth Historic Dockyard Trust; Peter Goodwin, Keeper and Curator, HMS *Victory*; John Stedman, Katy Ball and the staff at Portsmouth City Museum; Mike Rumbold and Beryl Williams, Weedon Bec Historical Society; Jenny Wraight, the MoD (Admiralty) Librarian; Nick Bridges, Ettwein Bridges Associates; Rose Marney, Institution of Civil Engineers; Peter Kendal, David Brock, Liz Gawith and Robin Taylor, English Heritage; Ronnie Schnable, John Weedon, Maggie Lindsay-Roxburgh and the staff of the Royal Engineers Museum and Library; Tony Firth and Linda Coleman, Wessex Archaeology; Paula Freeland, New Forest District Council; Jean Bowker and Alex Naylor; Peter Clark; Christine Hodgson, *Encyclopedia Britannica*; Sarah Sykes and Gayle Moult, Science and Society Picture Library; Nick Catford and Mark Bennett, Subterranea Britannica; Sarah Jackson, CentreScreen Productions; Esther Dugdale, Event Communications; John Jordan, Editor of *Warship*, DK Brown; Mike Dent; Paul Wells; Geoffrey Dennison; Stuart Grant; Martin Robson and Dee Dent.

The author and production team have made every effort to contact all copyright holders, and any errors or omissions are entirely unintentional. We will be happy to rectify any such instances, upon notification, in any subsequent edition of the book.

Preface

The contraction and rationalisation of the Ministry of Defence estate after the end of the Cold War coincided with an appreciation by English Heritage of the need to inform the wider public understanding and where appropriate the conservation of military sites. Over the last decade, a wide range of sites has been researched from barracks and naval dockyards to airfields and the archaeology of the Cold War. The results of much of this work have been published. During a re-evaluation of the designations within the Royal Naval dockyards, and new research focused on the Victorian Navy, it became apparent that very little was known about the ordnance yards, which were built for the storage and manipulation of armaments and explosives.

Much of the effort was focused on three sites about which little was known: the sites around Upnor opposite Chatham dockyard; Bull Point, a set-piece complex dating from the 1850s just to the north of Plymouth Dockyard; and Priddy's Hard in Gosport. Gosport Borough Council, ably assisted by Hampshire County Council, were in the vanguard in the protection of Priddy's Hard, acquiring the site within the earthworks in 1989 and designating it as a conservation area in 1990. It was, however, a major challenge for a host of reasons: the borough, already one of the poorest in the country, was facing job losses through reductions in its defence infrastructure, and it was proving difficult to understand the character and significance of the site. This is where English Heritage stepped in, commissioning studies of the ordnance yards in the Chatham, Portsmouth and Plymouth areas. These studies underlined the importance of Priddy's Hard as the one site where the physical evidence of the navy's transition from the age of sail, powder and solid shot to the Dreadnought era of the early 1900s was retained in a well-preserved range of structures. New housing and transport infrastructure is bringing life back to this fascinating complex, now home to the Explosion! Museum of Naval Firepower.

This research has proved to be a challenging task due to the fragmentary and dispersed nature of the documentation. It has revealed for the first time at a national scale the high-level political and military decisions that determined the way in which these sites developed, the rich variety of technologies employed within them and their importance in an international context. It was considered that the wider public would benefit from the publication of this work. This book, funded by English Heritage with additional assistance from Hampshire County Council, is the result. It is a contribution towards the study of these sites which, as the wonderful exhibition at Explosion! makes clear, embrace so many different facets of military, political and social history.

Jeremy Lake
Inspector of Historic Buildings, English Heritage

Introduction

This is a book about how buildings can develop in response to technological changes: from barrels of gunpowder stored in the driest room in a castle, to a vast network of depots, each with their own internal transport systems and reliant on the national transport infrastructure; from vulnerable storehouses to strongholds in the bowels of the earth. The book is about how the rate of technological change quickens by a geometric progression, leading to crises when the major components fall out of sync; about the rise and fall of bureaucracies and about human fallibilities. It is about how building types originally constructed to be as strong as possible became, after some false starts, as flimsily constructed as possible, and in a final twist, were made truly impregnable for the first time by going underground. It is about one of the key infrastructures underpinning the armed forces, where civilians provided the workforce; about places where the most advanced contemporary armament technology was prepared for use by the most basic of manual processes. It is about places where if you made a mistake you were dead.

The ever-growing dependence of land and naval forces on gunpowder weaponry from the 15th century onwards necessitated secure storage. A whole new branch of logistics was called into being. Many questions, particularly concerning the 16th century, remain largely unspoken and unanswered, and are perhaps now insoluble. How did European adventurers maintain their precious stores of gunpowder in a usable condition while traversing rainforests in South America and elsewhere? The volcanic landscape of Mexico provided ample materials for the manufacture of powder, but that was another matter. The same difficulties, slightly mitigated, must have presented themselves in the voyages to these destinations on small and leaky vessels. Reliance must have been almost wholly placed on the thoroughly established techniques of the cooper in preparing watertight barrels, and ships' carpenters must have numbered this among their battery of skills. The barrels were watertight enough, but what happened when they were opened and their contents distributed? With the great increase in the use of cannon both to attack and defend fortifications during the 16th century, the corresponding revolution in fortification design incorporated secure magazine accommodation to hold the masses of gunpowder now required, though this was not generally annotated in textbooks on fortification produced at the time. The fortification of cities and towns on the continent proceeded apace during the 16th and 17th centuries, with the incidental consequence that armies operating in the field were rarely at a great distance from reserves of gunpowder.

England was situated differently from the continental countries. There were no massively fortified cities and the army (save during the Civil War and the Protectorate) was insignificant, counting for nothing on a European scale. It was the Royal Navy, growing by fits and starts during the 17th century, that became a major player in the game by the end of that period. The bulk of powder and shot, therefore, needed to be kept in proximity to the dockyards, which, apart from Portsmouth, were at that time ineffectively fortified, and so without built-in magazine accommodation. As will be seen, the arrangements even at Portsmouth were very much on an ad hoc basis. The emphasis on the storage of explosives and projectiles in England was, therefore, almost from the start concentrated on the strategic holding of large stocks in proximity to the bases of the principal user, the navy, rather than maintaining depots to be drawn on by field armies or furnishing fortified areas with the means of self-defence. The magazines in Scotland (such as at Fort George near Inverness, the only work in the British Isles executed on a continental scale) and Ireland were also strategical in purpose, vital parts of the machinery of an occupying power.

During the 18th century the unsatisfactory arrangements at Portsmouth and Plymouth were replaced by purpose-built magazine facilities, and the Revolutionary and Napoleonic Wars saw a notable expansion of the Ordnance Yards, including, for the first time, a major inland site at Weedon, and a degree of modernisation of the arrangements on the Medway. During the first part of the 19th century the introduction of the explosive shell as a naval weapon necessitated the introduction of specialist buildings for filling them as well as storing them, together with the fuzes required to make them detonate as required. The Russian War of 1854–6 saw a massive expansion of the storage near the dockyards, and an addition to Weedon. Changes in guns dictated the further development of the Ordnance Yards: the rifled muzzle loaders carried on the new generation of ironclad warships and also used for coastal defence required new types of projectile and massive cartridges filled with new types of gunpowder. Their replacement by breech-loading ordnance during the 1880s started a programme of expansion of the yards, accelerated by the introduction

Map 1 The ordnance sites in Great Britain, showing major dockyards, stores and other locations mentioned in this book. Maps 2 to 5 show Portsmouth, Plymouth, the 'Thames Gateway' and Chatham. The depots at the three principal dockyards each evolved in a quite distinct way, because of the peculiarities of each individual site.

Map 2 (inset) The 'Thames Gateway', showing the relationship between the rivers Thames and Medway, their various naval and ordnance establishments, and the important gunpowder mills at Faversham.

(Maps drawn by Stephen Dent)

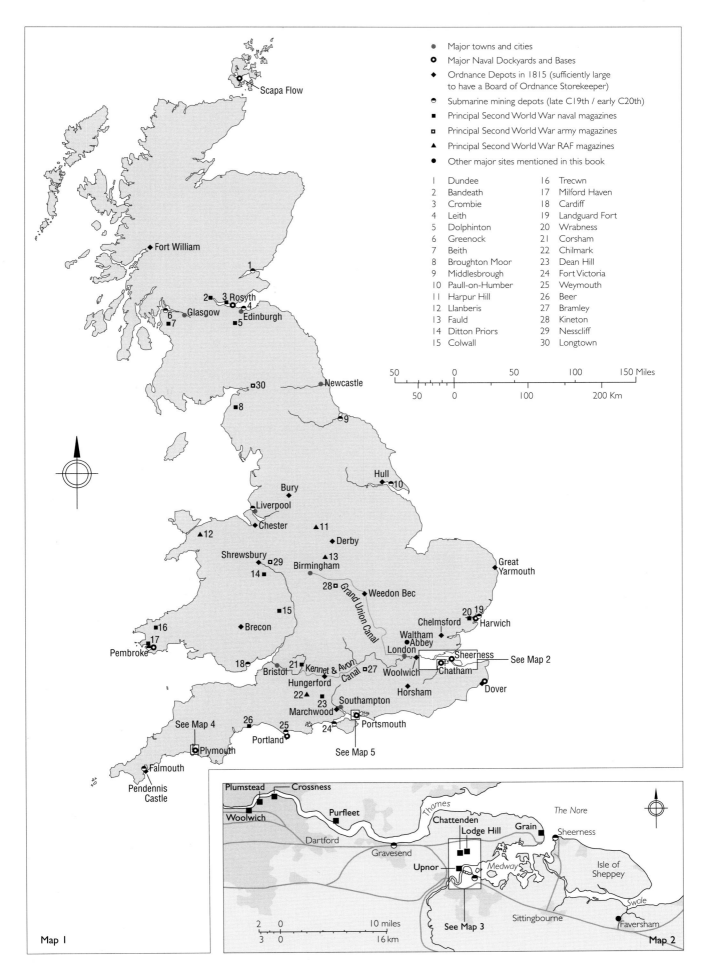

Major towns and cities

Major Naval Dockyards and Bases

Ordnance Depots in 1815 (sufficiently large to have a Board of Ordnance Storekeeper)

Submarine mining depots (late C19th / early C20th)

Principal Second World War naval magazines

Principal Second World War army magazines

Principal Second World War RAF magazines

Other major sites mentioned in this book

1	Dundee	16	Trecwn
2	Bandeath	17	Milford Haven
3	Crombie	18	Cardiff
4	Leith	19	Landguard Fort
5	Dolphinton	20	Wrabness
6	Greenock	21	Corsham
7	Beith	22	Chilmark
8	Broughton Moor	23	Dean Hill
9	Middlesbrough	24	Fort Victoria
10	Paull-on-Humber	25	Weymouth
11	Harpur Hill	26	Beer
12	Llanberis	27	Bramley
13	Fauld	28	Kineton
14	Ditton Priors	29	Nesscliff
15	Colwall	30	Longtown

Scapa Flow

Fort William

1

2 3 Rosyth 4
6 Glasgow
7 5 Edinburgh

30 Newcastle

8 9

Hull 10

Bury
Liverpool
Chester
12 11 Derby
Shrewsbury 29 13 Birmingham
14 28 Weedon Bec
Great Yarmouth
15 Grand Union Canal
20 19
Chelmsford Harwich
16 Waltham Abbey
17 Pembroke 18 21 Kennet & Avon Canal 27 London Sheerness See Map 2
Bristol Hungerford Woolwich Chatham
22 Horsham Dover
23 Southampton
Marchwood
See Map 4 26 25 24 Portsmouth
Portland See Map 5
Plymouth
Falmouth
Pendennis Castle

50   0   50   100   150 Miles
50   0   100   200 Km

Map 1

Plumstead Crossness
Purfleet
Woolwich
Thames The Nore
Chattenden
Lodge Hill Grain
Dartford Sheerness
Gravesend
Upnor Medway Isle of Sheppey
See Map 3 Swale
Sittingbourne Faversham

2   0   10 miles
3   0   16 km

Map 2

Map 3 The Medway, showing the location of the gunwharf, Upnor Castle and the various other ordnance establishments in relation to the naval dockyard.

Map 4 The developments at Devonport were dictated by the local geography and by the demands of the navy. Naval establishments shown include: Bull Point, occupying a narrow coastal strip next to the St Budeaux restoving establishment; and Morice Yard, in between the North and South Yards; Mount Wise. Also indicated are the sites of various works proposed but not carried out.

(Maps drawn by Stephen Dent)

of cordite, the new propellant, and quick-firing guns, which demanded much greater supplies of ammunition to be carried by an ever-increasing fleet. A crisis of accommodation for naval ammunition followed in the 1890s, until new building types to store cordite were settled on and land acquired for expansion, as safety dictated ever-increasing spaces between buildings holding explosives. By 1910 the magazines serving the dockyards were ready to serve the needs of the Grand Fleet; however, having their origins when first the Dutch and then France were the potential opponents, they were in the wrong place to confront the new enemy, and fresh logistical problems had to be faced. Following the First World War new magazines were built underground, to counter the new threat from the air, and these were largely completed when the next conflict broke out.

All these changes were initiated and monitored by a succession of committees, usually convened for a limited purpose in the first place, whose recommendations often had far-reaching consequences. Some, such as that which investigated the reprovisioning of ordnance facilities on the Medway, had a life far longer than originally visualised; some urgent proposals were repeated down the years by committee after committee, but never implemented for financial reasons until decades had passed. A considerable proportion of this book is taken up by accounts of these investigations and recommendations, for to a great extent

the history of ordnance storage during the latter part of the 19th and the early 20th century is, inescapably, the history of these Committees. The reader will find that several personages well known in other fields played their parts in the story.

The First World War, for the first time, saw a British army comparable in size to those of the major European powers operating on the continent, with demands for ammunition such as had never been experienced before. The consequent crises in the supply and effectiveness of shells, were, however, essentially those of manufacturing and did not affect the established Ordnance Yards, the masses of ammunition being simply held in massive dumps behind the lines. This book is, therefore, centred around the facilities for storing, maintaining and preparing ordnance materials that developed around the naval dockyards, and is in effect a parallel history of the Royal Navy from a new perspective, though such inland sites as the remarkable complex of buildings at Weedon (in the perspective of traditional architectural history the most notable of all) will also be discussed.

Scope and aims of this book

The buildings erected in the Royal Dockyards for the sailing navy from the late 17th century, and the organisation and performance of the labour force, have been the subject of several studies.[1] There are several reasons why the multitude of building

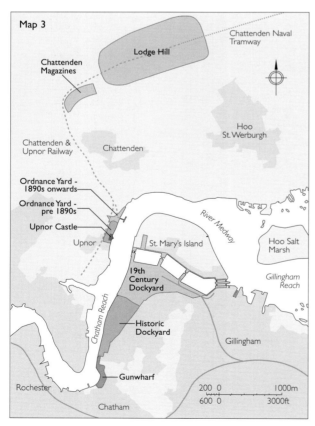

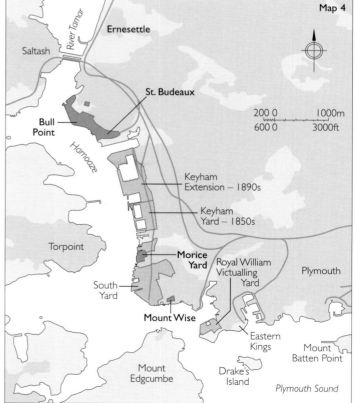

types developed for ordnance purposes, which were such a vital contributory factor to the navy's effectiveness as a deterrent and promoter of British naval power throughout the world, have escaped study till now. One is the physical complexity and generally utilitarian architecture of these establishments. Another is the very extensive and dispersed nature of the documentation, due partly to the multiplicity of bodies that have been engaged in the storage and maintenance of ordnance materials: the documentation of each have quite different degrees of survival, ranging from exhaustive in the case of the Board of Ordnance to the virtual total expunging of the records of the Control Department. The 18th and 19th centuries were not notable for security on military matters by modern standards, but storage of explosives seems to have been an exception. These topics, unlike subjects such as the matériel of the navy, were not discussed in Parliament, and a great mass of papers seem to have been deliberately weeded shortly after their generation. Not surprisingly, this applies today. A major reason has been the extremely limited access to these sites until recent years, a situation that changed with the contraction and rationalisation of the Ministry of Defence estate after the end of the Cold War. This coincided with an appreciation of the need to record these sites, to inform the wider public, and where necessary conserve military sites, commencing with a review of barracks in the mid 1990s.[2] Extensive demolition had already followed the closure of the 18th-century magazine complex at Purfleet on the Thames, and plans for redevelopment had in 1996 and 1998 resulted in a comprehensive survey of the Napoleonic complexes at Weedon in Northamptonshire and Marchwood on the Hampshire coast. At the same time, during a re-evaluation of the designations within the Royal Naval dockyards, and new research focused on the Victorian Navy, it became apparent that very little was known about the Ordnance Yards. Although Jonathan Coad's book on naval dockyards – *The Royal Dockyards, 1690–1850* [1] – includes a chapter on Ordnance Yards it does not go further than 1855 (the abolition of the Ordnance Board).

A very large number of building types, some extremely specialised, still survive in these establishments, many of which have been vacated by the services for some time, while others are clearly approaching the end of their useful life. The purpose of many of these buildings is unintelligible without an elementary knowledge of the processes that went on in them. It follows that the importance of individual buildings cannot be judged without this knowledge and a realisation of the way in which they functioned together as part of a system, varying from the simplicity of Weedon to the extreme complexity of Priddy's

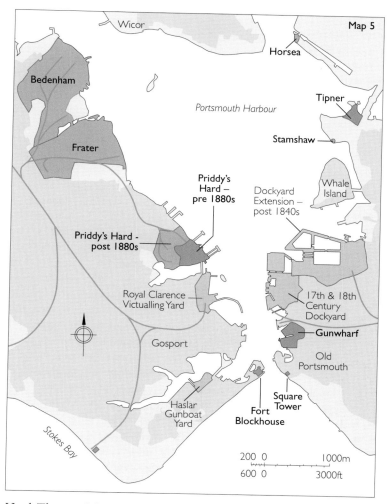

Map 5

Hard. The need for a national survey was heightened in particular by the disposal by the Ministry of Defence of Priddy's Hard, and attempts by Hampshire County Council and its new owners, Gosport Borough Council, to bring an informed understanding of context and significance to bear on its development and conservation. English Heritage was by this time engaged in pioneering the study of sites associated with explosives manufacture and storage, which had already informed the designation and development of the former Royal Gunpowder Factory at Waltham Abbey in Essex. The publication of *Dangerous Energy* (English Heritage, 2001) provided the broad framework for understanding Ordnance Yards, and the decision was then taken to investigate the documentation for sites around Chatham, Portsmouth and Plymouth, enabling the identification and evaluation of what had survived to be placed within their broad typological and historical context.[3] This work, which is summarised in Appendix A, has already contributed to an informed approach to the reuse and conservation of the most significant sites and components. It is hoped that this book, which draws the results of this pioneering work together, will contribute to a wider appreciation of these remarkable sites.

Map 5 At Portsmouth the ordnance and related establishments have been sited all around the harbour at various times, as well as submarine mining in Stokes Bay to the south of Gosport. At Priddy's Hard, the buildings accumulated within their own fortifications until the late 19th century, when the site was greatly extended outside the ramparts. Bedenham and Frater, under development before and during the First Word War, eventually replaced Priddy's Hard and are still in active use.

(Map drawn by Stephen Dent)

Chapter 1 # From Castle to Magazine

This book takes as its theme the development of the great strategic deposits of ordnance, where gunpowder and subsequent explosives were held in vast quantities. The origin of the accommodation for explosives, however, deserves a brief summary. The origin of explosives storage lies in the 14th century, when the first defensive uses of the gun were made evident by both the appearance of gun ports and the modification of fortress design in castles and urban fortifications throughout Europe. Also quick to develop was the administrative machine for organising the storage and distribution of this new form of ordnance. Nicholas Merbury was appointed the first Master of the Ordnance in 1414, and the scale of operations directed by him was large: in 1418 he procured, among many other ancillary stores, 7,000 stone cannon balls and 20 barrels of willow carbon gunpowder. During the 16th century, the office of Master of the Ordnance became, and was to remain, a high political appointment, its holder having the responsibility of overseeing all kinds of ordnance stores both for land and sea service. The earliest such sites were the gunwharves (see pages 26–7), which were established at the three major naval dockyards of Chatham, Portsmouth and, from its foundation in the 1690s, Plymouth (or Devonport as it became widely known). These were built for the receipt and issue of all kinds of ordnance from naval ships – from cannon balls and muskets to gun carriages and clothing – both for the navy and the land forces bound for foreign campaigns. The first site was at Chatham, established by the early 17th century on the site of the Tudor dockyard. Long narrow storehouses were positioned along the wharf for the storage of light weaponry (from cutlasses to boarding pikes), gun carriages and ammunition, with gun carriages laid up under cover and – according to one account of 1808 – '…numerous pyramids of ball and bomb-shells constructed in various parts of the wharf'. The

The Ordnance Board and the Royal Engineers to 1856

Throughout the centuries of change, when Ordnance Yards all over the British Empire developed gradually from small fortifications to highly complex networks, vast numbers of personnel worked in all aspects of ordnance. The decision makers (the Ordnance Board, the Inspector-General of Fortifications, the Storekeepers, myriad committees) were custodians of the sites, and as such affected the routines and practices of the general workforce who lived and worked on both the land sites and on the waterborne storage and supply vessels afloat in the harbours. They also had to deal with the extremely complex issue of safety, in terms of securing the sites from attack, limiting any danger to the workforce and keeping the local population's fears at bay.

The Board of Ordnance, as it became known, was to remain the custodian of ordnance stores of all descriptions, both for land and sea service, until its abolition in 1855. Under the Master General (a high political appointment, but often held by a man with military experience) were the Lieutenant General, who controlled the personnel (which included artillerymen and engineers as well as the stores department); the Surveyor General, in charge of all kinds of matériel (including buildings); the Clerk of the Ordnance, who apart from keeping the correspondence, dealt with finance; the Storekeeper; and the Clerk of the Deliveries [see also Appendix B: The Engineer Officers]. The Surveyor General was responsible for checking all plans and estimates for new works and repairs. After 1750 the post became a political appointment. The Duke of Richmond's reforms of 1782 (see page 23) established the Tower Committee of Engineer Officers, who took over the Surveyor General's technical duties until 1802, when the Inspector-General of Fortifications succeeded to that responsibility.

The direction of the ordnance outstations at an intermediate level was in the hands of the Principal Officers, who were the local Storekeeper, the local Commanding Engineer and the local Commanding Artillery Officer. These men all reported directly to the Board, without reference to any military superiors, a situation that had the potential for considerable friction. A Clerk of the Cheque and a Clerk of the Survey assisted the local Storekeepers in finance and matériel respectively; these men were responsible for the day-to-day running of the station and were known as the Respective Officers. At the three Royal Dockyards, the Ordnance Office was located in the gunwharf, and the Storekeeper there, being in overall charge of the whole range of ordnance activities, outranked the Storekeeper in charge of the separate magazine establishments. Both communicated directly with the Board, which could lead to difficulties in the event of personality clashes, and each magazine Storekeeper was provided with detailed instructions by the Board (see Appendix C). As will be seen elsewhere, this basic administrative structure was to become more complicated over the years.

1.1 The scale of the Great Storehouse in Chatham is clear from this photograph of 1942, taken before its demolition. (NMR A44/1481)

enormous Great Storehouse of c.1720, one of the crowning glories of Ordnance Board architecture, was demolished in the 1950s, the early 18th-century offices and Storemaster's House, and a store of 1805 being the principal survivals.[1] A gunwharf at Portsmouth was established by 1718. At Plymouth, the gunwharf was in 1718 moved from Mount Wise to Morice Yard, just upriver from the dockyard. Building work was completed around 1724.

Contemporary with the Portsmouth and Morice Yard Gunwharves was the beginning of the great development of Woolwich Arsenal. Gunfounding on a large scale began with the completion of the Brass Foundry in 1717, the construction of gun carriages being added from 1728. An equally significant activity at Woolwich was the establishment of the Royal Military Academy in 1741, instituted, in the words of the Royal Warrant, for 'instructing the raw and inexperienced people belonging to the Military branch of this office [of Ordnance], in the several parts of Mathematics necessary to qualify them for the service of the Artillery, and the business of Engineers…'. The Shop, as it became universally known, remained at Woolwich on another site, preparing cadets for the two scientific branches of the army until just before the Second World War.[2]

Evidence for gunpowder storage is more fragmentary. Cannon balls, as we have seen, could be stacked in open ground, but powder needed to be placed in a part of a building complex that was dry, well aired and secure. Apart from some small recesses, probably for ready-use ammunition, the earliest identifiable purpose-built magazines are 18th century. Surviving examples, notably at the Cumberland Bastion at Berwick-upon-Tweed, are relatively small structures intended to supply a single fortification.[3] The White Tower in London remained the principal deposit for land-service powder, and also supplied ships fitting out at the naval dockyard at Woolwich until the mid 1690s, at which time a large magazine was constructed at Greenwich, causing alarm among the local population. Powder was delivered there from the manufacturers and proved to test its quality. This building was a flimsy affair, which made matters worse. In 1668 Upnor Castle, made redundant as a defence by the provision of powerful gun batteries further downstream on the Medway, was converted into a store and magazine. By 1691, 5,206 barrels of powder were housed there, and it was the largest magazine in the kingdom, the tower holding 3,692 barrels. The powder was stored on two floors in the main building of the castle, which, as will be seen, was to see continuous service as an ordnance store for a longer period than any other building. A timber roof crowned the substantial 16th-century walls, an arrangement that was, fortuitously, probably the best that could have been contrived at the time. The question as to whether or not the magazines should be made bombproof (able to withstand contemporary artillery bombardments) was to remain unsettled. Upnor's location on the other side of the river from Rochester and Chatham provided those built-up areas with a reasonable degree of security in the event of any mishap. The contrast with the situation at Portsmouth was striking. The Square Tower dating from 1494 was probably no worse a magazine than Upnor, but it was situated at the bottom of Portsmouth High Street, with all the consequent risks. Nevertheless, it was to remain in use until well into the 18th century (see Figure 1.7, page 16). Plymouth Dockyard was not established until the 1690s, and the principal store of powder was in the Citadel fortress, a site that could not have been more inconvenient, with the transit of powder barrels being exposed to the same risks as at Portsmouth.

Magazines

The storage requirements of gunpowder, as an American naval officer observed in 1862, were straightforward enough:

'In the storage of gunpowder especial pains should be taken to secure it against the effects of moisture and dangers of explosion. Powder magazines are generally built of brick or stone, in a very substantial manner, and in places free from moisture and remote from danger... They should be so constructed that the air may circulate freely through them, and the powder casks should be so arranged as to rest neither upon the ground nor against the wall.' [4]

On the continent, the fortified towns and cities (such a rarity in Britain) were the natural place to locate powder magazines. These were usually placed for convenience as close to the ramparts as possible, but the great French siege engineer Marshal Sebastien le Prestre de Vauban

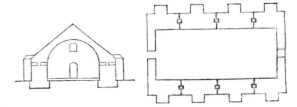

1.3 A typical Vauban magazine. (*From Lieutenant Colonel Charles Pasley Course of Military Instruction, Vol. III, p.373.*)

1.4 The restored magazine at the 17th-century Fort Nieulay, west of Calais. (*David Evans*)

(1633–1707) preferred to place his within hollow bastions, as the explosion of a magazine close to a rampart was liable to cause a major breach in the wall. Powder magazines were peculiarly suitable for construction to standardised dimensions, as the principal contents, the powder barrels, were themselves standardised. The calculated contents – 1,050 barrels piled three high, with adequate space left for moving between the barrels and stacking and removing them – determined the dimensions of the building. Vauban settled on 64 feet as the standard length (expressed in English measure) and 26 feet 8 inches as the width. The door was placed at one end of the building, the side walls strengthened by buttresses and pierced with ventilation holes, not running directly through the wall, but circulating around a solid pier in the centre of the wall. A steeply pitched vaulted roof, with about 8 feet 6 inches of solid masonry, offered protection against bombardment by mortars. It was impossible to maintain sustained fire against a particular spot with this weapons system, making it unlikely that repeated battering would break down the roof. The application of a layer of earth several feet deep to absorb the force of the blows, necessary to make a structure truly bombproof, was impossible in such a magazine because of the pitch of the roof (as can be seen in the heavily restored magazine at the Vauban-designed Fort Nieulay, Calais).

Despite his enormous prestige as a designer of fortifications, Vauban's magazine was taken as a broad framework but never as a detailed model in Britain. Thus at the Morice Yard, the replacement magazine of 1744 – with cavity walling and copper-sheathed doors and shutters – differed from Vauban's in having four vaulted compartments, a

1.2 The Square Tower, Portsmouth. This engraving from 1847 well illustrates the tower's less than ideal location, surrounded by residential and commercial properties. No longer used to store powder by this time, instead there was a semaphore tower on top to allow communication between ships and the shore. Erected in 1822, it was removed in 1848 with the arrival of the electronic telegraph. (*Priddys Hard Archive, 1998.4.21*)

1.5 Upnor Castle from the air, looking west. A pier extending out from the water bastion enabled stores to be landed and conveyed into the central block of the castle. This originally residential block was altered after conversion into a magazine in 1668 and again significantly in the early 19th century (see figure 3.3). The gatehouse and moat to the rear of the castle, and the top of the water bastion, was rebuilt between 1599 and 1601. To the extreme left can be seen the barrack block of 1719, while on the river wall to the right are instructions to shipping not to anchor close by. *(NMR 23185, frame 16)*

1.6 A ground-floor plan showing the phasing of the castle and adapted to show how the two magazines were placed to the rear of the bastion. *(English Heritage)*

15

1.7 The Square Tower, Portsmouth. Clarkson Stanfield's watercolour (left) of 1829 clearly shows both its convenient shoreside location at the harbour mouth, and the major disadvantage of its siting close to the buildings of the town. The modern view (below) shows the tower after restoration work carried out by Portsmouth Museums and Records Service between 1979 and 1986, when many original features were rediscovered. *(Portsmouth Museums and Records Service)*

The interior of the Square Tower (inset) photographed in January 1983, during restoration. The brick vaulting dates from the 18th-century conversion as a meat store, but the blocked fireplaces and windows are original Tudor features. *(Portsmouth Museums and Records Service)*

plan revived in the early 19th century at other ordnance yards. The magazine was lit by a window in each gable end, opened and shut by means of a ladder. The major difference was that British engineers used narrower arches, necessitating the use of two or more aisles to get the required capacity. This was probably the result of excessive caution, particularly in view of the proven resistance to bombardment of Vauban's magazines. Light roofs, which would be blown off easily with the minimum of debris, allowing the explosion to vent upwards, seemed to have become the norm by the end of the 19th century, but after the First World War, in contrast, much effort was spent on burrowing vast underground magazines.[5]

The necessity for new magazines

Reasons of safety eventually led to the abandonment of Greenwich and the Square Tower as powder storage and proving sites and their replacement by state-of-the-art facilities, but this was not to happen for many years in the future. In December 1750 the inhabitants of Greenwich, in fear for their lives, petitioned that the magazine might be removed. The Board of Ordnance ordered it to be surveyed, an opinion to be given as to what damage might be caused if it exploded with 300 or 400 barrels of powder in it, and suggestions to be made for a suitable alternative site. The apprehensions of the locals proved to be fully justified. The foundations were sunk, the walls cracked and bulged out, and the ends of the joists were decayed. In short, the building was irreparable, and it was agreed that an explosion would cause great damage.

Purfleet, which was isolated and on the north bank of the Thames, offered an ideal site, with solid, dry foundations and a creek that would facilitate the supply and shipment of powder. However, nothing was done, and by 1755 it was reported that the magazine was in an even worse state, liable to collapse, and quite unsafe as a repository for gunpowder. Even then, the land at Purfleet was not acquired until 1760, with construction of the new magazine establishment beginning the following year and only the magazine buildings being structurally complete by 1765. The final proving of powder took place at Greenwich in July 1768, the first proving of powder at the Purfleet Proof House (which survives today, see figure OA.38, page 141) apparently being performed in August 1769.

The whole site, with its wharfage and ancillary buildings, was completed by 1773. The five magazines each had a capacity of 10,400 barrels of powder, making Purfleet easily the largest store of powder in the country. The planning was very simple: the magazines were arranged in a row, with no attempt at protection from blast damage in case of an accident. The buildings followed the established English magazine design with double arches; the theory behind this was explained 50 years later, in the most authoritative textbook on the subject to be published by an Engineer Officer. Colonel Pasley (see Appendix B, The Royal Engineers) pointed out that in two magazines of equal length and capacity, with arches of equal thickness, one formed with a single wide arch was weaker structurally than one of two smaller arches, the strength of an arch diminishing in proportion to the distance between the supporting piers. He noted, however, that in practice Vauban's magazines had repeatedly been found bombproof. The establishment at Purfleet immediately became the great strategic deposit for powder, where all new powder was delivered and proved, and from where it was distributed. But it was soon realised that the site was too large and too close to London for safety.[6]

At Portsmouth, feeling against the magazine was just as strong as at Greenwich, but there was a multiplicity of possible sites on which a new one could be built. Apart from the Square Tower,

1.8 The single-chambered magazine of 1683 within the 17th-century fort of Port Louis, on the south coast of Brittany. Many magazines of this type were built within French and other European forts in the 17th and 18th centuries. Note the pitched roof, buttresses and ventilation shafts. (Jeremy Lake)

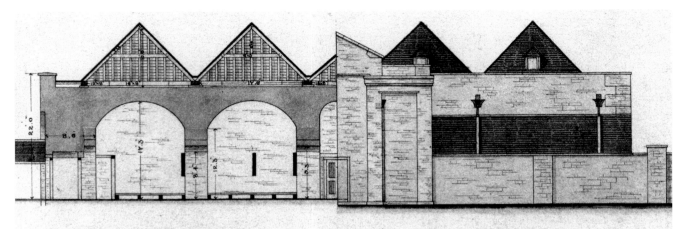

HALF LONGITUDINAL SECTION   HALF ELEVATION

1.9 An 1880 drawing of the Morice Yard Magazine, begun around 1744, which replaced one of 1722. *(TNA WO 78/3101)*

another magazine had been built in the camber bastion, part of the late-17th-century *enceinte* added by Sir Bernard de Gomme. This had a capacity of about 5,000 barrels, but its situation was no more acceptable than that of the Square Tower, and it had been emptied in 1764 because of its dangerous proximity to two smitheries. The arguments over the best site in the area were to continue, as will be seen, for 150 years. In May 1766 Commissioner Hughes, who was in charge

1.10 Morice Yard from the Hamoaze, showing (above) the magazine and (below) one of the two original storehouses (with the dormer windows) and the officers' terrace sited on the high ground to the rear. For a plan of the site, see figure 3.6. *(Stephen Dent)*

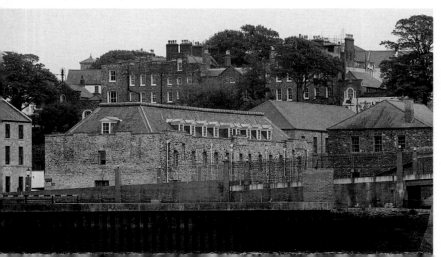

of the dockyard, wrote to the Admiralty that Priddy's Hard was certainly very convenient for receiving and shipping, but in the event of an explosion its proximity to the storehouses at Weevil, the gunwharf and the centre of the line of capital ships laid up in the harbour, meant that all these would be at risk. He concluded that if it were necessary to have a magazine within the precincts of the harbour, Horsea Island would be a much better place. The Admiralty were convinced by these arguments, and the Board ordered the Respective Officers at Portsmouth, in conjunction with the Commanding Royal Engineer (CRE) at Portsmouth, Captain Dixon and another Engineer, Captain Brewse (see Appendix B), to give a full report of the various advantages and disadvantages of the possible sites. They visited Horsea Island, Portchester Castle, Priddy's Hard and Boatswain's Hill's Coppice, and consequently Dixon was ordered to prepare plans and estimates for a magazine at Boatswain's Hill. The plans were referred to the Engineer in Chief, Major General Skinner (see Appendix B), and the matter rethought. An estimate was then prepared for erecting three magazines at Priddy's Hard, together with barracks, lines of defence, a guardhouse, cooperage and wharf, which amounted to £21,327. Because of the expense nothing was done besides taking steps to remove the tenants from the lands within the earthworks recently created around Priddy's Hard as part of the Gosport defences. In December 1767 the Mayor and leading citizens of Portsmouth petitioned the King to have the magazine removed. The officers at Portsmouth were already well aware of the apprehensions of the local community: earlier in the year it had been decided to move the powder from a magazine under the King's Bastion, and this was sent by water to the Square Tower rather than causing alarm by sending it through the town in wagons. To meet the requirements of the fleet 10,000 to 12,000 barrels of powder needed to be held at Portsmouth; the Square Tower held only

1.11 The rolling way at Priddy's Hard today, as converted into a gallery in Explosion! Museum. (Stephen Dent)

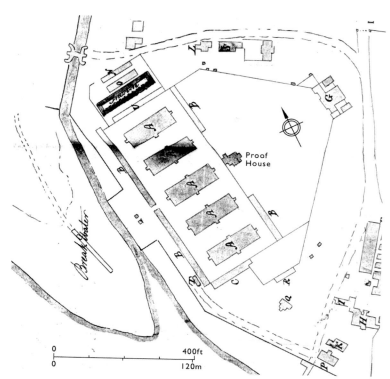

1.12 Purfleet in 1811. See Figure OA.38, page 137, for the Proof House. (Adapted from TNA WO 44/643)

6,000 barrels, and so a larger replacement was required. However, nothing could be done quickly. It took three years before newly built magazines were dry enough to receive powder, and the Board could not erect any without royal approval and orders for presenting the cost to Parliament. By November 1768 the Ordnance Board had conferred with the First Lord of the Admiralty, Sir Edward Hawke, and decided upon a reduced programme of works. Instead of three magazines at Priddy's Hard, there would be only one, with a cooperage and other ancillary buildings, at an estimated cost of just over £6,921. The other two magazines were to be postponed until the Admiralty and Board of Ordnance agreed a convenient situation.

Nevertheless it was to be nearly a decade before even this much smaller site could be completed. On 23 November an Order in Council announced the scheme and at the end of January 1769 the Board viewed a plan of Priddy's Hard with one of the magazines and the cooperage. Following this preliminary study, the CRE at Portsmouth, Captain Archer (see Appendix B), was ordered to prepare further plans and estimates. Like many military building projects before and since, Priddy's Hard was to be corporate architecture, with many hands contributing to the design. Archer was told to make any further alterations he thought desirable to the Priddy's Hard plan, and submit these to the Board before proceeding with the construction. Major General Skinner decided which section would be constructed, and also relocated the magazine and the rolling stage for unloading vessels. (Despite any implications in the name, powder barrels were never rolled, as this had a bad effect upon the contents, but were wheeled in barrows or tumbrils.) The necessity for a new magazine was becoming increasingly pressing, and in January 1770 the Board was told that the Portsmouth magazines were so full it would be very difficult to renew 400 barrels due to be taken out of a Russian ship. In September 1772 a minor crisis declared itself. Archer reported that when the protective chalk rubble was being laid over the top

of the arch of the magazine, the sidewalls gave way a little. He immediately stopped laying on any more weight, and without delay threw up buttresses, which remain a feature of the magazine to this day. These buttresses might enable the magazine to be completed as designed, but Archer thought it would be safer to substitute a lighter roof construction from that originally intended. Skinner came immediately to the site to make the decision. He proposed to leave the roof under its temporary covering of thatch until the next spring, and then to cover it with plain tiles instead of the heavier Delabole slate. Archer had different views as to the construction of the roof, but the view of the superior officer prevailed and he was ordered to finish it according to Skinner's plans, and to attempt to complete it before the autumn of 1773.

1.13 The sole surviving magazine at Purfleet (No. 5 Magazine), was built in 1763–5 to designs by James Gabriel Montressor. (NMR BB94/8152)

1.14 Purfleet.
Top: Some of
the softwood
partitioning that
divided the
two aisles into
numbered storage
compartments
have survived.
(NMR BB94/8154)

Bottom left: detail
of roof support
and crane. The
barrels were
moved by timber
cranes designed to
be pushed along
a gantry frame;
these are
precursors of the
travellers familiar
to 19th-century
engineering
workshops. The
massive and closely
spaced roof trusses
were designed to
resist an explosion,
in contrast to later
designs.
(NMR BB94/8158)

Bottom right: One
of the perforated
tin plates, and
hatched opening,
which enabled
internal humidity
levels to be
controlled.
(NMR BB94/8154)

By the end of September 1773 Archer reported that the floors and inside work at the cooperage and shifting room had been laid and were nearly finished, the floor of the magazine was nearly done and the arches had been cleaned off and pointed. The basin was laid out and largely cleared, 284 piles having been driven, and they were about to lay a sluice to scour it from mud. He began to form the basin and lake on 1 May 1775. By September 1775 the magazine, cooperage and shifting house were completely lined, all window and doorframes were fixed, and good progress was being made with the basin. As the magazine was required for use in such a short time, Archer proposed a re-arrangement of stacking the barrels, so as to accommodate 5,742 instead of 3,904, but was told that the original arrangements were to stand for the present.[7]

In the summer of 1776 an accident on the vessel *Marlborough* rekindled the alarms of the citizens and it was with great difficulty that they were prevented from again petitioning the King for the removal of the powder from the Square Tower. The Officers were asked to report on whether the magazine at Priddy's Hard was fit to be used and, if so, to re-house the powder from the Square Tower there immediately. Unfortunately, further work was required: the rolling way connecting the magazine to the basin had to be covered to secure the powder from bad weather; the landing place

was not finished and the mud in the basin required removal for vessels to have clear access; and a guard and guardhouse had to be provided. Archer took the necessary steps to speed these improvements and to allay the fears of the locals. He proposed to cover the rolling way with a pitched roof supported on oak stanchions, and requested to know if he should proceed according to the plan and estimate for the guardhouse, barracks and houses for the officers that he had transmitted to the Board in 1773. He also wished to know, as the basin and lake would soon be completed, whether to proceed with the two other magazines as first proposed. He was told to proceed with the line of the fortifications on the supposition that these were to be erected, and plans for the new magazines were produced, the only ones to survive from Priddy's Hard. The delays in making the magazine usable tried the patience of the local community, and in January 1777 they sent a further letter to the Board begging for the immediate removal of powder from the Square Tower, 'to prevent any Accident happening as the many recent Attempts of Villainous Incendiaries at that Port & other places have given them great alarm & filled them with great Dread & Apprehension for their Lives & every thing that is dear to them.'

The Board now ordered that Archer use every possible means for getting the magazine ready to receive the powder immediately, erecting tempo-

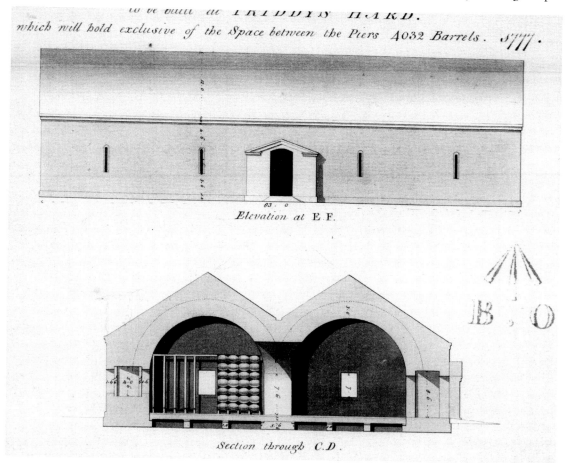

which will hold exclusive of the Space between the Piers 4032 Barrels. 1777.

Elevation at E.F.

Section through C.D.

1.15 Archer's design for projected additional magazines at Priddy's Hard. Note the storage racks and the airing passages built into the thickness of the walls. (MPHH 1/703)

rary sheds for the guard. At the same time that these events were unfolding in Portsmouth, circular letters were sent to all the outports cautioning the Respective Officers to be very careful of the magazines and storehouses, as attempts had been made to set fire to those at Bristol.

At last events began to move swiftly. On 28 February 1777, the Master General appointed William Bache as Storekeeper and on 7 March James Wright as Clerk of the Cheque at the newly completed magazine. The magazine was fit for receiving powder, except for a sliding crane for stacking barrels in the different bays which Archer ordered to be immediately put up. On 19 April the Principal Officers at Portsmouth were ordered to remove all the powder to Priddy's Hard as soon as it was ready: 'this is the Boards positive Order and must be comply'd with, without a Moment's Loss of Time.' Within a few days, cranemen were loading the *Amherst* powder hoy (see page 34) with barrack bedsteads, tables and forms, for the use of the guard at Priddy's Hard, and by 26 April all the preparations had been made. The *Amherst* was accordingly loaded with 300 barrels at the Square Tower and unloaded at Priddy's Hard by gunwharf labourers. *Amherst*, *Charlotte* and *George* shuttled to and fro, with the final lift accomplished on 14 May. [8]

Additional magazines at Plymouth

At Plymouth, the magazine at Morice Yard was not an object of alarm to the townspeople, but following the precedents of Purfleet and Priddy's

Hard, it was clearly policy now not to mingle the storage of gunpowder with other activities on a single site. Furthermore, the dockyard was to be expanded, with a corresponding increase in the need for magazine space, and there was no obvious room available at Morice Yard. There was no dispute as to where new magazine facilities should go; Keyham Point, an apparently safe distance upriver and at that time not with any significant housing in the vicinity, was the selected spot. It was not a unanimously favoured view, however. In August 1770 Lieutenant Colonel Roy (see Appendix B), Surveyor-General of the coasts for the Board of Ordnance, recommended providing security for the dockyard by fortifying the high ground around the Tamar, noting that, 'the position of the intended Powder Magazine at the mouth of Caham [Keyham] Lake is very much exposed from the heights beyond that Lake.' In November 1774 Major Dixon, who had become CRE at Plymouth (having been replaced by Archer as CRE at Portsmouth), was asked for his opinion on the proposed purchase of the land. He prepared an initial estimate in April 1775, for two magazines containing 10,000 barrels in all. Skinner had suggested a third magazine building, to be devoted to examining powder received from ships. Dixon did not intend to follow this up, as these operations had always been performed in the cooperages, and he intended to adhere to this practice. However, the will of the superior officer prevailed again and Dixon was told that the Board had decided on a third magazine for receiving and issuing powder, which was to have a capacity of 1,000 barrels.

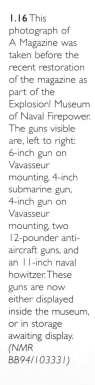

1.16 This photograph of A Magazine was taken before the recent restoration of the magazine as part of the Explosion! Museum of Naval Firepower. The guns visible are, left to right: 6-inch gun on Vavasseur mounting, 4-inch submarine gun, 4-inch gun on Vavasseur mounting, two 12-pounder anti-aircraft guns, and an 11-inch naval howitzer. These guns are now either displayed inside the museum, or in storage awaiting display. *(NMR BB94/103331)*

The complex, which included two cooperages and a canal for access by water, was very different from Purfleet, reflecting its role not merely as a store but also an establishment where, for the first time, powder was also inspected on a large scale. It was also different structurally. The two main magazines were not to have bombproof vaults. Dixon's recommendation to use Rawlinson's patent slating, which did not require as much timber in the roof as conventional slating and was lighter, was accepted. The reasons for this decision have not been located, but it can be surmised that either Keyham Point was thought to be too far up the Tamar to be at risk, or that the trouble-free existence of the flimsily built Greenwich Magazine showed that that there was no need for such a construction in buildings used simply as stores. Dangers arose in manipulating gunpowder, not in storing it, and the Examining Magazine was provided with a thick vault – the intention being presumably to attempt to contain an explosion rather than to protect from bombardment. However, there appear to have been second thoughts as to the wisdom of dispensing with the vaults on the main magazines in the final plan, decided on by Skinner and Dixon.

Excavations began in July 1775, the cooperages being constructed first to act as stores for tools and materials. Dixon intended to lay the foundations of the three magazines before April 1776, and to complete the two cooperages and boundary wall, and raise the magazine walls to the spring of the arches, by the end of October. By then Dixon had been replaced by Colonel Bramham (see Appendix B), who designed the chiselled work on the cooperage and gateway. By November 1780 only the floors, doors and windows of the magazines had to be completed. The canal was far from ready, but the magazines would take two or three years to dry out before they became usable. It was, therefore, not until May 1783 that the naval refitting magazines and the North Cooperage were ready to receive powder. It was hoped that the South Magazine and the South Cooperage would also be fit for use by August, but the schedule was bettered: on 11 June 1783, Dixon informed the Board that the magazines were ready, and the keys were delivered to the first Storekeeper at the end of July.[9]

Safety and security (Richmond's fortification plans)

While the magazine establishment was being formed, Lieutenant General Lane Parker, the commanding officer at Plymouth, took up the concerns about security voiced by Colonel Roy. Parker thought Dixon had underrated the danger posed to the military and naval installations by a hostile force occupying the Maker Heights on the

Gunpowder preparation

At Priddy's Hard, as completed in 1783, the key stages in the handling and storage of gunpowder can be observed. Barrels were hoisted up from ordnance vessels (see Powder Hoys, Chapter 2) onto the Camber or, on other sites, a long jetty that ran beyond the low-water mark. The barrels were then loaded onto barrows, and conveyed towards the magazine along a rolling stage, after personnel had replaced their footwear with felt shoes in the Shoe Room. The powder was then assessed for condition in the Examining Room. Barrels, which had to be absolutely watertight in order to prevent moisture penetration or powder leaking out, were inspected and if necessary replaced. Shifting houses (see Glossary) were built for this purpose. The barrels were marked with their date of arrival to ensure that the oldest powder was used first. Once back on board ship the barrels were stored towards the forward part of the hold, with access from the magazine to a filling room, where the powder was emptied into cartridges ready for action.

See Appendix C, Instructions for Running Ordnance Magazines at Marchwood, 1814; Brian Lavery, The Arming and Fitting of English Ships of War 1600–1815, Conway Maritime Press, London, 1989, pp.144–150

1.17 Priddy's Hard as completed in 1777, with the projected additional magazines. The plans show the basin for powder vessels, a powder magazine, a rolling way (for moving powder in barrows or trollies), officers' houses and – built against the east side of the magazine enclosure – a shifting house (for the examination of powder) and a cooperage for the repair of powder barrels. The latter were later incorporated into a single range (see figures 2.12 and 3.1–2). Though never built, the additional projected magazines had a permanent effect on the shape of the site, as the Commanding Royal Engineer of the Portsmouth district, Captain Archer, was ordered to strengthen the line of fortifications – which until 1779 comprised temporary pallisades and fascines – to allow for them. The space so provided was to prove invaluable during the site's expansion in the next century. By 1844 these defences were in ruins, and beginning in 1846 the earthworks were reformed, with the ends of the ditch protected with caponier galleries, and provided with a drawbridge, sally port, expense magazines, gun positions and access ramps. (MPHH 1/703)

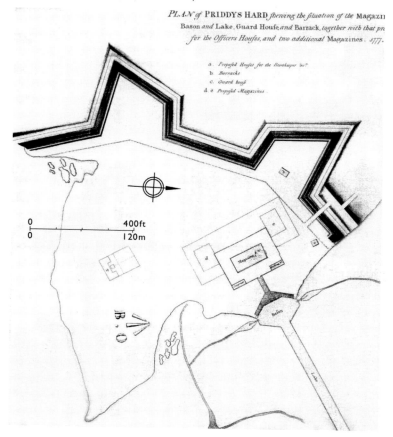

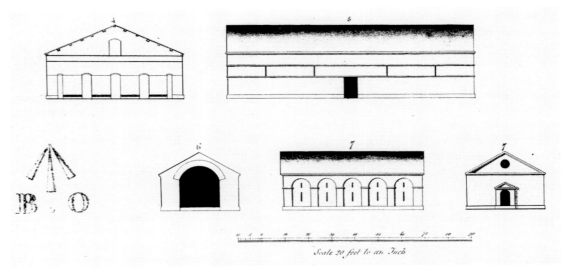

Scale 20 feet to an Inch

other side of the Tamar. However, nothing had been done about this weak point in the defence by the summer of 1778, when Roy again stressed that the Heights should be held to the last if attacked, as the security of the dockyard depended entirely upon that position. Field fortifications were proposed for Maker, and troops were encamped there. In August 1779 the subject became more than a matter of mere theoretical consideration, for the combined Franco-Spanish Fleets were off Plymouth, intend-

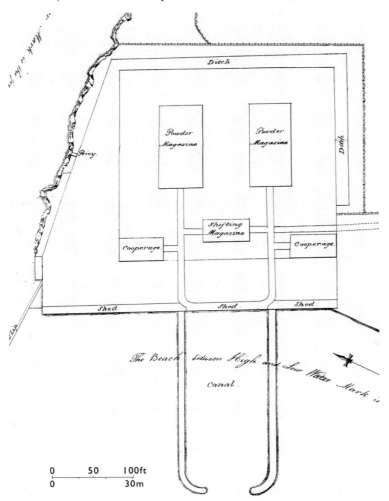

Ditch

Powder Magazine

Powder Magazine

Ditch

Privy.

Shifting Magazine

Cooperage.

Cooperage.

Shed

Shed

Shed

The Beach between High and Low Water Mark

Canal.

| 0 | 50 | 100ft |
| 0 | | 30m |

ing to land near Falmouth. This attempt proved abortive for various reasons, but the reality of the threat had been made apparent. A second threat by the Combined Fleets in August 1780 also came to nothing, but kept the pot on the boil.

On 30 March 1782, Charles Lennox, the third Duke of Richmond and Lennox, was appointed Master General of the Ordnance (see Appendix B). In April 1780 he had asked the House of Lords for an enquiry to be made into the defences of Plymouth, asserting that it was not tenable against an attack. The Master General was not expected to have any detailed knowledge of fortifications or other ordnance matters, being concerned with matters of high policy, but Richmond did, in his own estimation at least, and possessed what his opponents described as a 'passion for fortification', which he was now in an unequalled position to gratify. Dixon was ordered to fortify Maker Heights and a chain of redoubts was quickly completed. However, Richmond's first tenure of the Master Generalship was brief. Declining to serve in a Cabinet with Lord North, he resigned his post on 3 April 1783, and was succeeded by Viscount Townshend (see Chapter 2). Though out of office, his activities continued behind the scenes. The size of the Keyham establishment seemed a liability to him: the greater the store of powder, the greater and more tempting the target. But Keyham was small compared with Purfleet. In October 1783 Richmond thought relocation of the magazines was the answer: 'surely some plan should be offered to Parliament, for correcting as much as possible the impending Calamity from our enormous Powder Magazines. Won't it be necessary to apply to Parliament for some certain to purchase Lands where we may construct proper Magazines to separate this enormous quantity of powder so improperly placed.' On 26 November he followed this up by writing simultaneously to the King and the Treasury:

1.20 An early 19th-century painting of the Priddy's Hard Officers' Residence, which was built by 1786 and demolished in 1952. *(Explosion! Museum of Naval Firepower)*

'I ought not to omit ... mentioning the great danger which exists here both to the Dock, Magazines Navy and Inhabitants [of Portsmouth], as well as at Plymouth and indeed to His Majestys Garrisons in General, as well as the Embankment of the Thames and even the Metropolis, from the unfortunate and injudicious size of our Powder Magazines, which with the Aid of Parliament and every prudent measure in our power, we hope to remedy, as soon and as effectually as possible. The vast expenditure of the Service certainly induced in some degree these enormous and dangerous Depots – but it is an impending danger which ought to be removed as soon as possible.'

Richmond resumed office under William Pitt (the younger) in December and attempted to bring into effect elaborate schemes of fortification at both Plymouth and Portsmouth. Had he succeeded he would, no doubt, have turned his attention to the question of magazine accommodation, but his plans aroused intense opposition and were rejected in Parliament in 1786, though only by the casting vote of the Speaker. Some idea of his projects can be understood from a memorandum of August 1787 from Major William Congreve, then Deputy Comptroller of the Royal Laboratory at Woolwich (and later to reappear in this story, see Chapter 2). He agreed with Richmond on the dangers posed by Purfleet:

'As large Store Houses will be Required to contain the Salt Petre and Brimstone necessary for the stock of those articles which His Grace the Duke of Richmond means to keep in Store, it is a very favourable opportunity to get rid of the danger which daily threatens the Capital, by keeping a large quantity of Gunpowder at Purfleet – as the Magazines at that place will make excellent Store Houses for Salt petre & Brimstone.'

However, after his rebuff in Parliament any extensive projects Richmond might have had in mind remained in the realm of ideas, though he remained in office until his dismissal in February 1795, and did, as will be seen, establish a second Magazine in the Portsmouth area.[10]

By then England was engaged in a prolonged war and the Ordnance Depots so recently created were put to the test.

Chapter 2 # The Revolutionary and Napoleonic Wars

2.1 The New Gunwharf at Portsmouth as developed by 1799. This effectively doubled the size of the existing gunwharf. See figure 9.30 for a later plan of the whole gunwharf site. *(From TNA WO 55/786)*

Before the Revolutionary and Napoleonic Wars the relatively few magazine depots could be operated with small staffs of men accustomed to the routine. The navy created the greatest demands for ordnance since it was frequently involved in operations, including the transport of the army to foreign campaigns. The wars were the most complex and most prolonged military and naval undertaking that the United Kingdom had ever experienced, and the Board of Ordnance was forced to undertake a great expansion programme, which carried it into types of manufacture never contemplated before. The

existing facilities were quite inadequate for war demands, but a regular magazine could not be constructed any quicker, as it was essential that the buildings dried out before they could accommodate powder; it was not until quite late in the wars that the new buildings at Weedon and Upnor were completed, and Marchwood was still not in use by the time they ended. Consequently, emergency magazines were required, but there was no reversion to the insecure and dangerous accommodations at Portsmouth and Greenwich. Indeed, the temporary magazine at Hungerford was, in part, taken as a model for the immense permanent depot at Marchwood, and many others had the security (as far as the public were concerned) of being located within existing fortifications. Safety concerns also led for the first time to the creation of traverses to reduce the effects of blast, should a mishap occur. Improvements in the understanding of gunpowder composition led to the establishment of dedicated facilities at Portsmouth and Plymouth for the repair of damaged powder: naval powder in particular was liable to become degraded through storage on board ship. At both these locations laboratories were built for filling and emptying shells and cartridges.

The Gunwharves

Guns, gun carriages, small arms, powder and shot were removed from ships returning from a commission and stored in the gunwharves. At Portsmouth they were stored in the Square Tower or the Camber Magazine and the armoury; the weapons were then cleaned and maintained; and when a ship was put in commission the operations were reversed. No sophisticated storing techniques were used for the powder, but in May 1771 the following regulations were issued. Store Powder was to be shifted (i.e. inspected) twice a year in the months of March and September. Powder that had been in store for more than three months was to be inspected before issue, the powder stored longest being issued first. The powder with the largest grains was to be supplied to ships embarking on foreign service. All powder returned from ships was to be inspected, and if necessary, to be sifted to remove any lumps that formed through

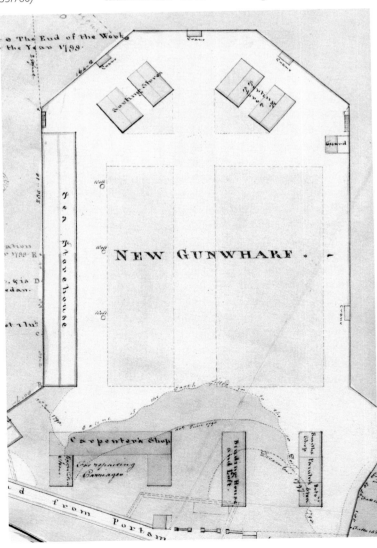

damp. The magazines were to be opened and aired as often as convenient.

Land-service weapons were also stored, and in 1767 a storehouse was built to hold the Battering Train of artillery (which, in 1776, was to be despatched to America, together with the appropriate laboratory stores). Solid shot, obviously, required no preparation before firing, but mortar shells and cartridges had to be filled, requiring special scales and funnels, ancillary equipment and empty cloth cartridge bags. Other equipment held included swords, pikes, canteens, haversacks, camping equipment, entrenching tools and greatcoats. Small arms cartridges were made at the gunwharf, the men being paid 5/- (shillings) per thousand; in February 1776, 7,549 x 4⅝-inch mortar shells were in store. Guns and stores were also supplied to coastal batteries in the Portsmouth district. Other items of storage were not for use against the enemy: in April 1777 Lord Howe's Flag-Captain asked the gunwharf Storekeeper for bilboes and shackles for ten mutineers. The Old

2.2 An 1854 engraving of the ordnance stored at the gunwharf. The principal building resulting from the rebuilding of 1800–1814, the Grand Storehouse, is shown. Compare with figures 5.23, 5.24 and A.40. *(Priddy's Hard Archive 1998.4.20)*

2.3 Photograph from c.1900 of the north wing of the Grand Storehouse on the gunwharf. In the foreground is a 16.25-inch, 110-ton gun, as mounted on the battleships *Victoria*, *Sans Pareil* and *Benbow*. *(Portsmouth City Museums and Records Service)*

2.4 A photograph
from 1897 of the
Shell Ground at
the gunwharf.
*(Portsmouth City
Museums and
Records Service)*

2.4 A photograph from 1897 of the Shell Ground at the gunwharf. *(Portsmouth City Museums and Records Service)*

Gunwharf was only a lesser risk to Portsmouth than the Square Tower had been by virtue of the smaller amount of explosives it held. The Master General, then Lord Townshend (see Appendix B), had appointed one of his footmen as overseer of the new defence works, and as a sideline this man had been raising flowers in the armoury yard. An anonymous letter sent to the Board reported a conversation:

'between two Gentlemen in Portsmouth some time since one of the Gentlemen … said [a] great deal about the new Magazine not being Ready to receive the Powder the other Gentleman said… that there was a Place in Portsmouth Allmost as dangerous as the Magazine. [The other man] said whare [sic] is that why Sir it's the Old Armoury Pray Sir what is keep their? Garrison Stores What are they composed off Why there is some Thousands of live Shelles some thousands of Infuses Meal Powder &c.[1] And in case of a fire there is no Water but what Runs from the Storehouses into two or three tubs … [and because of the attraction of the flowers]… All the last Summer The Armoury was as Publick as the Market from Six a Clock in the Morning often till Nine at Night.'

However, no catastrophe occurred, and since the practice of working by candlelight was not discontinued until 1796, this must have had more to do with luck than judgement. Further perils were averted during the famous Spithead mutiny on 8 May 1797, when, 'on account of the State in which the Seamen are on board the Fleet', all the fixed ammunition was removed from Priddy's

Hard to be lodged in the garrison, and all arms were removed from the gunwharf. The incident in fact passed off without any attempt to seize arms.[2]

The gunwharf workers

The New Gunwharf, separated from the old one by a camber spanned by a bridge, was begun on 10 August 1797, and by the end of 1799 the sea walls had been formed and work begun on the first storehouses. By October 1805 the CRE pronounced it to be usable, though still unfinished, and new offices were designed for the Old Gunwharf for the Respective Officers and the clerks. A brief historical account of its formation was prepared in 1850, and from this it is known that between 1798 and 1815 the establishment comprised the Storekeeper, the Clerk of the Survey, the Clerk of the Cheque, 9 clerks and 154 men. At various periods between the years 1800 and 1814 were built an armoury, a magazine for filled shells and Congreve rockets, workshops for armourers and smiths, a guardhouse and the Grand Storehouse. The armoury was designed in 1804 to accommodate 12,000 muskets, 5,000 pairs of pistols, 10,000 swords, and was supplied with workshops and forges. The main smithery was completed in the summer of 1805. In November 1799 the Old Gunwharf was engaged in making up 1,000,000 rounds of musket ball cartridges, which were to be sent to Priddy's Hard. This was an activity that ebbed and flowed, unlike the regular wartime work of the establishment, and by 1801 the expertise appears to have been lost, as the Royal Laboratory at Woolwich then sent a labourer, who had been chiefly employed in making up ball and blank cartridges, with three boys, to superintend and assist in making them up at the gunwharf; the necessary tools were sent by coach. The gunwharf staff now needed to ask what was the usual day's output for a man and a boy, and were told it was not prescribed, as care and attention should have priority. Civil labourers were paid 1/6 (1 shilling, 6 pence) per day, military 9d (9 pence). Young boys on first coming to the Woolwich Laboratory got 6d a day, when they could make 500 a day 9d, when still more expert 11d. The complexities of holding and issuing stores at the gunwharf are clear in this list of laboratory stores to accompany twelve medium 12-pounder guns.

Shot fixed to wood bottoms	Round	3,600
	Case	1,056
Flannel cartridges filled	4 lb	3,600
	3½ lb	1,056
Tin tubes		6,600
Portfires		900
Tin tube boxes		24
Portfire sticks		24
Cutting knives		12
Scissors		12
Worsted		12 oz
Needles		24
Empty flannel cartridges		600
Cartouches of leather		24
Copper powder measures	8 oz	12
	4 oz	12
	1 oz	12
Thumbstalls		24
Spherical case shot		720

(these have 17 different classes of implements & fuzes accompanying them)

Quick match	1,440 lengths
Paper Bursters 4½ oz	720
Fuzes, Drove, 8 inch	1,440
Flannel cartridges for spherical case shot filled with 1 lb powder	720

The workload of the men was immense, as demonstrated in the list of work undertaken on *Victory*'s armament during the fortnight before she sailed on the voyage that would culminate at Trafalgar in 1805:

August 23 Carpenters employed repairing *Victory*'s carriages; searchers (who inspected ordnance) employed washing the *Victory*'s guns

August 24 Carpenters employed repairing *Victory*'s carriages

August 26 (25th was a Sunday) Storehousemen receiving unusable stores from *Victory*; carpenters and smiths repairing *Victory*'s carriages

August 27 Storehousemen sorting *Victory*'s stores; carpenters and smiths repairing *Victory*'s carriages

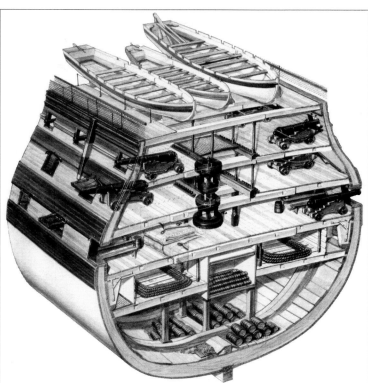

2.5 Midships section of HMS *Victory* showing armament and stowage of powder and shot in a typical three-deck ship in the age of sail. Recent research by Peter Goodwin, Keeper and Curator of HMS *Victory*, has revealed that the magazine would actually have been lined with copper, and would have contained racks of cartridges rather than small barrels. The decks of the cable tiers (each side of the magazine) would have been painted with red paint to prevent rotting resulting from the stowage of damp cables, while the hold would have contained a layer of iron ballast, topped by a layer of shingle ballast, with the barrels of provisions stowed on top of these. There would also not have been a barrel at the end of each mess table – the ropes from which the table was hung would have interfered with anyone sitting here trying to eat – and the top of the capstan would have been plain, the decoration being a Victorian invention. *(Illustration by Ross Watton, from The Arming and Fitting of English Ships of War 1600-1815 by Brian Lavery, Conway Maritime Press, 1987)*

August 28–31 Smiths repairing *Victory*'s carriages; searchers painting them

September 2 Storehousemen looking out stores for *Victory* and shipping them on board the *Richard* and *Sarah*; carpenters repairing *Victory*'s carriages; searchers painting guns and carriages

September 3–5 Carpenters repairing *Victory*'s carriages; searchers on board *Victory*

September 6–9 Carpenters working on carriages of *Victory*. [3]

Gunpowder, restoving and the first laboratories

By this time, considerable improvements had been made in the performance of English gunpowder, which had been notoriously inferior, as testified by a letter of 26 June 1795 from Captain Sir Erasmus Gower, HMS *Triumph*: 'I cant forbear mentioning a very old and repeated Complaint made of the Gun Powder, it is Really so notoriously unequal to that employed by the French, that an English Man of War is in a certain degree disabled before she

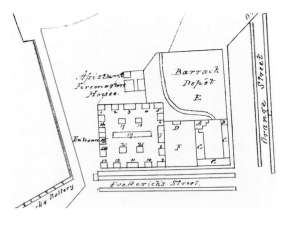

can get a Shot to reach the Enemy.' The man responsible for the improvements was Sir William Congreve (see Appendix B), the Comptroller of the Royal Laboratory at Woolwich, who generated a minor revolution in the field of gunpowder production and preservation. Congreve and his successors, as the appointed authorities on the technicalities of gunpowder, were to play significant parts in this story. The use of cylinder charcoal, which had been processed in iron retorts, effected a great improvement (see wartime sites, page 48). Under service conditions, powder was very liable to become damp, particularly when afloat, and Congreve devised means for drying and restoring these damaged powders through the installation in 1791 of restoving machinery (see Glossary) at the Royal Gunpowder Factory at

Waltham Abbey. The dried powder was then, according to its condition, mixed with a proportion of fresh powder and re-issued for service. Some of the restored powder was only suitable for blank, drill or saluting ammunition, but there was a constant demand for these inferior grades. By September 1796 Purfleet had in store 4,553 barrels of restoved powder, which required to be mixed with 3,414 barrels of cylinder powder to give the proportion of 7:3. In October the Board of Ordnance laid down that until a supply of gunpowder manufactured entirely with cylinder charcoal could be supplied from the store magazines, for land as well as for sea service, the powder to be issued for the navy was only to consist of that manufactured with the old pit charcoal and that formed from returned powder, dusted and restoved and mixed with a proper proportion of cylinder powder. In 1804 at Congreve's instigation, the Master General, the second Earl of Chatham, decided to set up laboratories at both Portsmouth and Devonport Dockyards. The storehouses at Woolwich had been the subject of attempted incendiary attacks, and Congreve suggested that the most effective form of decentralisation would be to create facilities for making up the different types of ammunition required by the navy, supplemented by specialised buildings for the restoration of damaged gunpowder.[4]

By June 1804 Lewis Wyatt (of the architectural dynasty) had sent the exterior elevations and plans

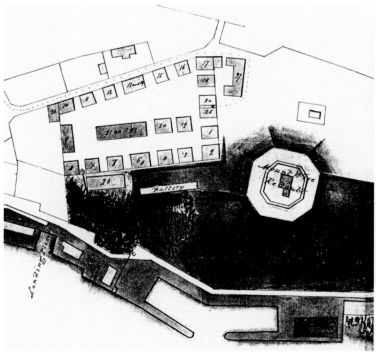

of an ideally arranged set of laboratory buildings to the Portsmouth and Plymouth CREs for local adaptation. The Laboratories at Portsmouth and Plymouth had different ground plans. The Portsmouth site, near the gunwharf, allowed for the ideal symmetrical layout. At Plymouth, the site was cramped and a different arrangement had to be adopted, but it had the advantage that Mount Wise acted as a natural traverse between it and Government House. The Laboratories were intended to repair ammunition and furnish laboratory stores for the naval service, and also to cast lead bullets and make up small arms ammunition for the army. As soon as laboratory stores had been finished they were to be sent to the gunwharves and no more powder was to be brought from the magazines than required for the day's work in the Laboratory. The initial establishment at Portsmouth was to be:

1 Assistant Firemaster
1 Clerk
1 Foreman of Labourers
1 Assistant Foreman
1 Master Carpenter
1 Master Turner
1 Master Smith
1 Master Cooper
1 Master Tinman
1 Master Painter
1 Master Taylor
1 Brass Founder
12 Civil Labourers

The Firemaster was in charge of the Laboratory, and this introduced a new complication into the running of the two main outports, as he was subordinate to the Storekeeper at the gunwharf but reported directly to the Board of Ordnance. When a site was shared, as happened later at Priddy's Hard, friction occurred. The purpose-built facilities for restoving powder were also the Firemaster's responsibility, but these were placed at relatively distant locations for safety reasons. Congreve laid down the number of drying stoves necessary, and the CREs were ordered to co-operate with Mr Dugleby, Second Assistant Firemaster at the Royal Laboratory, in the details of the design. The CRE at the Faversham Powder Mills was to give directions and patterns for copper plates, boilers, pipes etc. for the steam stoves; the Clerk of Works at Faversham was to go to Plymouth to superintend construction of the stoving house, mixing house for two sets of hoppers, a dusting house with eight beds to be worked by hand and a house to unhead and head powder barrels.[5]

Dugleby was to do the same at Portsmouth. There, the facilities were divided between Little Horsea Island and Stamshaw Point. The dusting

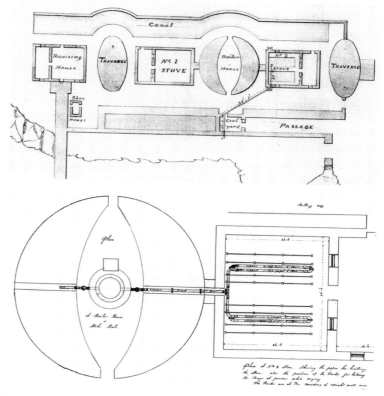

house and mixing house (see Glossary) were at Stamshaw, which was the first stop in the cycle of powder transit. Dugleby described the entire process:

'The Gunpowder which will require Restoving, being deposited in Tipnor Magazines [see page 41], will at early flood each day be shipped on board in such quantities as can be got through the Keels; and proceed to Stampshaw, where it will be unloaded and deposited in the Cooperage of the Mixing House, here it will be unheaded, and passed thro a Coarse Sieve, of 10 Meshes to the Inch, to separate from the powder all lumps, and other impurities; it will then be convey'd to the Dusting House and there dusted in the Keels, which when done, it will be weigh'd, & headed up, and returned to the Mixing House, from whence on the following day, it will be put on

2.9 Plans of the restoving complex at St Budeaux, showing the boiler house which heated the stoving houses. Note the shoe house for changing into magazine clothing. *(From TNA WO 55/805)*

2.10 The mixing house of 1804–5, reconstructed in 1830, is the only original building surviving on the site. By 1866 it was used as a dining room. *(Stephen Dent)*

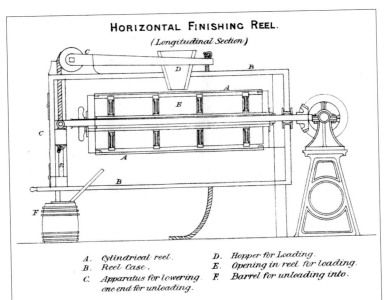

HORIZONTAL FINISHING REEL.
(Longitudinal Section)

A.   *Cylindrical reel.*   D.   *Hopper for Loading.*
B.   *Reel Case.*   E.   *Opening in reel for loading.*
C.   *Apparatus for lowering*   F.   *Barrel for unloading into.*
     one end for unloading.

2.11 The design of the dusting reel did not change. The powder was dusted by being passed through a cylindrical reel of copper gauze through which the dust fell, and this dust was then reworked into new powder. After passing through the reels, the powder was then removed from the dusting house and taken to restoving houses, in which it was placed on trays and dried out by hot water pipes fed from a boiler house placed outside the buildings and isolated from them by massive earthen traverses. The dried powder was then, according to its condition, mixed with a proportion of fresh powder and re-issued for service. Some of the restored powder was only suitable for blank, drill or saluting ammunition, but there was a constant demand for these inferior grades.
(Treatise on Service Explosives (HMSO), 1900)

board the barge which will convey it to the Stoves [at Horsea] where it will be stove dried and returned to Tipnor Magazines; and this operation will continue daily, until a quantity is collected, which it shall be deemed proper to mix: when 198 Barrels will be conveyed to Stampshaw, and Mixed, and returned back to the Magazines, each day this operation continues. But as Gunpowder from Ships of War coming in to refit will require restoving only. This powder will be sent from Priddy's Hard Magazines, direct to the Stoves where it will be examined by passing it thro a Sieve of 10 Meshes to the inch, to divest it of lumps & impurities, then Stove dried, weighed, headed up, and returned to the said Magazines, thus continuing until all this kind of powder is finished, when the operation of restoving will again commence, and go on as before.'

Coopers (barrel makers) from the two magazines would attend to unhead and head their own powder:

'At early flood the Barge being loaded will as soon as she floats proceed down Tipnor Lake, which at the time of tide can be done by shoving her to the entrance of the small Lake leading up to Stampshaw Point, by the time she gets to this place, the tide will have made up so, as to enable her to approach the platform, where unloading the

powder to be dusted, and taking in that already done, she will proceed with the tide up Porchester Lake, to the Stoves, where the powder to be restoved will be unloaded, and that which has undergone the operation will be put on board, and the Barge will take the shortest Rout to Tipnor Magazine, which she will be enabled to do (as by this time it will be high water) by going close along the shore of Little and Great Horsey Islands, this being the best & least laborious track at this time of tide. Thus the round of the buildings will be accomplished during flood. The Communication of Priddys Hard magazine with the Stoves, will also be carried on during flood tide, as vessels at high water can load, and unload, at the platform at Horsey Island, and return with the ebb tide back to the Magazine with the powder restoved; & thus this business can continue daily as long as it shall be deem'd necessary.'

This was the overall shape of the operation; the details of what went on at Stamshaw and Horsea are also known. The Foreman of the powder barge *Bull Dog* kept accounts of receipts and issues and superintended the mixing; two labourers and two bargemen navigated the barge, loaded and unloaded it and assisted to mark the mixed gunpowder. At Horsea seven men worked in three stages: firstly, the cooper, the stoke hole man and four men emptied the barrels into separating hoppers to pick out lumps and impurities, while another man swept up loose powder in the weighing room and cleaned the stoves; then, two men removed the examined powder assisted by the stoker, and two men on the landing place steps delivered it to one man in a punt. Finally, two men assisted by the stoker, emptied the barrels of powder into a loading tub, and took empty cases from stacks in the weighing room to be loaded with powder to be stoved. Three men loaded racks in the stoving house with cases when filled with their proper proportion of powder. The cooper and six labourers then went to the dusting house at Stamshaw, leaving the foreman and stoker in charge of the stoving operations. In the Stamshaw dusting house, which was equipped with two double reels, one man set each reel in motion; one fed the hopper, regulated the receiving tubs and relieved the man at the reel; two men took restoved powder from the mixing house, loaded and navigated the punt, returned with the dusted powder, swept the place out occasionally, sprinkled the platforms with water and washed the punt. Two men on the other double reel did the same. It might have been supposed that all these men came under the firemaster at the Laboratory, but further complications in the chain of responsibility were introduced by the fact that the cooper, lightermen and labourers were paid by the Storekeeper at Priddy's Hard. These complications did not exist at Plymouth, where both sections of the establishment were set up at St Budeaux, further up the Tamar from Keyham, and separated from it by Weston Mill Lake.[6]

These potentially dangerous operations were shielded by massive earthen traverses supported by brick revetments with wet moats in the rear (the buildings faced the waterside). The design of the gunpowder repairing facilities was duplicated in contemporary buildings at Waltham Abbey, whose foundations were exposed in the 1990s. Traverses had not previously figured in the design of magazine complexes; henceforth they were considered a valuable addition. The origin of the traverses came in July 1804 when Colonel D'Arcy had proposed making Purfleet safer by turning alternate magazines into traverses. In particular, they were essential to guard against the danger of an accident in the examining houses at Priddy's Hard, which occupied the corners of the magazine enclosure on the Camber side, a particularly objectionable feature being windows looking into the yard of the main magazine, only 30 feet away. Consequently, in 1807, the Board decided that the facility should be moved outside the magazine enclosure and traverses be built between it and the magazines. In response to an order from General Morse (see Appendix B), the Inspector-General of Fortifications (a title that in 1802 replaced Chief Engineer), the CRE, Colonel Evelegh, prepared an estimate – but nothing was done. Elsewhere similar measures were taken, and plans were prepared for examining houses and traverses for the magazines at Sheerness. By December 1811 Congreve had second thoughts on the value of traverses; an explosion at the Press House at Waltham Abbey threw burning debris over the traverse to the Corning House, which blew up in its turn. 'The Explosion in the Corning House would not have been thought so tremendous if the force could have expanded over the Extensive Level Meadows below the Town of Waltham

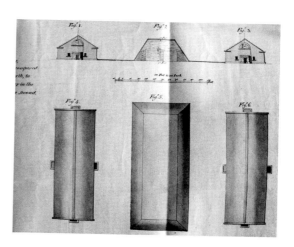

2.13 In July 1804 Colonel D'Arcy proposed making Purfleet safer by turning alternate magazines into traverses. This is surely the origin of the traverses at Weedon. (See figures 2.18 and 2.19) *(TNA WO 55/765)*

Abbey, instead of being pent up between the Traverses No. 2 & No. 3 ... the effect of the recent accident shews the inconvenience of confining Explosions between two Traverses because it gives a contrary direction to the force than that which would afford a free Expansion to the Elastic Fluid.' As a consequence, traverses were not to be a universal feature of the three new large magazines that were required to meet the demands of the war.[7]

Building in response to the conflict

The demands of war, predictably enough, placed great strain on the existing magazine infrasctructure. The greatest quantities of powder were required for ships in active service and for overseas expeditionary forces. A First Rate 100-gun ship, for example, typically held 480 barrels of powder, each weighing 90 lbs, and a Third Rate 74-gun ship (the backbone of the navy in this period) held 402 barrels for foreign service and 365 for Channel service. Siege warfare was a particularly high consumer: a quarter of a million tons, for example, being used at the siege of Badajoz in 1812 alone.[8]

The use of floating magazines went some way towards meeting this demand. Floating magazines had been used to provide essential extra storage from the time that the ordnance depots were initiated. For over a hundred years sailors visiting the principal naval anchorages would have noticed mastless roofed-over hulks painted an eye-catching red. These they would have kept well clear of, especially if their funnels were likely to emit sparks (not uncommon in the early days of steam). These superannuated wooden walls, their lower decks stacked with barrels of gunpowder, often leaky and abominably cold in winter – moored as they were in exposed positions away from the coastline and with no fire permitted apart from the galley – must have been an unenviable posting. It was probably even colder on the Medway than on the south coast. The crew, typically a foreman with two or three labourers, led an isolated life; the men

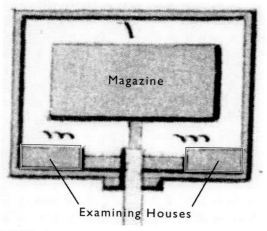

2.12 This detail shows the proximity of the highlighted examining houses to Priddy's Hard Magazine. *(From TNA WO55/2033)*

on the Priddy's Hard floating magazine *Grampus* could only hear the bells from the nearest ship in Ordinary (out of commission from active service) when the weather was very moderate or the wind from the south, and so often had little idea of time. Only the visits of the powder hoys (and of an occasional officer checking up on them) provided contact with the outside world. Viewed as a necessary evil, always posing a risk – the galley on

Grampus caught fire in 1858 and had to be modified – they nevertheless provided a storage capacity that the naval Ordnance Yards could not do without. In 1818 the three floating magazines at Priddy's Hard, *Fortitude*, *San Antonio* and *Atlas*, held respectively 6,128, 11,015 and 12,692 barrels, or twice the capacity of Priddy's Hard and Tipner Magazines combined, and this form of storage, however criticised (see page 108 for the disputes

Powder hoys

Hoys, a type of sailing barge, were a vital element in the operation of the coastal Ordnance Depots, supplying ammunition to and unloading from naval vessels, which as a safety precaution never tied up alongside for these purposes. As well as the explosives and the labourers to handle them, the hoys also carried ordnance officials and clerks to maintain records of the transhipments. As the construction of Priddy's Hard got underway in 1774 the officers set out their requirements. As the demands of the service might mean that delays were kept to a minimum, they wanted a boat capable of carrying 300 barrels of powder, together with officers and clerks, in weather that would make the use of an open boat impossible. It was thought that it would be cheaper to hire a boat than to have one built; two local men both offered 40-ton boats, to be navigated by three men at 8/- per day, on a 21-year contract, and one of these was selected. This was probably the *Amherst*, still in use in 1809. By the time the magazine was ready she had been joined by *George* and *Charlotte*. *George* was a bigger vessel, capable of holding 500 barrels; she, together with *Charlotte*, appears to have been attached to the gunwharf, while *Amherst* 'the contract powder hoy', moored in Priddy's Hard basin, her Master being allotted a house at Priddy's Hard, which was enlarged for him in 1809. By 1797 *George* had been joined by *Wootton*, but by 1804 *Amherst* was no longer adequate, both because of the pressure of wartime work and the daily transits of powder to the newly established restoving facilities at Stamshaw Point and Horsea Island, and the Priddy's Hard Officers were ordered to purchase a new vessel. A boatbuilder of West Cowes offered a new vessel on the stocks: 44 tons, complete with mast, sails, boat and fittings for £650. The Board ordered it to be bought. Until it was available, the Board ordered the gunwharf to lend a hoy to carry on the communication between the floating magazine (see below) *Fortitude* and the drying stoves on Little Horsea. The Master of the new hoy *Pitt*, like that of *Amherst*, was provided with a house at Priddy's Hard.

Powder hoys like these were normally confined to harbour duties, not going beyond ships moored at Spithead. Larger coasting craft, powder vessels, were employed for shipping powder in bulk in and out of the depots; in 1812 piles and buoys were fixed at Priddy's Hard at the Storekeeper's request for warping powder vessels in and out in contrary winds. By 1815 *Amherst* appears to have come to the end of its long career, being replaced by *Ebenezer*. *Pitt* was still at work in 1827, though the restoving activities at Horsea and Stamshaw were then on a much reduced scale. The advent of the shell-firing gun introduced a new class of supply ship, the gun hoy. These were coasting vessels that transported shells to the gunwharves and laboratories from Woolwich; *Letitia* and *Wellington* were regularly employed in the middle years of the century, a replacement for

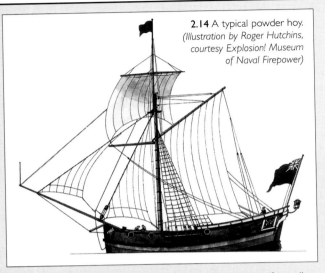

2.14 A typical powder hoy. *(Illustration by Roger Hutchins, courtesy Explosion! Museum of Naval Firepower)*

the former being needed in 1867. This needed to be a fast sailer rather than of large capacity, as it was to make constant runs to the floating magazine *Grampus*, whose berth was very awkward at low water; with adverse winds a large hoy had to be warped up. In 1869 five vessels were attached to Priddy's Hard; in addition to serving the ships in harbour and at Spithead, they also provided for the Coast Guard ships at Southampton and Weymouth, the local depots of Tipner and Marchwood, and the floating magazine *Grampus*. Under ill-advised pressure from the Control Department, it was decided to transfer the powder vessel (the term *hoy* seems to have gone in abeyance for the gunpowder craft) *Annie* from Priddy's Hard to the gunwharf, lay up the powder vessels *Hardinge* and *Gorilla* at Priddy's Hard and the gun hoy *Wellington* at the gunwharf.

Larger craft were in use for bulk transfers of explosives. In 1873 *Earl de Grey & Ripon* arrived at Purfleet with 700 barrels from Cork and Dublin, *Lord Panmure* was also at Purfleet unloading 2,000 barrels from Marchwood. This was ancient powder, some 15 or 20 years old, being amassed to supply the Ashanti expedition. Like *Amherst*, some of these vessels had long lives. In 1891, following the division of depots between the two Services, *Earl de Grey & Ripon* was transferred to the Admiralty, attached to Woolwich and renamed *Buffalo*. Whimsical nautical names appear to have replaced normal military ones – *Marquess of Anglesey* became *Growler*, *Winifreda* became *Plumper* – though there seems no reason why *Cuckoo* became *Owl*.

WO 55/5, WO 55/2147, WO 55/2010, WO 55/2158, WO 55/2029, WO 55/2163, WO 55/2164, WO 55/786, WO 49/128, WO 54/516, WO 55/1887; ADM 131/35, WO 33/53 contains 1893 *Report of Committee on Conveyance of Government Explosives on the River Thames*. For information on 20th-century ammunition ships up to *Regent* and *Resource*, both built in 1967, see E.E. Sigwart, *Royal Fleet Auxiliary*, London, 1969.

over their value in 1890) was to be resorted to continually, up to and including the Second World War, as there was always a pool of obsolete ships to be drawn on. [9]

In November 1799 *Queen* was adapted as a floating magazine at Portsmouth, and in 1802 was joined by *Fortitude*. This form of storage had manifold drawbacks, one of which was the impossibility of closely supervising the men, illustrated in October 1804 when the crew of *Fortitude* were all found asleep in their hammocks. This human failing, however, had also happened in the early days of Priddy's Hard, where three sentries had been found asleep in 1777, after which labourers were used as watchmen in preference to soldiers. In 1805 *Bull Dog* was fitted up as a floating magazine, as were the French prize *San Antonio* and the 90-gun ship *Atlas* in 1814. *Bull Dog* was a working magazine, holding 2,600 filled barrels and a proportion of empties, with no less than three or four receipts and a similar number of issues from it every week. By the end of the war all gunpowder received at Priddy's Hard from warships was sent to *Bull Dog*, which kept Priddy's Hard free from all powder unfit for immediate service. The other hulks served as deposit magazines, and *Fortitude*, *San Antonio* and *Atlas* held respectively 6,128, 11,015 and 12,692 barrels. Just how vital a role these ships played is demonstrated by the fact that Priddy's Hard, even with the stacking arrangements reorganised, held less than 6,000 barrels, and Tipner under 8,000. *Mont Blanc*, *L'Alexandre*, *Gibraltar* and *Vanguard* supplemented Keyham, with the capacity to hold 11,700, 11,200, 11,160 and 6,900 barrels respectively. Upnor was even more dependent on the floating magazines, being supplemented by *Marquis of Huntly* (3,000 serviceable powder, 6,000 unserviceable); *Delft* (5,600 and 3,400); *Princess of Orange* (7,500 and 4,500); *Polyphemus* (3,800 and 2,200); and *Brunswick* (7,000 and 4,000). In 1815 *Texel* was also in use. In addition, Sheerness used *Canada*, which held 11,259 barrels; 11 casemates fitted up in the fortifications at Chatham had a capacity of 26,000 barrels; the three similarly employed at Dover Castle held 14,364. [10]

All these hulks supplemented a substantial building programme of magazine depots. In 1804 the first sketches were made for a completely new establishment at Weedon, a site in the heart of England, but adjacent to the newly completed Grand Junction Canal. A branch of this connected the establishment with the nationwide system of canals, and, most importantly, to London. Thus, a viable large-scale alternative to the coastal shipping of explosives was established for the first time. The canal system enabled military ordnance and explosives to be moved about without risk of unwanted enemy attention.

Weedon was conceived as a great universal

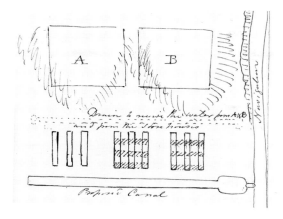

2.15 Colonel Pilkington's first sketch for Weedon included the canal but was quite different from the finished design. *(From TNA WO 55/719)*

arsenal (see Glossary), not just a deposit magazine: the plan included vast storehouses for small arms and military equipment, together with a Horse Artillery barracks. It stands alone in Britain as being conceived on a grand architectural scale, the buildings being grouped to offer two grand frontages, one featuring the storehouses, the other the officers' buildings. The architect of Weedon, Robert Pilkington (see Appendix B) selected a variant of the most prestigious design, Palladianism, not only for the officers' houses but also for the warehouses, the southern range of which were supplied with massive projecting central platforms (resembling portes-cochères), which appear to be solely for display. The whole ensemble reconciled the display of status with a functional layout; the accessibility by canal of the great small-arms industry of Birmingham was much in mind and the storehouses were grouped around this. The internal design of the storehouses appears to have sacrificed practicality for effect; the ceilings are so high (14ft 6in on the ground floor and no less than 16ft on the first floor) that in the absence of stacking equipment it is hard to see how much of the available space could have been used. They were originally used to house saltpetre, which would have been brought in by barge and

2.16 An 1859 engraving of the Royal Military Depot at Weedon, showing the storehouses (right) and one of the lodges with its portcullis (left). *(NMR BB65/999)*

Weedon Barracks, Northamptonshire.

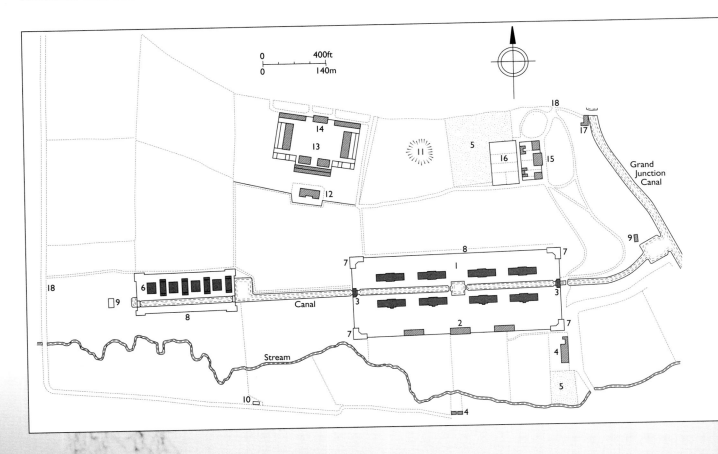

0   400ft
0   140m

14

13

12

11

5

16   15

18

17

Grand
Junction
Canal

9

18

6

9

8

8

7   7

3   3

1

2

7   7

Canal

Stream

4

4

10

5

2.17 The Royal Military Depot, Weedon Bec, as built, 1830. The storehouses and magazine placed around the canal are all surrounded by bastioned walls, their musket loops and field-gun standings providing a perimeter secure from a lightly armed enemy force. It was extended when an additional magazine was constructed at the west end. The Horse Artillery Barracks, Ordnance Row and the civil officers' houses (the so-called 'Grand Pavilion') have been demolished.

Key

1	Storehouses
2	Workshops
3	Engineer and Storekeepers' Offices
4	Master's Artificers' Dwellings
5	Plantations of Walnut
6	Magazines with Traverses
7	Caponiers
8	Boundary walls
9	Guardhouses
10	Labourers' cottages
11	Gravel pit used for roads, pathways etc.
12	Hospital
13	Soldiers' Barracks
14	Officers' Quarters
15	Houses for Civil Officers
16	Walled gardens
17	Occupied by military
18	Carriage entrance

Solid shading indicates surviving buildings, cross shading those that have been demolished.

(Plan by Stephen Dent, based on Beryl Williams, p.170, TNA WO55/2697 and other sources)

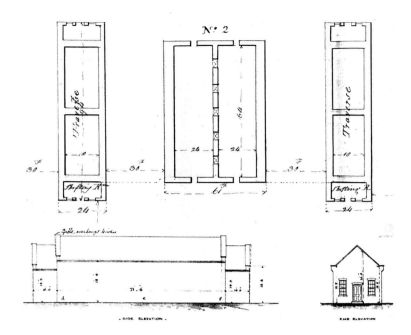

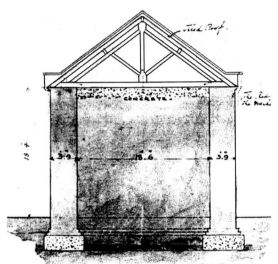

2.18 Above: an October 1806 plan of the magazines and traverses at Weedon, which gives no idea of the remarkable design of the latter. *(From TNA WO 55/719)*

2.19 Left: Section of one of the traverses at Weedon. *(Royal Engineers' Library, W58/2)*

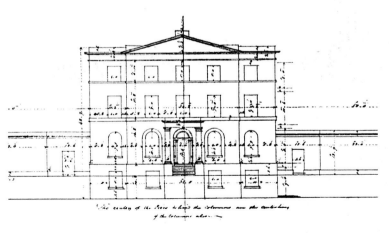

2.20 Left: A view of the Grand Pavilion (no. 15 on plan) from the east. This fine classical range, now demolished, was built for senior civil officers on the site. *(NMR BB65/932)*

2.21 Above: An early 19th-century drawing of the front elevation of the central block of the Grand Pavilion at Weedon. *(From MPH 1/771)*

2.21 Ordnance Row, Weedon,
demolished in 1975, was built as housing
for senior storekeepers. *(NMR BB75/66)*

despatched to Waltham Abbey using the canal system. The magazine complex was placed some 500 feet away from the group of storehouses, an extension of the canal connecting the two sites.

The first range of storehouses was well advanced by the autumn of 1805, the canal basin had been formed and wells were being sunk for the artillery barracks. The four magazines, the first two of which were begun in 1806, parallel the slightly later magazines at Upnor, being two-celled buildings with catenary vaults. Pilkington corresponded about the design of Weedon with Colonel D'Arcy (see Appendix B): he thought he would 'not be at a Loss in any particular, save what may relate to a Powder Magazine'; a curious statement, as he had just been transferred from the post of Chief Engineer at Faversham Powder Mills. Possibly he had been deliberately placed there to give him experience before being sent to Weedon. D'Arcy was to design Upnor (see page 44), and the design of the vaults of the magazine there probably derived from his correspondence with Pilkington. The traverses owed nothing to anything that was to follow at Upnor, or, indeed, anywhere else. With few precedents to go on, Pilkington came up with a unique design in 1806. The resulting traverse resembled externally half a magazine, with a shifting room or office at each end. The structures had wooden roofs and harmonised visually with the magazines, but were filled with rammed earth – in effect, stuffed buildings. Had this type of traverse caught on, the term 'blast house' might have been added to the vocabulary of fortification. However,

2.22 The east elevation of the West Lodge. The chimneystacks heat offices to either side of an unheated central room, which retains a winding mechanism for raising and lowering the portcullis. *(NMR BB65/958)*

2.23 A general view of the storehouse complex at Weedon from the north west. In the foreground is West Lodge, one of the two lodges with portcullises that straddled the canal at each end. *(NMR BB65/967)*

2.24 Above: One of the traverses at Weedon, with its front shifting room. *(NMR BB97/5472)*

2.25 Right: One of the heavy studded doors to the vaulted basement rooms, which originally held saltpetre. *(NMR BB97/5481)*

2.26 Below: The south-facing stores make full use of the fall of the land to accommodate a basement storey on the south elevation; this is treated in a robust classical manner, with semi-circular arches over nail-studded plank doors set beneath shuttered openings for ventilation. The centre bay projects out to the central loading area. *(NMR BB65/994)*

by 1812 Pilkington thought that, in the light of the damage caused at Waltham Abbey the previous year, the presence of wooden roofs was a design fault; should such a misfortune occur at Weedon the timbers would be projected as missiles. The final pair of magazines at Weedon was authorised at the beginning of 1808, and all were ready to receive powder in the summer of 1810. The four buildings each had a capacity of 4,140 barrels; a fifth, single-celled building was designed but not built. It is probable that Pilkington's design, with the emphasis placed on giving protection from blast, was influenced by the short time he had spent at Faversham: defensible walls with corner bastions surrounded both complexes. These defences would have posed no challenge to an ordinarily equipped army; William IV spelled out the threats they were meant to counter (apart from pilfering) when he stated that if a rebellion came about through failure to pass the Reform Bill he would raise the Royal Standard at Weedon. No doubt the imposing appearance of Weedon and the promise of domestic comfort there played some part in the royal strategy.[11]

While Portsmouth Gunwharf was undergoing its great expansion, a new magazine was added to the area. As has been seen, the Priddy's Hard establishment was given one magazine instead of the originally intended three because of its proximity to the dockyard, and Archer's subsequent plan for the additional magazines was never implemented. A First Rate, 100-gun ship of the line, stowed about 480 barrels of powder in its magazine. The amount of powder held was clearly inadequate to meet the needs of the navy, for at just below 4,000 barrels, the magazine's capacity was only equal to that of eight First Rates. In January 1783, at the end of the Seven Years' War, the ships of the navy included five First Rates and nineteen Second Rates of 98 and 90 guns, which would have

carried almost as much powder, and no less than eighty-one Third Rates of 74 guns, in addition to smaller vessels. Furthermore, in addition to the navy's needs, the considerable military forces in the Portsmouth district also had to be supplied, and even with the expedient of using the magazines that served the fortifications of Portsmouth and Portsea it was clear that extra capacity was needed. Richmond, following his policy of spreading out magazine accommodation, decided on acquiring a site at Tipner Point, well to the north of Portsea and well situated for water transport.

A preliminary estimate made in December 1788 was for a magazine containing 5,000 barrels. By June 1789 the CRE, Colonel Mulcaster, had been entrusted with the preliminary steps. He did not make a preliminary survey and section of the land, as he had been ordered to do, as he thought too obvious a determination to purchase would induce the owner to raise his terms, and so the less said or done before the price was settled the better. Ten acres were for sale, and he advised a quick purchase which was agreed on Boxing Day. A further parcel of land was acquired in May 1791, and by July Richmond had received Mulcaster's plan for Tipner [alternative spelling of Tipnor, see pages 31–2]. The whole expense had been stated to Parliament as £11,500. Following the rejection of his earlier plans he did not wish this project to founder by going over the budget. The land had cost £2,000, and the estimate for the wharf was £2,730. Richmond wished to know if the remaining £7,130 would cover the magazine, and the CRE reassured him that a magazine with shifting house and surrounding walls could be done for £7,121, and it would hold 7,776 barrels, better than the original projection. However, the building was not to be finished, let alone employed, during Richmond's Master Generalship.

2.27 Above: Interior of one of the magazines at Weedon. *(NMR BB97/5473)*

2.28 Below: Wooden pegging instead of nails was used to secure the magazine floor. *(NMR BB97/5475)*

2.29 Below: The magazine complex from the south west, showing on the left the magazine added in the 1860s. Also visible are the traverses with their front shifting rooms alternating with the double-gabled magazines. *(NMR BB65/968)*

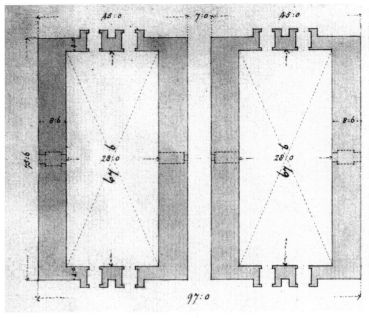

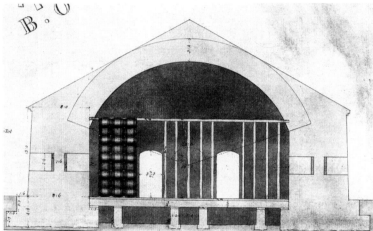

2.30 The original plan for a double magazine at Tipner, and a section of one of the magazines. *(From MPH 1/760)*

The ground proved to be very bad, and all the walls needed piling. The wharf was constructed first, to enable a large stock of bricks to be sent from Stokes Bay during the winter. Stokes Bay was one of two brickyards operated by the Board of Ordnance in the Portsmouth area, the other being at Fort Cumberland, where Richmond was engaged in enlarging an existing building. The first designs, drawn up by a committee appointed by the Duke, were for two Vauban-type magazines side by side, with semicircular vaults (see page 39). Richmond was not keen on this, as an accident in one building would affect the other, and he thought the two magazines should be thrown into one building with two arches, the tried and tested model. Mulcaster agreed with the Master General, adding the further point that there would not be a proper circulation of air with the magazines so close together. Furthermore, the committee's plan made the principal passages 3 feet 11 inches wide, although wheelbarrows required 4 feet 6 inches to pass, the bays were not wide enough, and it appeared that an arch of the thickness and span proposed '…would require uncommon attention in its own Construction and the Construction of the side Walls to make it support its own Weight.' Mulcaster suggested that models be made or '…the learned Dr Hutton, who we believe is universally allowed to understand the Theory of Arches better than any Author…' consulted. Charles Hutton FRS was professor of mathematics at the Royal Academy, Woolwich, with publications including *Principles of Bridges, containing the Mathematical Demonstration of the laws of Arches*. The final design of Tipner was probably prepared in consultation with him, and was for a building

2.31 A watercolour of Tipner Magazine in 1858, artist unknown. The ship alongside is probably moving gunpowder. In the background is Great Horsea Island, converted into a torpedo range in the 1880s (see figure 9.17), with Portsdown Hill beyond. *(Portsmouth City Museums and Records Service)*

composed of three rows of parabolic arches, connected laterally by seven transverse arches (see Appendix A, page 235). No masonry ridges were formed above the groined vaults, the whole structure being covered by a wooden roof clad in copper. By May 1798 the building was still not in a condition to receive powder, and it was not till July 1800 that the magazine and shifting house were completed, but the cooperage was still unfin-

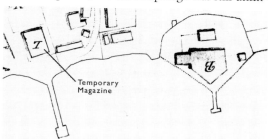

2.32 The temporary magazine at Upnor had its own pier. (TNA WO 44/143)

ished and the accommodation buildings were also unready. The Storekeeper was finally supplied with all his wants in October 1801.[12]

Upnor, like Priddy's Hard, did not have to wait for the war to reveal its inadequate capacity. In February 1763 the Master General, Lord Ligonier, wrote to the Treasury asking to buy a storehouse and land near Upnor. The Seven Years' War had recently terminated and Upnor was overwhelmed by the great number of ships arriving to be disarmed and laid up. There was no room to store the powder, and the Admiralty refused to allow the ships laid up in Ordinary to be used as magazines. The local ordnance officers had been offered a storehouse near Upnor, which would contain nearly 10,000 barrels. It would take at least two months to adapt the building, but there was no alternative. It was procured, and served as a temporary magazine for some 50 years. In August 1787, Congreve proposed that, if Richmond's plan to

2.33 Tipner from the air, in January 1980. Comparison with the phased plan on page 235 shows the extent to which the spit in the foreground post-dates the sharply-angled outline of the enclosure to the 1790s complex. The photograph shows, from the left, the shifting house, the magazine with its vaulting exposed, the larger 1856–7 magazine and the cooperage. (Portsmouth City Museums and Records Service)

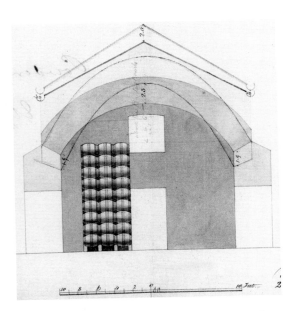

2.34 The catenary arches of the soldiers' quarters at the Drop Redoubt, Western Heights, Dover. The roof was originally covered with earth and slate tiles, the latter being presumably for the collection of rainwater – the Redoubt not having its own well. *(Stephen Dent)*

2.35 Right: A drawing of 1808, showing the proposed semi-circular vault amended to a catenary vault at Upnor. *(From TNA MFQ 1215)*

use the Purfleet Magazines as storehouses were to materialise, eight magazines (not bomb proof) might be built half a mile apart upon the north side of the Medway above Rochester Bridge. If each magazine were to hold 5,000 barrels, the eight would hold more than a year's stock for the most expensive war; and their spacing would ensure that an accident at one would not affect the others. All this could be partly financed by the sale of Upnor Castle and the temporary magazine. Purfleet was not converted and the new magazines were never built.

By 1806 it was decided to take the situation in hand. The temporary magazine, clearly past its sell-by date, was being used as storage and stables, and the Castle was in use for a multiplicity of functions, most of them unsuitable. The South Tower was a laboratory, the North Tower a store, the basement held unserviceable powder, the ground floor

was a store for ammunition, the second floor contained returned rockets and blue lights, while the third floor was a lumber room. The gateway was in ruins. In March 1808 it was decided to build a magazine for 10,000 barrels. Colonel D'Arcy, who years earlier advised Colonel Pilkington about Weedon, drew up the design, employing the same catenary arches. Centering for the arches was already to hand; probably this had been in use at Dover for the construction of Drop Redoubt in 1806. Unlike Weedon, the four cells of the magazine were grouped together in a single block, instead of being spaced out and traversed; this was probably due to the constricted nature of the site, though the Morice Yard Magazine provided a precedent. The magazine was completed by 1811 and was the first to be provided with a traversed shifting house, as had been recommended by the Ordnance Board in 1807. The whole set up was completed by the summer of 1812. A powder pier was built to supply the new magazine. Ordnance vessels bringing powder from Purfleet had to round the Isle of Grain and double back up the Medway, but when the new magazine was being planned a shortcut by canal was suggested. This was the Thames and Medway Canal, which was intended to connect Gravesend and Strood. Ralph Dodd, promoter of

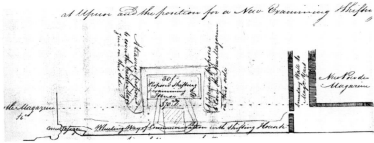

2.36 Sketch for the proposed traversed shifting room at Upnor. *(From TNA WO 55/767)*

2.37 A section through Upnor magazine as executed. *(From TNA WORK 41/89)*

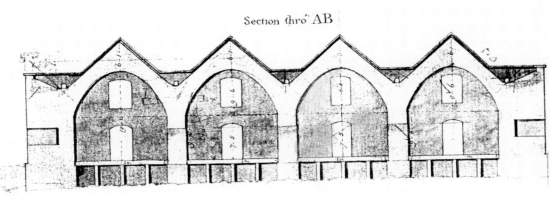

Section thro' AB

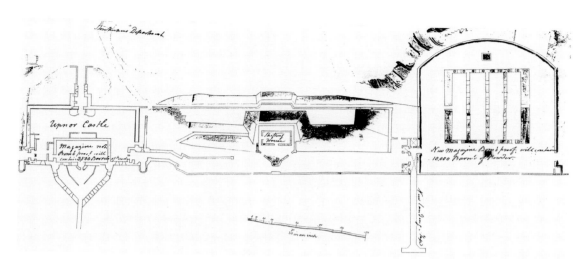

2.38 Upnor as completed in 1812. *(From TNA WO 44/140)*

the canal, stressed its value in wartime. Work began in 1800, and it must have appeared to the Board that great savings in transport would soon be made, but the canal was not completed until 1824 and it is not known if the Board ever patronised it. The bricks for the magazine, as at Priddy's Hard, came from the local ordnance brickfield.

Upnor was apparently unique in another ancillary industry run by the Board of Ordnance. This was the Ordnance Plantation (see Glossary), located behind the magazine area, which raised a variety of trees and shrubs useful in fortifications, presided over by a Foreman of Plantations. So useful was it that it survived the general asset-stripping of the Board's subsidiary activities which took place after the cessation of hostilities, a typical demand being that of 29 December 1824 for 2,000 five-year-old walnut trees (the wood was used for gunstocks), 5,000 five-year-old ash trees, 17,000 four-year-old quicksets for fences, and 20,000 to 40,000 willow cuttings. It appears to have survived until the demise of the Board itself, as in 1851 32,000 quicksets were ordered for the exterior slopes of the re-formed Gosport fortifications.[13]

Canal communications were also seen, initially, as an asset for the third great magazine depot to be originated during the war. In April 1811 the Master General and the Board determined that magazines to contain 20,000 barrels should be erected in the neighbourhood of Southampton, to serve as a depot, from which Priddy's Hard could draw on when necessary. Marchwood was to be a Store Depot only, like Tipner. The site lay on the opposite bank of Southampton Water from the historic port. There were three possible navigations in communication with Southampton Water, or in prospect: the Redbridge–Andover canal, completed in 1794, the Northam–Winchester navigation on the Itchen, and the Bursledon–Botley navigation, which never materialised. It was, according to a misinformed individual at the Board of Ordnance, only 9 miles from Andover to the Wiltshire and Berkshire canal,

which gave access to the whole system. In fact, it was some 15 miles from the Kennet and Avon canal. Clearly, enthusiasm for canals was at its peak in the deliberations of the Board. As with Upnor, these communications were never to be used, and Marchwood was to be supplied by ordnance craft throughout its history, though, as will be seen, it was to get a canal of its very own.

The site at Marchwood fulfilled the necessary criteria of being inferior land (and therefore cheap) and also 'at a considerable distance from any respectable House'. The original intention was for two magazines of 10,000 barrels rather than one of

2.39 Plan of Marchwood magazines and canal, as originally built. Note the pier and how the rolling stage is flanked by the examining rooms outside the magazine enclosure. (See page 245 for a phased plan of the site.) *(New Forest District Council)*

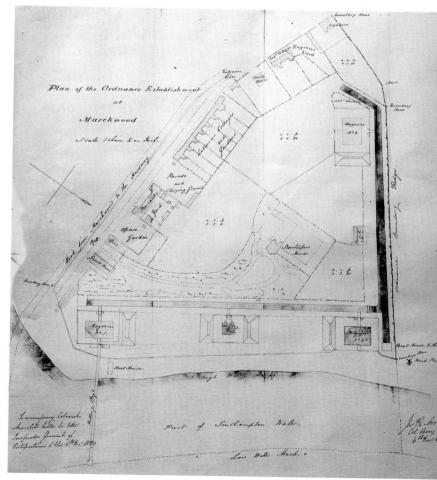

20,000, and in June 1812 plans were submitted for a 10,000-barrel magazine, of a construction very similar to Upnor. The Inspector-General of Fortifications, by then Lieut. General Mann (see Appendix B), thought that a bomb-proof construction was not necessary given the location. As has been seen, this was not a novel idea, and had been behind the original design for the main magazines at Keyham.

By August the CRE at Portsmouth, Major-General Fisher, was asked to report on the cost of four 5,000-barrel magazines, and orders were given for completing the purchase of the land. Unlike Pilkington, Fisher had never been closely involved with explosives stores before – not many Engineers had – and was supplied with a plan to explain the general construction of magazines. Mann suggested that if more than one magazine was built traverses should be provided, like those proposed for Waltham Abbey, and a drawing of these was sent to Fisher. By September Fisher had costed an establishment of three magazines, two traverses and a shifting house; as the buildings were not to be bombproof he suggested that they be roofed on the plan of the saltpetre storehouses at Faversham and Waltham Abbey. The bricks were to come from the ordnance brickyards at Stokes Bay and Fort Cumberland. Mann felt that the recently completed magazines for 10,000 barrels at Picket Field, Hungerford (incidentally, and surely not accidentally, on the Kennet and Avon canal) might serve as a useful model and Fisher inspected that establishment early in 1813. He had been told in February that his design bunched the magazines too closely, and that the land had been bought with a view to keeping them as far apart as possible. After visiting Hungerford he prepared two alternative plans, one utilising the Hungerford design and another of his own, which he naturally preferred. Instead of a rolling way to serve the magazines, a canal was to be cut, the excavated earth being used to form traverses. Cavity walls were to be so constructed as to form flues in which fires could be lit as soon as the building was

up, in order to dry it out as speedily as possible; also, lime mortar would be mixed with Harwich cement so that setting would be more rapid. Fisher's buildings would also be fireproof, if not bombproof, with 14-inch brick arches and slated roofs on timber, much like Weedon.

However, this design was not to be. General Congreve had drawn up plans for magazines with a capacity of 5,000 barrels, which would cost £2,850 each, while Fisher's cost £3,588. This was a decisive argument, though Fisher had the consolation of seeing his canal accepted. In the event, Congreve's design was modified to include Groves' patent wall construction, intended to secure against dry rot by the inclusion of voids in the brickwork, some connected with the open air, others totally enclosed. Fisher was to use this system at his discretion on buildings other than the magazines. Specifications for three magazines of 6,800 barrels capacity each were issued on May 25 1813. These insubstantial buildings were constructed far more rapidly than the conventional type of magazine, and by July 1814 the only buildings remaining to be constructed were the Officers' houses, working drawings for which were forwarded in October. The canal had been cut, but the manner of filling it was still in question in March 1815; storm water was adequate at first but the use of a spring proved necessary.

The establishment was nearly ready to open when it was given a preliminary inspection in June 1815 by officers from the Royal Laboratory, who had various adverse comments to make. Elementary errors had been committed: wooden spouts were fastened with iron holdfasts and there was iron door furniture on the gate of the boundary wall to the magazines; the platform on which the barrows were wheeled led through No.1 Magazine through which all the receipts and issues of powder to and from the other magazines had to pass; No.1 and No.2 Magazines were only 11 inches above high-water mark at spring tides, and the air holes to their floors afforded a lodgement for water, which had to affect the walls adversely.

2.40 Opposite: Aerial view of Marchwood magazines, 1947, looking east. The main line of magazines facing Southampton Water is shown, with the canal to the rear. (See Appendix A, page 245 for a phased plan of the site.) (New Forest District Council)

2.41 Marchwood – No.1 Magazine (1814–16). Opposite (inset): the magazine as it survives today, minus roof, within its surrounding walls.

This page, left: the receiving rooms built to the seaward side of the magazine in the 1840s, with one of the brick revetted traverses in the background; right: detail of a ventilator in the magazine wall. (Stephen Dent)

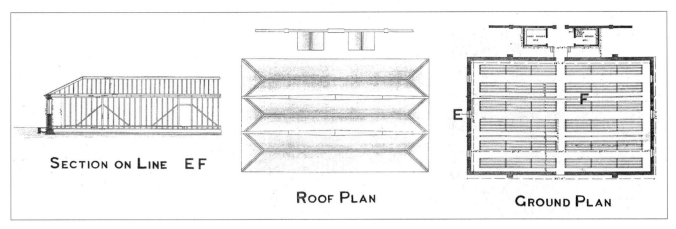

SECTION ON LINE EF

ROOF PLAN

GROUND PLAN

2.42 Marchwood – No.1 Magazine, Royal Engineers plan from 1871. This is the only Napeolonic-period magazine to have survived at Marchwood, the other having been destroyed through enemy bombing in 1940. It has brick cavity walls for the prevention of damp and temperature control, built according to a system patented in 1809 by John Groves. *(New Forest District Council)*

This depot was completed too late to play any part in the Napoleonic War, and was marginalised; though, as will be seen, it was to attain a prodigious size 40 years after its initial completion.[14]

Temporary wartime sites

The Board of Ordnance's activities in this period were very wide-ranging, including barracks, forts, magazines and the supply of building materials. Mention was made above of Harwich cement and Hungerford Magazine, which typified the two extremes of the Board's activities. Harwich Cement Factory (whose enclosure walls survive today) contained a cement mill and cooperage and provided high-grade cement for ordnance works. A highly specialised activity was the production of cylinder charcoal for gunpowder manufacture, and several of the buildings connected with this

process survive at Fernhurst and Fisher Street in Surrey. A gun-barrel factory was first planned at Enfield Lock in 1812, and the establishment was under construction in 1814. Fireships were still a weapon of war and in 1809 two sheds for fireship stores were built on Portsmouth Laboratory wharf. Great Yarmouth became a major fleet anchorage, and a major ordnance establishment was begun there in 1806, probably designed by James Wyatt, the considerably better known uncle of the designer of Portsmouth Laboratory. This comprised a magazine, six Storehouses, an Armoury, a workshop, Officers' quarters, a barrack and gatehouses. The whole establishment was abandoned in 1815, but despite partial demolition it survives as a uniquely complete site. Hungerford was but one example, though probably the largest, of store powder magazines constructed during the conflict and disposed of afterwards. A smaller

2.43 Marchwood – offices and guardhouse (today the offices of the yacht club), photographed in 1947. Note the fire buckets and, to the right, the cannon and the 'thunder bell' as it became known, a device used to warn of fire and, later, thunder – the precursor of lightning. (See also Appendix A, page 244). *(New Forest District Council)*

2.44 Marchwood No.1 Magazine, receiving rooms. This is a view from the foreshore, where the rolling stage was situated. *(Stephen Dent)*

example, for 2,000 barrels, was begun in 1808 at Dorchester. Others were established in old fortifications, such as Chester Castle. In addition to Tipner, Priddy's Hard, Upnor and Hungerford, the Board of Ordnance had, in 1811, magazines at Tilbury and Gravesend forts and, serving the capital, at Hyde Park. The latter, of c. 1805, and remodelled c. 1830 to the designs of Decimus Burton, survives. Two magazines in Shrewsbury's Armoury were built to the designs of James Wyatt in 1806, of which one with associated stores and housing survives. In 1817, there were thirty sites in Britain – mostly in existing barracks and forts – that had magazines of sufficient size to warrant the appointment of a Board of Ordnance Storekeeper.[15]

By the end of the war the responsibilities of the

Board of Ordnance ranged far beyond the relatively simple provision of powder, shot and guns that had been their stock-in-trade in the early years of the 18th century. After 1815 some of its activities were to be pruned, but there was to be no return to the uncomplicated past.

2.45 One of the firebarns built at Portsmouth in 1809. *(From TNA WO 55/786)*

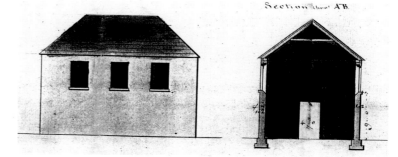

2.46 The Armoury, Great Yarmouth. The Armoury divided the Royal Ordnance Store at Southtown into two halves, namely a wharfside area with a magazine and bounded by storehouses, and a landward side with barracks, workshops and gate lodges. Most of the latter survive. Its design has been attributed to James Wyatt, architect to the Board of Ordnance during the Napoleonic Wars. *(NMR BB97/05968)*

Chapter 3 **Consolidation**

The facilities accumulated during the war were not disposed of hastily, although the number of ships in commission had reduced from 99 ships of the line and 495 cruisers in 1813 to 13 ships of the line and 89 cruisers by 1817. In December 1817 the Board decided to break up the depot for Fireship Stores at Portsmouth, but most of the floating magazines remained in service for several years, *Fortitude* being disposed of in 1820, *Atlas* having its fittings removed in 1821 and *San Antonio* being cleared of powder in 1823. *Bull Dog* appears to have been the last survivor at any of the dockyards, owing to its use as a depot to supply Little Horsea with repairable powder, and it lingered until September 1828. The inland magazines were soon sold, the buildings and land at Hungerford going in March 1821 for £6,457. The charcoal-making establishments in Surrey were sold in 1824. The brickyards at Fort Cumberland were disposed of between 1820 and 1824, but those at Stokes Bay, relocated further inland, were still in existence in 1830. Their survival was due to their proximity to one of the major building projects of the time, the Royal Clarence Victualling Yard at Gosport: in 1828 the contractor for this project, Hugh McIntosh, was allowed to buy Stokes Bay bricks. After the completion of the yard in 1832 the brickyards were disposed of, and it was also around this time that the Harwich cement factory was sold.[1]

During the 1820s the most significant routine maintenance undertaken at the retained yards and depots was the renewal of nearly all the timber-work of the roof of Priddy's Hard Magazine in 1821–2. In 1827 two unsuitably placed shifting houses were connected by a two-storey insertion for the reception of empty barrels, a significant addition that gave the magazine enclosure the appearance it retains today. So connected, the complex became known as the Long Storehouse, later altered to B Magazine to reflect its changed use. The covered passages connecting the camber with the original A Magazine and shifting houses were rebuilt in their present form in 1826–7. At the same time, Upnor Castle was modified. The laboratory buildings on the water bastion were rebuilt, probably because of their ruinous condition, and the central tower was drastically refitted to provide better access between the laboratory and the ground floor of the castle, now used as the Laboratory Storehouse, with a spiral staircase being built in an enlarged well, with revised hoisting arrangements that survive today. The laying up of the bulk of the ships in ordinary meant that the gunwharves were occupied with the storage and maintenance of their armaments; in 1824 at Portsmouth there were 7,154 guns, 2,422 of which were in good order, 4,067 required their bores lacquering, 4,203 needed external anti-corrosion paint, 316 wanted venting, and 1,850 were piled in stacks and needed to be taken down. The other gunwharves were undoubtedly similarly occupied. But the chief event of the decade was the prolonged enquiry made by a committee set up to enquire into the role of the laboratories and make decisions about their future.

Redevelopment of the laboratories

The value of these establishments during the war had not been a matter for any doubt. Portsmouth Laboratory had chiefly been employed in the manufacture of small arms ammunition, and between 30 August 1807 and 7 April 1814, 52,953,970 rounds had been made. At its height, in December 1813, it employed 353 people – of whom 294 were boys. But in 1827 the staff comprised only eight men, who during the first six months of 1827 had completed the following work:

Made flannel cartridges and packed them in lead-lined barrels	13,317
Made small arm cartridges, ball	682,000
Made small arm cartridges, blank	195,690
Repaired empty flannel cartridges	3,779

3.1 Isometric showing the development of B Magazine, which occupied the east of the magazine enclosure. The two original separate structures, one a shifting house (for the inspection of incoming powder) and the other a cooperage (after 1783 converted into a shifting house) had by 1812 been joined by a single-storey passage and in 1827 by a central two-storey unit to form a continuous range parallel with the magazine; between 1849 and 1856 the front was brought into a uniform line and the central roof line was raised by 1859. The east side of the range incorporates the original traverse wall to the magazine. (Illustration by David Evans / Stephen Dent)

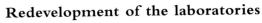

1812

1827

1849

The range of buildings heightened and refronted shortly after 1856

50

Examined empty flannel cartridges	7,823
Examined filled flannel cartridges	11,338
Examined small arm ball cartridges	1,044,199
Examined small arm blank cartridges	94,027
Repacked small arm ball cartridges	370,914
Repacked small arm blank cartridges	42,300
Broke up unserviceable small arm ball	673,285
Broke up unserviceable small arm blank	51,727

Plymouth Laboratory had manufactured 70,000,000 cartridges between 1806 and 1814.

The staff must have been comparable to that at Portsmouth, but it had been similarly reduced and in 1827 numbered only one foreman and four labourers. The duties of this small body of men comprised:

Examining and breaking up all ammunition returned from ships or issued from store
Making ball and blank cartridges
Filling and packing flannel cartridges in lead-lined barrels for the navy

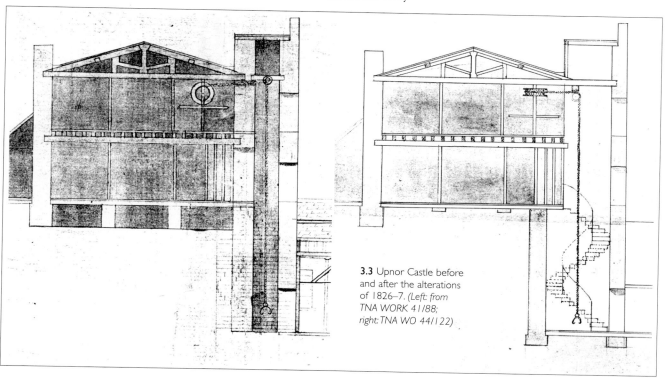

3.3 Upnor Castle before and after the alterations of 1826–7. *(Left: from TNA WORK 41/88; right: TNA WO 44/122)*

3.4 Upnor, the first floor of the main building today, showing a reconstruction of its use as a magazine. Note the hoist to the external door, shown in the section of the plan. (See also figure 1.6 on page 15.) *(English Heritage Photographic Library, K951091)*

Making rockets, miners' portfires, priming tubes, blue lights

Repairing common and lead-lined barrels, unheading and heading up powder and ammunition barrels

Making rocket sticks, and cases to contain rockets

Weighing and nailing up lead ball – strapping shot boxes and making lids

Quilting grape shot and filling case shot

Working powder boat between Keyham Point and laboratory

Cleaning and keeping in order all laboratory tools and engines

Airing fireship stores

The powder works had been an equally good investment. Little Horsea and Stamshaw had restoved and dusted 12,000 barrels during 1813, the year of highest output, and with a reduced staff were currently capable of dealing with 192 barrels a week. St Budeaux had restoved 86,617 barrels and dusted 83,548 between July 1806 and March 1820. However, in 1821 the receiving house and one of the stoving houses had been destroyed and the other stoving house badly damaged in an explosion caused by detaching shot from fixed ammunition, and operations were temporarily halted. The committee at first recommended that it be repaired to a degree to work one stoving house, which was adequate for peacetime. When St Budeaux had been established almost all powder returned from ships required restoving, but as a

consequence of the introduction of metal-lined cases the necessity was greatly decreasing.[2]

The committee decided that Portsmouth Laboratory, though badly situated, was so excellently arranged that the expense of moving it to a preferable site at Priddy's Hard was not justified. The location of the powder works was inconvenient, but the sites functioned well. The Plymouth Laboratory was also well arranged, but had the fatal disadvantage of being one and a half miles distant by water (the shipping difficulties in the Hamoaze must have been greater than in Portsmouth Harbour), and about the same by land from the magazines at Keyham Point. In November 1828 the Board decided to suppress it forthwith. The fate of Portsmouth hung in the balance. The best site for the relocation of any of the facilities at Plymouth would be Keyham Creek. The committee recommended that St Budeaux be restored to full production, and that the three stations of Devonport (as the naval base was now known), Portsmouth and Faversham, with the collateral aid of Ballincollig (in Ireland) should be made capable of restoving the whole mass of powder in the service in ten peacetime years. In the end, it was decided to retain all the Portsmouth establishments, with the powder works dealing with 10,000 barrels a year, while St Budeaux was initially to be restored to handle half that number, but eventually would work at the same rate as Portsmouth. The laboratory workers were to be transferred to the revamped St

Budeaux, as their experience in handling powder and knowledge of all the necessary precautions made them ideally suitable. Sir Augustus Frazer, Director of Royal Laboratory, Woolwich, suggested that St Budeaux be enlarged to handle 10,000 barrels a year, with a wooden railway instead of a rolling way connecting the dusting house to the present expense magazine (which was to be enlarged) and the magazine with the stoving houses.[3]

The closure of Plymouth Laboratory initiated the redevelopment of Keyham, as the new arrangements depended on the erection of a filling works there. The CRE, Colonel Morshead (see Appendix B), designed the Keyham additions, which comprised a shifting house, cartridge filling house and a breaking up house. As the breaking up operations required greater care, the breaking up house was detached from the other two for greater security. Morshead, aware of the importance of spacing, regretted that the site did not permit their being placed 400, 500 or even 600 feet from the magazines. Further significant additions were made at Keyham; in November 1829 estimates were prepared for a new examining house, filling house and railway, with traverse, a quay, traverse and rolling way, a jetty at Keyham Point and a new boathouse for four boats, the existing boat house site being used for the examining house. These buildings were to be of frangible construction, wooden with slated roofs, and the recommendations for Priddy's Hard envisaged by the Board in 1807, but apparently not implemented anywhere, were at last put into practice.[4]

Laboratory relocation

After 1815, there was an unnaturally prolonged period of European peace. Despite this, the navy was involved in numerous operations around the world, and it was naval pressures that brought about a renewed burst of activity by the Board of Ordnance during the 1840s. The explosive shell, a new weapon (or rather an old one updated and used on a vastly greater scale), required specialised accommodation. General Paixhans' shell-firing guns were introduced into the French service in 1824, and immediately after into the Royal Navy, though it was not until 1838 that the 8-inch gun, the favourite seaborne weapon of the day and the principal armament of British line-of-battle ships until the revolution in ordnance of the 1860s, was introduced. In November 1845 the First Naval Lord, Sir George Cockburn, minuted:

As the introduction of Shells filled with Gun powder into the Naval Service will frequently occasion a return of them into store at Stations both at Home and Abroad, it appears to me very desirable that it should be ascertained whether

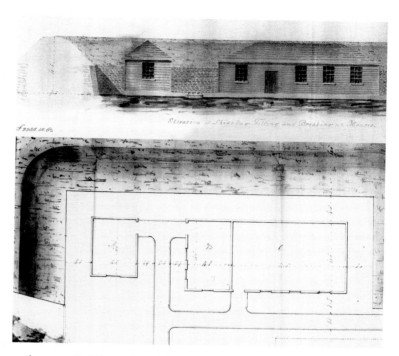

there are Buildings adapted for the examination and safe storing of those shells which cannot of course be deposited in Magazines.

Reports were ordered to ascertain if any suitable buildings existed. At Devonport, it was proposed to use the gunwharf cooperage as an examining room, though a fire in the carpenters' shop there the following month (caused by carpenters using heated irons when working on gun carriages) probably put a halt to this suggestion. It was recommended that the armoury (situated directly adjacent to the cooperage) be isolated, and the roofs of the carpenters' shop and armoury be replaced by iron pillars and corrugated iron. The Portsmouth Storekeeper replied that on the gunwharf there was a magazine (dating from before 1814) of three compartments with brick arched roofs, in which filled shells, carcasses and

3.5 The danger buildings designed by Colonel Morshead for Keyham. (From TNA WO 44/307)

3.6 Devonport Gunwharf as in 1847. The two 1720s storehouses flanked a quay with cranes. (From TNA WO 55/806)

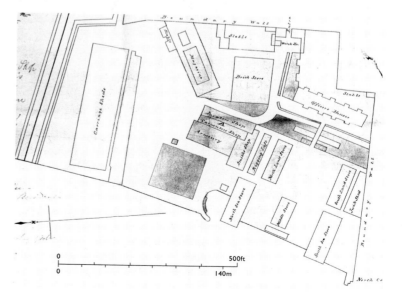

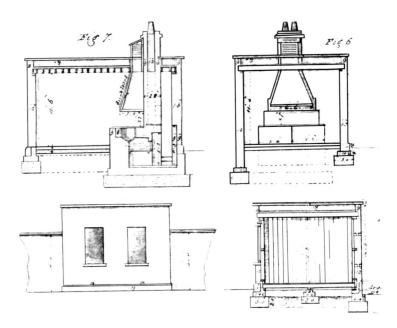

3.7 Two of the laboratory buildings at Priddy's Hard. Above: the lead-melting room; below: the building for filling small arms cartridges.
(From PTM/2936)

ble in case of Fire, and also the great danger there is of an accident surrounded as she is with an 100 Men (Excavators) the most depraved who in a moment of their insane drunkenness might be the means of hurrying hundreds of lives into another world and a severe loss of property.'

Captain Denison, the Engineer Officer in charge of the modernisation of the dockyard, recommended Priddy's Hard as a site for the laboratory, and the Admiralty concurred, but the Board of Ordnance saw no necessity for it to be moved. Of the alternative sites, Tipner was rejected, and Admiral Hyde Parker, the Admiral Superintendent of the Dockyard, considered that the industrialisation of the yard then in progress would make the gunwharf site dangerous. The decision in favour of Priddy's Hard was made rapidly and a site selected on 27 June 1846, and by April the next year Colonel Lewis, the CRE, had drawn up plans for the buildings. As the relocation was made at the Admiralty's request, they were prepared to defray the cost (estimated at about £9,684), on the understanding that the present laboratory and firemaster's house would become Admiralty property. During the first financial year £5,000 was to be provided for the removal of the laboratory to Priddy's Hard. By August 1847 specifications and plans for the new laboratory were completed and an advertisement for tenders was placed in *The Builder*. In July, Lewis designed an expense magazine to serve the laboratory, to hold 200 barrels. A separate landing stage was provided, so that the camber and rolling way were reserved for magazine purposes. The principle of the provision of separate facilities for each function within an ordnance establishment was being recognised as the key to safe and efficient working.[5]

When Major Lethbridge, Assistant Firemaster (in

Congreve rockets (see Glossary) were stored. There was no building suitable for examining filled shells. The CRE and the Inspector-General of Fortifications, Major-General Sir John Burgoyne (see Appendix B), proposed Priddy's Hard as the best site in the area for a purpose-built shell store, but the Board turned this down. While the location of additional shell stores remained undecided (the Admiralty recommending Whale Island, just to the north of the dockyard), the laboratory was to be relocated. In the time-honoured manner, an anonymous letter complained of its dangerous situation (see page 79). Apart from its proximity, 'not 20 Yards from the flames of our Chimneys', a powder vessel had been lying by the laboratory for many weeks, 'a great portion of that time aground, thereby rendering her removal absolutely impossi-

3.8 All that now remains of the laboratory are the north-west and north-east ranges, their pitched roofs replacing the original flat ones. These represent the sole surviving examples of an Ordnance Yard Laboratory.
(Stephen Dent)

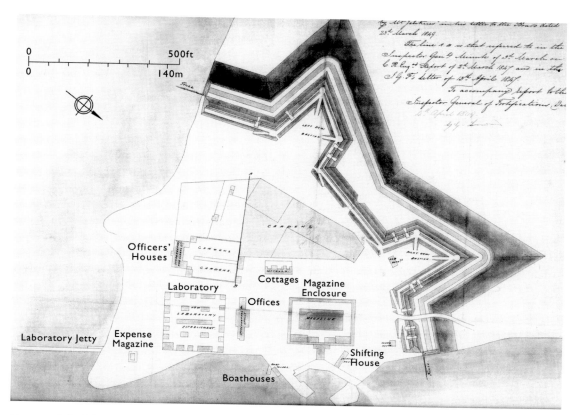

3.10 Priddy's Hard in 1849, after the completion of the laboratory complex and the improvement and restoration of the defences. Note the laboratory boathouse and, to the right of the camber, the first of the shifting houses for changing into magazine clothing to be built outside the magazine enclosure. (Adapted from TNA WP 44/284)

charge of the laboratory), was introduced into the command structure of Priddy's Hard, conflicts between him and Storekeeper Jenkins (in charge of the depot) were immediate, even before the transfer of the establishment. Lethbridge had been allocated rooms in the existing offices rather than provided with a separate office of his own, and Jenkins demanded that a partition and a new staircase be provided to isolate his department from that of the interloper. The CRE, not personally involved, wrote to the Board: 'I am not able to form any opinion as to the necessity of the separation of the two Departments … or the force of Mr Jenkins apprehensions, but as both are under the immediate Controul [sic] of the Board of Ordnance, I would suggest that Mr Jenkins' fears are rather imaginary than real'; no alterations were sanctioned.

The turf war continued, with the room occupied by Jenkins' messenger being appropriated for the laboratory attendant, after another struggle resolved by the Board. By 14 November 1848, all the stores had been shipped to Priddy's Hard, and the conflicts rose to a higher plane. Within a fortnight Jenkins was asked if the powder vessel *Letitia*

could be employed in conveying stores, including metal-lined cases and examined shells, between the gunwharf and the laboratory. Jenkins professed his willingness to assist, when the boat could be spared, but maintained that the available resources would 'seldom or ever' admit anything more than lending her and her Master when two of the crew of the gun hoys might be spared to assist, and that such a step would have to be sanctioned by the Board. The gunwharf officers were concerned with the efficient operating of the department, rather than squabbles between men lower than themselves in the hierarchy, and they added their weight to Lethbridge's request. Jenkins had to reply showing willing: 'if you will state the Number of these Cases and other Stores … & obtain the written Sanction of the Assistant Firemaster for their consignment to my charge I

3.11 The north-east block – a carpenters' shop converted into an examining room by 1880, to the right of the picture – has projecting from it the single-storey rolling way. This formed part of the tramway system that from the 1860s was devised in order to link C Magazine to the laboratory and its associated shell-filling complex. It extends round the rear of this building. (Jeremy Lake)

3.9 The laboratory expense magazine at Priddy's Hard, surrounded by a wall. (From TNA WO 55/794)

will then tell you what means I possess of transporting them to this Magazine, when metal lined cases are <u>urgently required</u>. At the present time both my Vessels have powder on board awaiting demands & directions in regard to its disposal.' He was, however, reluctant to do anything without sanction from on high. The Board exercised its authority and ordered that *Letitia* be used as proposed.

The situation was exacerbated by the fact that the laboratory landing stage was still unfinished, and use had to be made of the camber for laboratory purposes, a situation that enraged Jenkins. In February 1849 the Master of the gun hoy *Wellington* wrote to the Portsmouth officers:

'I beg leave to report for your information that agreeable to my orders I proceeded to Priddy's Hard to land Shell, in Situation in the Camber where I have frequently landed them before but on Mr Jenkins Seeing me he inquired what business I had to lye the Vessel there. I replied to him I had landed Shell there before with his sanction. Mr Jenkins then in a very ungentlemanly manner call'd me a <u>Liar</u> I then immediately reported the case to the Assistant Firemaster and by his direction landed the Shell without moving the Vessel.'

Jenkins gave a qualified apology:

'if I used the language imputed to me, I very much regret it. I must observe that when the Master brought the Vessel along side this Wharf the Laborers were engaged in wheeling powder from the magazine to the Laboratory Department and passed close to where the Vessel lay in the Camber loaded with live Shells without having given me any previous notice of the circumstance or I should not have interfered.'

The Board decided against him, ordering that,

'he will allow the Laboratory Stores to be landed at the Wharf under his Charge until the Pier for the Laboratory is constructed and they desire that such mutual arrangements may be made between him and the Assistant Firemaster as will prevent any Risk of explosion in conducting the public Service the Board at the same time beg to observe that it is the duty of public servants to carry on the duties of their respective stations peacefully, a contrary course being invariably prejudicial to the public Service.'

A chance for revenge soon arose, though on a sufficiently ludicrous scale. The following month Lethbridge asked the Board for permission to graze his animals within the ramparts of Priddy's Hard, but was turned down. Nevertheless, he

carried out his intentions, giving Jenkins the opportunity to denounce him to the Board.[6]

The transfer of the laboratory coincided with a downturn of business, and the establishment was reduced to a staff of just thirteen: 1 Foreman of Labourers (at 5/- per day); 1 Foreman of Carpenters (5/- per day); 1 Cooper (4/- per day); 1 Coxswain (2/4 per day); 8 Labourers (2/2 per day); 1 apprentice, to fill the first labourer's vacancy. The following work was on hand: 360 metal cases and 1,030 metal lined cases were to be cleaned; 10,670 flannel cartridges repaired; 1,050 shells examined and cleaned; 1,360 caps and fuzes; 800 metal-lined cases needed repair; 150,000 rounds of small arms ammunition and 400 powder barrels were to be examined. With the reduced staff now at his disposal, Lethbridge thought that he could cope better if the small arms ammunition were sent to Woolwich to be broken up.

At Marchwood, the predictions made in 1815 about the flooring duly materialised, and in 1846 the floors of two of the magazines were sinking from dry rot, the third having been already repaired by the insertion of brick arches beneath. In August 1849 the Board decided to close the establishment down entirely, and the stock was moved to Tipner, Priddy's Hard, Dover and Purfleet. Stamshaw and Little Horsea were also closed by July 1849, though the buildings were retained, and Stamshaw was used to hold fireship stores, being repaired for this purpose during the financial year of 1853–4. Restoving of powder had not been carried out at Horsea since 1833, and the practice was about to be generally discontinued, partly because of improved storage afloat following the general use of metal-lined cases and Dell's pentagonal metal cases (for use in steamers), and partly because of changes in the make-up of the powder itself, though dusting was still practised. St Budeaux had been still engaged in restoving, and it had recently been proposed to refit one of the stoves on the same lines as at Waltham Abbey, but it was underused and was closed down at the same time as the Portsmouth powder works. The final returns of barrels of powder held for restoving were Purfleet (2,200 doubtful, for examination); Chatham (2,763); Faversham (2,124); Priddy's Hard (13); Tipner (112); Keyham Point (201); St Budeaux (860). Since Portsmouth had stopped the process, it was only performed at St Budeaux and Faversham. St Budeaux, however, was to remain, and the buildings were to become a vital component of an enormous new magazine complex, whose story had begun a few years earlier.[7]

Keyham moves to Bull Point

Keyham Point had become the subject of local apprehension, although in February 1841 Colonel Cockburn, the Director of the Royal Laboratory,

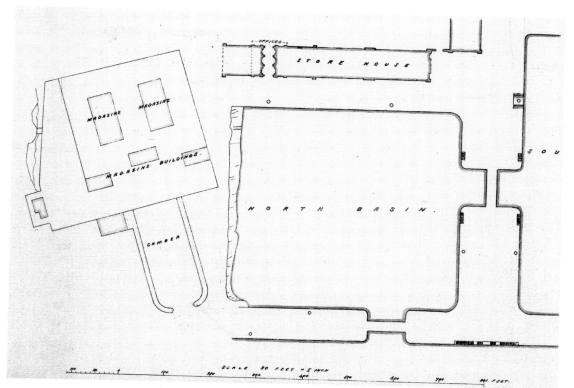

3.12 Keyham Magazine shown in relationship to the steady expansion in the late 1840s of the North Basin and the great quadrangle range. (From TNA ADM 1/5660)

rejected a petition against it. He asserted that the location had been selected as being a safe distance from the dockyard, with no contiguous buildings that would be endangered. Of late years the town of Devonport had gradually encroached upon the magazines, knowingly approaching the danger of which they now complained. If the inhabitants of Devonport were to succeed in getting the magazines moved a precedent would be established. The brewer, Samuel Whitbread, had complained some years previously about Purfleet (probably unaware that many gunners and engineers shared his fears about that establishment). Everywhere lay open to objections: Southampton might complain of Marchwood; Portsmouth and Gosport of Priddy's Hard and Tipner; Upnor Castle had a populous neighbourhood; the magazine in the Arsenal was situated between Woolwich and Plumstead and surrounded with buildings; the magazine at Leith would affect Edinburgh; Dover was vulnerable, and indeed so was every other place where Government magazines were stationed.

The Keyham Magazines were, however, to be moved, but not in response to any civilian agitation. In September 1843, Captain Burgmann, RE, in charge of the great expansion of Devonport Dockyard, wrote to the CRE Plymouth stating that the formation of a Steam Engine Establishment, with a basin for steam vessels, had impelled the Admiralty to approach the Ordnance Board over Keyham Point with a view to acquiring the site. As has been seen, the building of a magazine establishment using the conventional substantial construction was a lengthy process, requiring some kind of stop-gap, and the expedi-

ent of floating magazines was contemplated. Cockburn stated that two ships would be required: one a line-of-battle ship as the depot ship containing 10,000 barrels, to be moored above St Budeaux; the second, to hold 6,000 barrels of powder for examination, being anchored nearer the powder works. The examination of returned ammunition, breaking up and filling cartridges, was to be performed at St Budeaux as a temporary measure. The ships were to be fitted out in bays in the same manner as the Keyham Point magazines, and a temporary store found at the gunwharf for empty barrels and a cooperage. In April 1844 two ships were requested from the Medway. However,

3.13 The proposed use of St Nicholas' Island as a magazine. (From TNA WO 44/313)

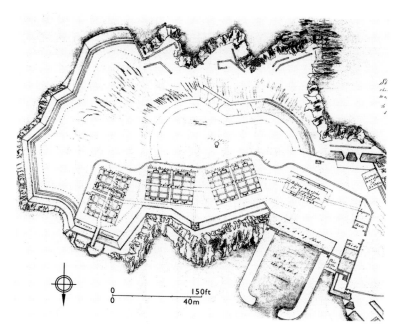

work on converting *Armada* to a floating magazine was suspended on 1 September 1845; if the job was taken in hand again it could be completed in about six months and would cost £8,500. *Medway* was also allocated but work on her was never begun. The conversion would cost at least £5,000 to £6,000 and by February 1847 the Respective Officers, the CRE Colonel Oldfield (see Appendix B), the Commanding Officer Royal Artillery (CRA) and Ordnance Storekeeper, did not think the expenditure worthwhile. It was far better to expedite the construction of Bull Point, which had in the intervening three years come to light as a suitable site for development.

On 22 May 1844, the Master General, Sir George Murray, had requested Colonel Oldfield to select a site for the new magazine establishment. There was no lack of possibilities. Petre Point, on the opposite bank of the Tamar from St Budeaux, St Nicholas' Island (now known as Drake's Island) and Mount Batten each had their advocates (see figure 3.13). Petre Point offered the possibility of extensive fortifications with barracks being provided to protect the magazines, but these were estimated at £55,700. The First Naval Lord, Admiral Sir George Cockburn, thought that two magazines might be preferable to one, and that a large magazine on St Nicholas' Island, backed up by a smaller at Mount Batten, might be the best solution. He also favoured a site at Millbay, but being in a built-up area it was thought to be out of the question. However, the Kinterbury estate, to the rear of Bull Point adjoining St Budeaux, and described as abounding with excellent water and good building stone, was on offer for £23,500. A committee, composed of naval and ordnance officers, reported that at Bull Point there was ample space for the magazines, which would be quite safe from any explosion that might take place at St Budeaux: 'A Traverse might be constructed, & by excavating an interior Canal between the two Establishments, the Powder might be transferred, after it has been restoved, to the Magazines by means of Powder Barges, without running the risk of a second voyage by Sea.' The Commander in

Chief at Plymouth favoured St Nicholas' Island, but there was not enough space. During the spring of 1845 matters remained in flux. In February the Master General and Board told the Admiralty they considered Point Petre a better site, but on 11 March tenders for work at Bull Point were called for. A fortnight later, however, a report was completed with plans, sections and estimates for magazines on St Nicholas' Island. Despite the fact that an apparent decision had been made in March for Bull Point, it was not until the following month that plans for Point Petre were abandoned. The development of the site had already been impeded by indecision on the part of the owner, who thought there might be a silver lode there. On 17 April Thomas Elliott, the owner of the Kinterbury estate, wrote to the Admiralty to ask if they wanted any part of it, but nobody there knew anything about the matter; tentative negotiations had been carried on in secrecy by the Admiral Superintendent Sir Samuel Pym.[8]

In the face of all this confusion, Colonel Oldfield decided to find out exactly what took place at Keyham Point to see if operational necessities ruled out any of the sites. It seems odd that this needed to be done, but it appears that ordnance officers liked to keep their activities veiled from outsiders in the services. He discovered that as soon as the Storekeeper received the Admiral Superintendent's authority to take the powder out of any ships, preparatory to their coming into the harbour to refit or be paid off, a powder vessel was sent into Plymouth Sound for that purpose. The powder was then landed and deposited in the magazines, and as soon as possible each barrel or case was taken into the examining house, separately opened and each cartridge minutely inspected, serviceable cartridges being immediately repacked and returned to the magazines to be again issued for service; the defective ones were separated from the others, returned to the magazines and broken up, the powder being sent to St Budeaux to be processed, and then returned to Keyham. The number of filled flannel cartridges issued to a 1st Rate was about 9,800, which required about 800 metal-lined barrels to contain them, and the filling of these alone would occupy all the workforce for one month. In the seven weeks before Oldfield's investigation, 6,037 had been made up, and 16,000 had been issued since the start of the year. It was clear to Oldfield that the restoving had to be carried out at a distance from the main magazines, but at the same time there needed to be convenient access between the two sites. This at once ruled out Mount Batten and St Nicholas' Island, with Bull Point clearly the best site. Colonel Cockburn thought there should be five magazines, separated by traverses, holding 6,000 barrels each, and a small building for percussion caps and detonating tubes.

3.14 Oldfield's first surviving plan of Bull Point, dated March 1846. *(From TNA WO 55/805)*

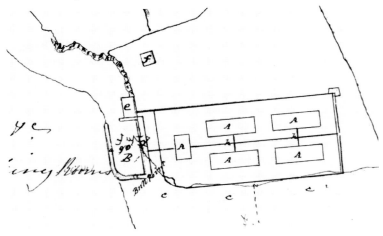

3.15 Poster inviting tenders for the building of Bull Point magazines. *(TNA WO55/807)*

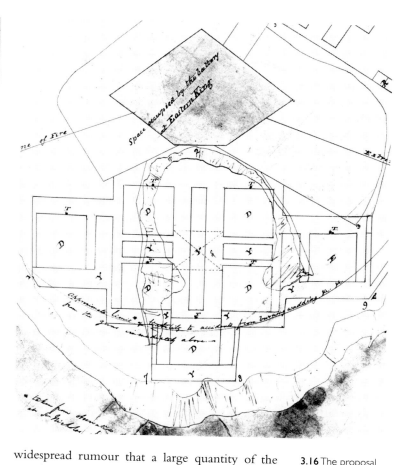

3.16 The proposal for a magazine establishment below Eastern King Redoubt. *(From TNA WO 55/806)*

The Purfleet Magazines were suggested as a suitable model for the buildings themselves, if not for the layout. A tram road should connect the magazines with St Budeaux, and, on account of the shallowness of the water at low tide, a long jetty would be absolutely necessary. Because of the relatively isolated situation, a small barrack would be required for the guard.

Following up these suggestions, Oldfield requested drawings of the Purfleet buildings and, commencing in the spring of 1846, began to produce a sequence of design studies. A basin was incorporated from the outset, though not among Cockburn's suggestions, while the recommendation to provide traverses was ignored. In fact, the spacing of the magazines was apparently intended to group them in as small an area as possible, an even worse arrangement than that of Purfleet. Possibly Oldfield thought that the advice to follow Purfleet's design applied to the layout as well as the buildings; he was clearly unaware of the long history of unease at the highest levels about the safety of the establishment. The danger buildings were, however, placed over 300 feet from the nearest magazine, though they were grouped in a single block. At the end of the year all these criticisms were levelled at Oldfield's designs. Though no satisfactory design had been produced, pressures were mounting for construction to begin as soon as possible, and in February 1847 Edward St Aubyn, the Steward of the Manor of Stoke Damerel, wrote to the Board of Ordnance of a

widespread rumour that a large quantity of the powder at Keyham Point would be sent to various places within the Devonport Lines; and explained that 'Very great uneasiness & anxiety have been created in the minds of the Inhabitants.' An anonymous letter reinforced the point, and Admiral Sir Thomas Hastings, the recently retired Captain of the gunnery training ship *Excellent* and now Storekeeper of the Ordnance, suggested that in view of the situation at Devonport the new magazines should be built as quickly as possible. Oldfield had in fact just drawn up specifications, and he informed Burgoyne, the Inspector General of Fortifications, that with an efficient contractor the magazines and boundary wall might be completed within two years of commencing work. On 26 April Baker & Son's tender for £181,000 for work at Bull Point was accepted – they were also the contractors for the Keyham Steam Factory, basin and docks.[9]

It might be thought that construction now proceeded smoothly, but in fact the whole question of the suitability of Bull Point was about to be re-opened. The instigator was the Storekeeper of Keyham Point, who addressed Oldfield directly. He thought a superior arrangement would be a principal depot at Bull Point, under the charge of the Firemaster, supplemented by an expense magazine by the Cattewater, which might be the best site for the whole establishment '... but for the opposition to be apprehended from the proximity to the town of Plymouth; the danger of which

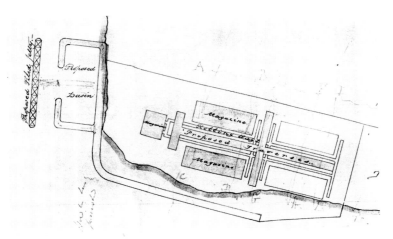

3.17 This design of June 1848 introduced traverses between the closely grouped magazines. *(From TNA WP 55/806)*

proximity is perhaps more imaginary than real.' As an alternative, Bull Point might be supplemented in case of emergency, when there was no time to send powder from there to vessels in the Sound, by land-service magazines at Devonport, or a magazine built within the walls of the Royal William Victualling Yard. This, rather than Bull Point, would be the place where all the most important parts of the duty of supplying ships, and removing powder from them when they were refitted or paid off, would be performed under the Storekeeper's control. But what the Storekeeper really wanted was to hang on to Keyham Point: 'I further submit that until the question of the extension of the existing Magazines be decided, or a new site be definitively approved by the Admiralty, that not another barrow be removed that can further impair the efficiency of what remains of the present Establishment.' Oldfield was won over by these arguments, and suggested that Keyham Point should remain, being separated from the Steam Factory by a traverse, to be formed by the excavations from the docks. 'It would certainly diminish the area of the Steam Dockyard, but with the strong objections urged against every site that has been proposed, and as Magazines are indispensable, I know not what other plan to suggest.'[10]

Other people did have suggestions to offer. Burgoyne, as Inspector General of Fortifications, was uniquely placed to put his oar in. He now listed four principal objections to Bull Point:

1 Its great distance up the Hamoaze for the transfer of the ammunition to and from warships.
2 The unfavourable nature of the shore, involving a very large expense for the formation of a basin with a deep water channel.
3 Being distant from any inhabited locality housing must be provided for the whole workforce, and a Barrack for the Guard.
4 It did not fall within any system of defensive protection.

The Admiralty's latest proposal had been a suggestion for dividing the facilities by constructing the depot magazines at Bull Point, provided merely with a stage for embarkation at high water, eliminating the basin there, and establishing an expense magazine of 6,000 barrels on St Nicholas' Island. Burgoyne thought the island was most unsuitable, and preferred to place six magazines holding 2,000 barrels each under Eastern King. Although only 300 or 400 yards from the town of Stonehouse, an intervening hill of solid rock, 60 feet high, would dissipate the shock of an explosion. Eventually, Burgoyne hoped, additional larger magazines would be added until Bull Point was made redundant, though this was not to be attempted '… till the public had become more reconciled to the measure, and better aware of the unreasonableness of their apprehensions.' But there was a fatal snag: the architect John Foulston had already planned a development on this ground on behalf of the Earl of Mount Edgcumbe, whose lawyer stated that however unfounded any alarm might be, it would materially affect the value of property in Stonehouse and that even were the Earl disposed to abandon his projects and make an arrangement with the Government (which he was not) it was most improbable that the perpetual tenants of the

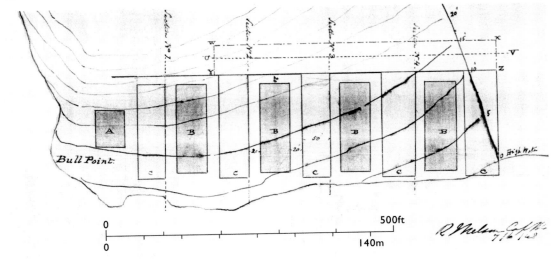

3.18 This plan from Oldfield's office in the same month was adopted as the basis for the final design, with a basin added. *(From TNA WO 55/805)*

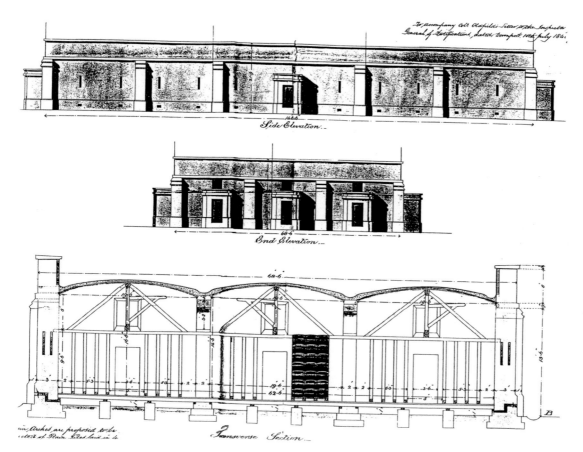

Side Elevation

End Elevation

Transverse Section

3.19 Oldfield's design for the main magazines at Bull Point. Note the traveller cranes sited within each of the three bays. (From TNA WO 55/805) Compare with the section of a Maltese powder magazine, on St. Clement's Bastion, Cottonera Lines, Malta. (Adapted from Quentin Hughes, Malta: A Guide to the Fortifications, Liverpool, 1985, p.101. Original in the Bibliotecca National, Valletta, Malta.)

Earl could be brought to agree. The Admiralty liked Burgoyne's proposal, but foresaw the opposition. In the spring of 1848 several alternative plans were prepared for these magazines, but nothing came of any of them. The estimated cost of £120,000, quite apart from other things, worked against the site near Stonehouse, but the planning resurfaced shortly among the preliminary studies for Bull Point.

By June it was finally decided that Bull Point was the best site available, and the question of its design was re-opened. Traverses were now to be provided, though the new Director of the Royal Laboratory, Colonel Hardinge, thought traverses were not required for store magazines; they were very expensive to build and it was not clear if they would be any use with large magazines. A first redesign merely interposed traverses between the four closely grouped magazines but subsequent designs offered more substantial traverses between much more generously spaced buildings, and Oldfield's plan closely resembled these. The magazines themselves differed from any previously constructed in England, but strongly resembled in

Spaccato per il largo del Magazzino

section an 18th-century magazine at St Clement's Bastion in the Cottonera Lines, Malta. The Maltese fortifications had been well known to the Royal Engineers, both practically as well as by repute, since the British occupied the island in 1800. The buildings, as shown in Oldfield's design of 1848, are fireproof rather than bombproof. No drawings survive of the final plans, which were the work of the succeeding CRE, Colonel Holloway, who drew up the specifications in July 1850. His modifications to the magazine design offered a capacity of 10,000 barrels each as against 9,500, and a saving of £3,528.[11]

Chapter 4 # The Impact of the Russian War

In June 1850 the final plans for the Bull Point magazines were approved, and the business of contracting for the work was set in motion. Characteristically, the lowest tender was accepted and the contractor ran into difficulties, going bankrupt and being replaced in 1852. Earlier in the year it had been decided to develop the under-used restoving establishment at St Budeaux as a laboratory, to be connected with the Bull Point magazines by means of a tramway. This would bring the magazine and manipulation facilities together on a single site, but with a much greater degree of separation than at Priddy's Hard. As a consequence there were never to be the same concerns about safety at Bull Point. A rationalisation of the various ordnance sites in the Portsmouth area had taken place following the move of the laboratory, with Stamshaw, Little Horsea and Marchwood all being closed. Stamshaw was retained for a time as a storehouse, holding the incendiary materials for fireships and being repaired for this purpose in the financial year 1853–4. Marchwood was kept tidy and advertised for letting; the coastguard took on the officers' accommodation, boat house and some other ancillary buildings, and in 1851 a retired sea captain by the name of Macrae rented the Storekeeper's house on a three-year lease, attracted by the secluded position and the sea air (for his wife's health). There were no takers for the magazines, but a local contractor enquired about using the examining room and landing stage to export white sand for the glass industry. The other depots and gunwharves remained unaltered.[1]

A lack of facilities

With the loss of the facilities at Stamshaw and Little Horsea there was now no means of proving powder in the area, and arrangements had to be made at Priddy's Hard. A suggestion that buildings for this purpose be placed in the traverse formed by the newly finished ditch of the fortifications, on which reconstruction had begun in 1846, was turned down by Major Lethbridge, the Assistant Firemaster, who thought that a bell tent and mortar platform would be adequate for the present. [This idea was implemented on a grand scale 50 years later (see pages 155–6).] In the spring of 1850 Captain Pickering replaced Lethbridge and soon had reasons to worry about the safety of the establishment. A Turkish warship landed stores in a condition that no ship of the Royal Navy would countenance. The powder cases were iron bound, with powder escaping from many of them; shells and carcasses were packed loose in barrels with priming exposed and quick-match hanging from them. The normal procedure was to lodge the packages of landed explosive and pyrotechnic stores in the magazine then take them to the examining room for opening; unserviceable or repairable items were sent to the laboratory for further examination. Pickering thought, not surprisingly, that stores in the bad condition of the Turkish ammunition should not be placed in or near a magazine, and that in any case the examining room was too close to B Magazine. The offending ammunition was repacked and sent to Stamshaw. A new examining room and rolling stage were proposed, but not proceeded with.[2]

Pickering did not stay long at the laboratory, being replaced by Captain Cockburn in 1852. There was a need now for increased magazine accommodation in the Portsmouth area; the temporary loss of facilities at Devonport until Keyham could be replaced by Bull Point threw a strain on the sister yard, with filled ammunition held in readiness for sea service being divided between Priddy's Hard and Tipner. The most pressing requirement was for a shell magazine, the local CRE and CRA holding different views on its location. The CRE preferred the Portsmouth side as better defended but the decision was eventually taken to build on the gunwharf, with construction of a second shell magazine beginning in the early summer of 1853, together with an additional powder magazine (see text box opposite). While these modest additions were made at Portsmouth, plans were prepared for the construction of a basin and jetty at Bull Point, where the magazines were proceeding steadily, with completion date set for the autumn of 1854. The storage problems were worse on the Medway than on the south coast. John Shepherd, Deputy Storekeeper at Upnor, was short-handed as well, with only three or four labourers engaged in filling cartridges in the laboratory, so that he had to ask Woolwich to supply the shortfall. One of the arches of the magazine was being refloored and the remaining space was crammed; after the repairs the building would still be full with no space available to take ammunition returned from ships.[3]

The war begins

The purse strings were to be released to partially solve these difficulties. During the early months of 1853 the relations between Russia and Turkey deteriorated rapidly. On 31 May an ultimatum was delivered to Turkey, and on 2 July Russian troops crossed the River Pruth into Moldavia. On 15 July the Portsmouth officers were asked to report on the current condition of the Marchwood magazines, and estimate the time and cost to put them

in a serviceable condition. Macrae, who had engaged in many violent disputes with the coast-guard officer and the retained foreman, was informed, to his fury, that the Board of Ordnance would repossess the premises when his lease expired in March 1854. Old employees, hearing of the plans, put out feelers about re-engagement. On 30 November shellfire from the Russian fleet destroyed a Turkish squadron in the Black Sea harbour of Sinope, confirming the lethality of the projectile against wooden ships. Britain finally declared war on 27 March 1854, and the following month a Mr Duncan was placed in charge of Marchwood with the rank of Deputy Storekeeper. However, the site was not to play any significant part in the conflict. The Admiralty had despatched

---

Gunwharf stores during the 1850s

In 1850 gunwharf stores included brass and iron ordnance for land and sea service, with carriages, shot, shells, muskets, pistols, swords, pikes, canteens, haversacks, camp equipment, entrenching tools and greatcoats. The only powder kept there was that contained in filled shells, it having been decided that a quarter of the shells were to be kept filled. Metal-lined cases were rapidly ousting wooden barrels as containers for powder, and shell guns were supplied to line-of-battle ships; the first-rate *Neptune*'s magazine and shell rooms could receive 740 metal-lined cases, 360 × 8-inch shells and 300 × 6-inch. New types of projectile began to be introduced, the prelude to a flood of new designs of ordnance. In the summer of 1852 8-inch and 10-inch Moorsom's shells were ordered for supply to all ships, in proportion of quarter of shells allowed. All ships were to be issued with 6-inch shells with Moorsom's fuzes (see Glossary) in the following proportions:

1st Rate	150
2nd Rate (*Princess Charlotte* class)	150
Other 2nd Rate	100
4th Rate	60
5th Rate	50
6th Rate	35
Sloops	25

By December 1853 the following proportions were laid down for screw ships:

		Per gun
Bow & stern pivots		180
8-in 65 & 60 cwt	Distant	40
	Full	20
	Reduced	20
32-pdr 56 cwt	Distant	40
	Full	20
	Reduced	20
Filled 6-in shell	Bow & stern pivots	60
	Side guns & carronades	10
32-pdr round shot	Bow & stern pivots	120
	Side guns & carronades	70

The war brought about the hasty conversion of five old two-

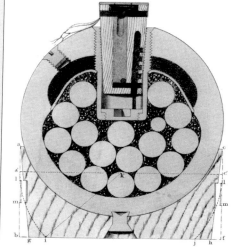

4.1 A section through Boxer's diaphragm shrapnel shell, fitted with Boxer's fuze. These replaced the older type of shrapnel shell. (*From Majendie and Boxer, Descriptive Plates to Ammunition, London, various dates; this plate 1863*)

deckers to screw propulsion as floating batteries, following the precedent of the first steam battleships, and the four blockships successfully converted in 1847. The gunwharf was ordered to supply each with:

lower deck –	24 × 32-pdr 56 cwt
	4 × 8-in
main deck –	26 × 32-pdr 50 cwt
upper deck –	2 × 68-pdr
	4 × 10-in

Mortar vessels, for assaults on coastal fortifications, were each to be equipped with a 13-inch mortar and 300 filled shells in boxes, 50 carcasses, 64 Dell's cases and 360 wooden fuzes. Private contractors failed to supply enough ironwork for new gun carriages, and the gunwharf smithery was asked to assist. Improved mechanical appliances for shifting all these warlike stores were needed and a sheerlegs was sanctioned early in 1856. The Spring Equipment (which was never issued because of the sudden termination of the war) was not to include Shrapnel shells. Instead they would be supplied with Diaphragm shells, which would require a new type of fuze.

WO 55/2105, WO 55/2106, WO 55/2108, D. K. Brown, 'The First Steam Battleships', in *Mariner's Mirror*, November 1977; WO 55/2111, WO 55/2113, WO 55/2114

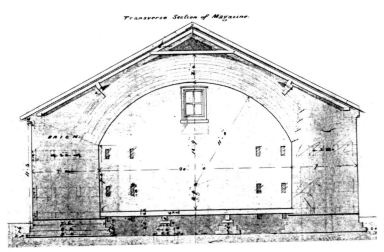

Transverse Section of Magazine.

4.2 The Portsmouth Gunwharf shell store of 1856 (see page 66) was a massive Vauban-type construction. Its bombproof vault was eventually reduced in thickness. Although shell stores were a new building type, there was little to differentiate them from earlier magazines.
(From PTM/1831)

fleets to the Baltic and Black Seas before the declaration of war, which required a supply of Dell's metallic powder cases. These had to be stowed at Upnor magazine, necessitating immediate modifications to the third arch in the autumn of 1854. The gunwharves were kept busy not only in despatching shells, carcasses and fuzes to these forces, but also stores, which were even more necessary for the survival of the troops: Portsmouth Gunwharf received 360,000 square feet of asphalted felt roofing for prefabricated huts in the Crimea. The storage problem naturally got worse and worse during 1855; the Assistant Firemaster at Priddy's Hard was asked if he could store live shells for which there was no room at the gunwharf in the Laboratory Magazine. He refused on the grounds of safety and the small size of the magazine, but offered to empty them and store them in the laboratory, refilling as required for

despatch. As an immediate measure a temporary shed at the gunwharf was approved, and a further shell magazine there proposed for the next financial year. At Upnor, John Shepherd represented that no more powder and shells could be accommodated if the depot was to remain a working rather than a deposit magazine, and that a shell store was urgently required; some 16,500 shells of various calibres needed to be housed there, and the only accommodation was on the first floor of the Castle. Shells had to be landed, taken through the laboratory and hoisted up (a windlass remains there today). The Storekeeper at Chatham thought that the facilities at Upnor were quite adequate for a peacetime establishment, but that was scarcely the point; the Baltic Fleet had to return home in the winter as the sea iced up, and all its ammunition would need to be unloaded, much of it in the Medway. Manufacture of a new weapon, Hale's war rocket, took place not only at Woolwich Laboratory but also at Stamshaw, whose fireship stores were sent to the still unoccupied magazines at Marchwood, where Hale was also authorised to make his rockets. The magazines started to come into use again at the end of 1855, when all made-up ammunition in store at Woolwich was transferred to Marchwood, and a military guard reinstated. [4]

Transformation of the Ordnance Depots

The main event of 1855 was the abolition of the Board of Ordnance, the Order in Council for its abolition being signed on 6 June. All ordnance

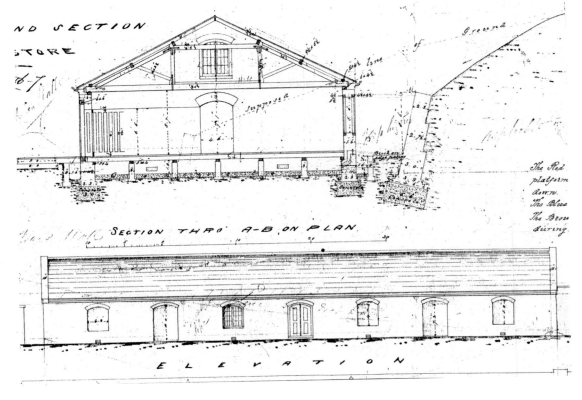

NO SECTION STORE

SECTION THRO' A-B ON PLAN

ELEVATION

4.3 By contrast, the lightweight design of the contemporary shell store at Upnor pointed the way forward for future Shell Stores.
(From AD13)

matters, save the control of troops, now came under the Secretary of State for War. Three new civilian posts were created: Superintendent of Stores, Superintendent of Contracts and Superintendent of Clothing. Five serving artillery officers were in charge of ordnance manufacture: Superintendent of Ordnance, Superintendent of Gunpowder, Superintendent of the Carriage Department, Superintendent of the Laboratory and Superintendent of Small Arms. It was under this new organisation, which was intended, among other things, to cut down the lag between decision-making and implementation, that a great expansion of magazine accommodation was initiated. It is not known if the Committee on Magazines, which reported by the beginning of March 1856, was set up under the new dispensation. Its recommendations were not restricted to England; a permanent store of 300,000 barrels were to be maintained, with increased accommodation provided at the Medway, Weedon, Alderney, Gibraltar and Malta. The Secretary of State for War, Lord Panmure, in approving the decision, noted that there were good sites on the Medway, but these locations remain unknown. In fact, the Medway was the position least favoured by geography for a magazine serving a major dockyard, as would become apparent later in the century. Of these recommended sites, nothing was done in the

event at Weedon, but additional works on a large scale were provided at Marchwood, Tipner and Plumstead.[5]

The year 1856 saw the beginning of the transformation of the Ordnance Depots on a scale not seen since the Napoleonic Wars. The construction of these new magazines proceeded with a rapidity that seems to have justified the organisational changes. At the beginning of April plans were initiated for a new powder magazine and a shell store at Upnor. Dedicated shell stores were a new building type, and there was disagreement about

4.4 Upnor magazine, interior view. Note the tracks for the overhead traveller crane. (Jeremy Lake)

4.5 An exterior photograph of Upnor in 1930, showing the 1808 magazines in the foreground and beyond them the 1856–7 magazine. The former has been demolished, the latter survives. Just visible on the right are the gates to the jetty. (Royal Engineers Library)

the degree of protection they required. As gunpowder was safely contained within a shell, did a shell store need to be bombproof (as the store currently being designed for Portsmouth Gunwharf was, though the vault was reduced in thickness from eight courses to three) or merely fireproof? Colonel Boxer (see Appendix B), Superintendent of the Royal Laboratory, was in favour of bombproof construction, but John Shepherd thought a slate roof would be quite adequate, and the building was so designed, setting the pattern for the future. The building was completed by November, by which time construction of the new magazine, designed by Lieutenant Colonel Savage (see Appendix B), had begun. This building followed the design of D'Arcy's original magazine (see page 33), although one and half times the size, and was built alongside it on the waterfront. It is probable that the purpose of replicating the established building was to expedite its progress, which was very rapid for such a large structure (it had a capacity of 23,000 barrels). It needed to be built quickly: the survey ship *Volage*, which had paid off at Sheerness in May 1856, had been pressed into service as a floating magazine and was filled by August, having to be supplemented by the Third Rate *Cornwall*. Despite wranglings with the Dover-based contractor, Joseph Diggle, the building was handed over on 24 June 1857 (the optimistic date for completion of the fabric, not allowing for drying out, had been 26 January). *Volage* and *Cornwall* were at once emptied and their staff paid off. However, possibly

because of the speed with which it had been built, structural faults soon became apparent in the new magazine.[6]

At Portsmouth, the CRE suggested that Marchwood was the best place to establish a depot magazine. There was plenty of room on the site for expansion and building materials would be easily procurable. This view was supported by the Superintendent of the Royal Gunpowder Factories and the CRE at Waltham Abbey, who forwarded sketch designs, not only for increasing the size of Marchwood but also that of Tipner. Construction at Marchwood had begun by October 1856, and by August 1857 four additional magazines had been completed; these followed the original structures in not being bombproof, and gave the whole depot the enormous capacity of 76,000 barrels, making it the largest in the kingdom. The enlargement of Tipner had not been called for by the Magazine Committee, but had been precipitated through Colonel Boxer's concerns for safety at Priddy's Hard. In January 1856 Boxer discovered that B Magazine at Priddy's Hard – the old North and South Stores, intended for empty barrels and cases and not bombproof – were being used to stow cases of filled cartridges (the Storekeeper maintained he had been pointing this out for over three years). Boxer wanted these to be removed immediately to Tipner and Marchwood and made several other recommendations, all of which were implemented. The facilities of the laboratory were to be expanded so that all shells and cartridges required for Portsmouth ships could be filled there, which would necessitate more men and the provision of wooden sheds. This work would probably require a supply of between 100 and 150 barrels of powder per day, to be supplied from Marchwood and Tipner. A floating magazine, *Grampus*, already earmarked for Priddy's Hard but not yet in service, would hold the made-up ammunition, but even so an increased workload would clearly be thrown on Tipner. By June 1856 the Assistant Inspector-General of Fortifications, Major Jervois (see Appendix B), had produced a rough sketch of how the capacity of Tipner could be increased by 20,000 barrels. This pre-supposed a construction similar to Marchwood. However, it was decided that the magazine, like the original building, would be bombproof and the CRE Portsmouth was asked to prepare designs accordingly, for a capacity of around 8,000 barrels. In the end around 12,000 barrels were accommodated, under vaults of a slightly different design from the originals, but the general effect is very close to them, and without prior knowledge it would be difficult to date the buildings apart. As on the Medway, the returning ships from the Baltic produced a crisis of accommodation. There was no room to store any more shells and in this emergency they were

4.6 Major Jervois' proposal to enlarge Tipner with magazines similar to those at Marchwood. (*Redrawn from POR/I/2*)

Guard House

Office

Cooperage

Proposed New Magazine

Original Magazine

Shifting House

0   50   100ft
0   30m

placed in the shell rooms and spirit rooms of the ships laid up in Ordinary. This situation was to be mitigated by the gunwharf shell store which had already been approved, and empty shells were to be stacked at Priddy's Hard, the soft ground being prepared by a foundation of old shells.[7]

Development of Bull Point

All these works came too late for the Russian War, which although expected to be a prolonged affair, was terminated by the Peace of Paris on 20 March 1856. However, the need for increased magazine capacity had been so clearly shown that they were proceeded with. The completion of Bull Point, where at the conclusion of hostilities a defensible barracks was under construction to replace a set of prefabricated huts, also continued. During the summer drawings were produced for the array of ancillary buildings at Bull Point, for which Samuel King was the contractor. These were the first set of buildings to be designed for all the requirements seen to be necessary for a Deposit, Receipt and Issuing Magazine Establishment of the mid-1850s. As completed Bull Point was a magnificent establishment, taking full advantage of a spacious site where geography imposed a linear arrangement on the buildings, which happily coincided with the operational requirements of dividing the depot into four areas – the laboratory, the ancillary buildings, the magazine enclosure and the basin area. The clear space between the magazine enclosure and the restoving works at St Budeaux, now adapted as the laboratory, was lined with a sequence of stylish buildings unnecessarily grand for their purposes. As the Board of Ordnance had approved the designs for Bull Point years earlier (in 1850), this could possibly be seen as a conscious final architectural statement on their part (and also possibly a vindication of those who had accused the Board of wasteful practices). It is not known precisely when the buildings operating in conjunction with the basin – shifting house, shell magazine, flannel cartridge store, landing shed and receipt and issue magazine – were constructed. No designs for this magazine and the cartridge store can be found in any of the preserved design schemes for the magazine area and basin. The firm of Clift & Drew made a tender of £46,572 for the basin, which was accepted in September 1854, shortly after the estimated completion date of the four store magazines; it is probable that these buildings surrounding the basin were contemporary. The unified procession of empty barrel and case store, tailor's shop, flannel cartridge store, printing and model room, hydraulic press room, two examining rooms, a further empty barrel and case store, carpenters' shop, tradesmen's store and painters' shop (see Glossary), presents an ensemble unmatched in any other Ordnance Yard. Most of

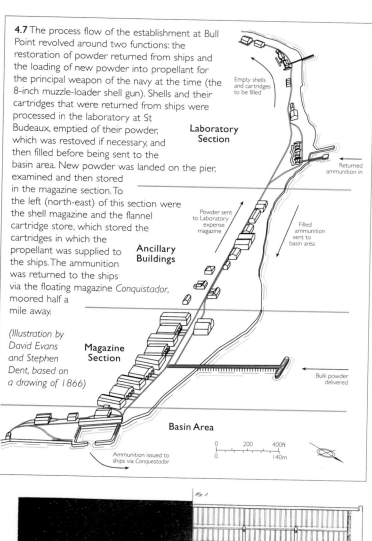

4.7 The process flow of the establishment at Bull Point revolved around two functions: the restoration of powder returned from ships and the loading of new powder into propellant for the principal weapon of the navy at the time (the 8-inch muzzle-loader shell gun). Shells and their cartridges that were returned from ships were processed in the laboratory at St Budeaux, emptied of their powder, which was restoved if necessary, and then filled before being sent to the basin area. New powder was landed on the pier, examined and then stored in the magazine section. To the left (north-east) of this section were the shell magazine and the flannel cartridge store, which stored the cartridges in which the propellant was supplied to the ships. The ammunition was returned to the ships via the floating magazine *Conquistador*, moored half a mile away.

(Illustration by David Evans and Stephen Dent, based on a drawing of 1866)

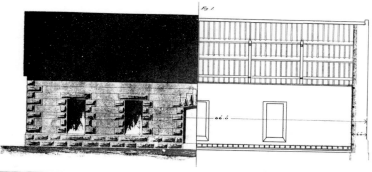

4.8 The filling and packing house at Bull Point displays the high-status craftsmanship that characterised the whole site. It was probably originally designed as an examining room, for inspecting shells and explosives. (*Drawing from DML fiche 038150; photograph by Jeremy Lake*)

4.9 The fuze store, looking north-west, used for storing percussion caps, fuzes and percussion tubes. In the 1850s fuzes for shells comprised relatively simple components which were stored separately, together with the firing tubes and percussion caps used to fire guns. The drawing (below) illustrates the lightning conductors provided for all the buildings. *(Drawing from DML fiche 038118; photograph by Jeremy Lake)*

these buildings remain to this date, externally virtually unaltered. The northernmost set of buildings at St Budeaux had been altered since 1847, only one stoving house being retained and the receiving house converted to a shell room. To the south of this was added a shifting house, foreman's quarters and an expense magazine for the laboratory. The southernmost buildings of St Budeaux, the dusting house and mixing house, were converted to staff facilities and later (after 1859) a small arms cartridge making room (see Glossary). Beyond these were built two filling rooms, one for shells and one for cartridges, each divided into three internal divisions.[8]

The system of separate supply lines for powder and shells evolved at Priddy's Hard was imposed here from the outset. The whole layout was geared around the supply of filled shells rather than the emptying of returned ones. The laboratory retained the two original jetties of the St Budeaux establishment; it is probable that the northern one (the most used, as it was enlarged, and supplemented by a quay) was used for receiving returned shells, which were then emptied in the shell room, the powder requiring restoving being processed in the surviving stoving house. The southern jetty was retained. The new shell filling room was adjacent to the cartridge filling room, powder being supplied from the expense magazine lying between the sections of the laboratory. The filled shells and cartridges were then dispatched to the basin area for storage and shipping. A single tramway led through the magazine enclosure to the receipt and issue magazine (see Glossary). This building was divided into two halves to keep the categories quite separate; as it functioned to receive ammunition from ships, working in

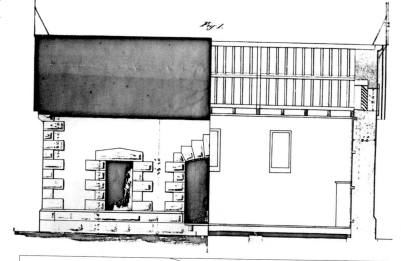

Fig 1.

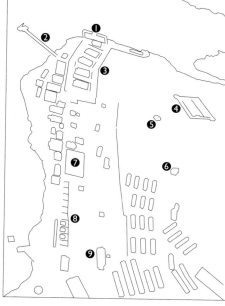

4.10 Opposite: a modern-day aerial view of Bull Point from the south east. For a full, phased plan of the site see Appendix A. Note the boundary walls on its landward side and enclosing the magazine area. *(Photograph by Frances Griffith, Devon County Council, 10 January 1992. Copyright reserved.)*

Key:
1 Basin and Receipt and Issue Magazine (1850s)
2 Powder Pier (now demolished)
3 Main magazine area
4 Bull Point Barracks
5 Kinterbury House
6 Bull Point House
7 Shell Store (1906)
8 Shell and Cartridge Filling Rooms (1890s)
9 Electrical Generating Station

conjunction with the landing shed, it is clear that the traffic flow was capable of being reversed, though with much of the transit system based on a single line, movements would have to be carefully planned. The expense magazine would have been replenished first thing in the morning and so its filling would not have created an obstructive counterflow. From the receipt and issue magazine the tramway led first to the cartridge store and then the shell magazine. Everything was then directed to the shifting room where examination took place before issue; this building does not survive and no drawings have been preserved, but

it was one of the smallest buildings on the site, to minimise damage in the event of a mishap. Powder was sent to the store magazine enclosure on an almost completely separate tramway. It was landed at the long jetty, which was accessible at all states of tide and completed in the autumn of 1853 (a year before the magazines). A double line of rails led to the principal transit line running through the magazine enclosure, from which the store magazines were supplied. A bottleneck existed at the connection, but as bulk deliveries of powder probably required most of the staff there was probably little conflict between magazine and labora-

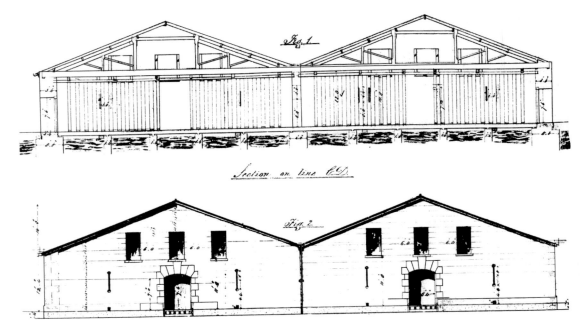

4.11 The barrel and case stores at Bull Point. Case stores are associated with the introduction of shells into naval service, each shell being individually packed into its own wooden box. Each box was 10 inches square by 11 inches high. A 92-gun ship with twenty-four 8-inch guns would carry an outfit of 600 shells, which would occupy some 380 cubic feet. These stores were accordingly sizeable buildings. *(From DML fiche 038144; photograph by Jeremy Lake)*

4.12 Above: The receipt and issue magazine, intended to receive ammunition from ships coming in to refit or be paid off. Powder barrels that had been checked were held there for issue. *(Jeremy Lake)*

4.13 Below: The monumental architecture of Bull Point Magazine and its traverses, photographed in July 1947. Note the hand-operated cranes, the railway and the lightning conductors. *(Plymouth Naval Base Museum)*

4.14 The pattern and class rooms of 1862–3. This building was later a school, doubled as a church in the 1890s, and from circa 1900 served as a cook house and galley. *(Stephen Dent)*

4.15 The steel screw sloop HMS *Phoenix*, in late Victorian livery, pictured off Bull Point. Visible beyond her bow is the powder pier and in the distance Brunel's Royal Albert Bridge (opened 1859), while Bull Point cottages can be seen on the skyline between the ship's masts. *Phoenix*, typical of the smaller warships of the era, was built at Devonport and completed in May 1896. Displacing 1,050 tons, she carried six 4-inch BL QF, four 3-pdr and three machine guns, and had a crew of 106. She capsized during a typhoon in Hong Kong in September 1906. *(Craig Leaske)*

tory operations. No other Ordnance Yard could boast anything like this elaborate system, for which a total of £4,000 had been approved (probably not including the laboratory layout); the system had a gauge of 3 feet 8 inches, not found anywhere else, and each tumbril could carry thirty powder barrels at a time. It remained operational until 1896–7, when it was converted to 18 inches and extended to serve the newly enlarged depot. The only significant addition to the buildings until the 1890s was the provision in 1862 of a pattern and class room building (see Glossary), which appears to have been unique, though it did not retain this function for long, being converted by 1866 to a school for children of the staff. Subsequently part was used as a church and after 1900 it became a cook house and dining room. Finally it was used as offices during the Second World War. The building

survives, though nothing remains of the original internal arrangements, which, however, are known through surviving drawings. Despite the lavish facilities at Bull Point, its operation required a floating magazine moored half a mile up the Tamar. This was the old Third Rate *Conquestador*, which was converted to a hulk in 1860, probably replacing the hulks that were used in the period between the demolition of Keyham and the new magazines coming into use. Unlike *Grampus*, which functioned as a deposit magazine, *Conquestador* played an active role, apparently supplementing or replacing the receipt and issue magazine. All ships returning their ammunition sent it to *Conquestador*, which in turn sent it to the laboratory for examination. Filled shells and cartridges were in turn sent to the floating magazine for issue. The great magazines were treated as a reserve store, the bulk of the business taking place between *Conquestador* and the laboratory.[9]

Decentralisation of ordnance facilities

The completion of Bull Point made the other magazine depots seem distinctly poorly arranged and inadequately provided with ancillary buildings. However, the initiation of new works was now unlikely after the end of the war. At the end of July 1856 the Storekeeper at Priddy's Hard was told to expect a great fall off in work during the autumn, and some of the exceptional measures were dispensed with: the powder and shells placed in the ships in ordinary were withdrawn to Marchwood and to *Grampus*. Carcasses stored in these ships were moved to Stamshaw and placed in the old dusting houses. The new magazine at

Tipner came into use early in 1858, enabling *Grampus* to be cleared and returned to the Admiralty. However, circumstances were to dictate that she was to remain on the scene, or waiting in the wings, for another forty years, for a sequence of events were now to take place at Priddy's Hard which, though not leaving any striking new buildings behind, had a great effect upon its operational history.[10]

In May 1858 a report on the best means of repelling an invasion noted that Woolwich was the sole military arsenal in the land, and recommended a large measure of decentralisation, with two or three large depots for stores of all descriptions being formed. Weedon – where the central depot for army clothing had been established in 1855 – and Chester were considered the best locations, and Portsmouth was recommended for development as a second great Arsenal. At the same time as this report was presented the wharfage at Priddy's Hard was found to be inadequate to meet the new naval requirement to ship the whole of the powder of the First Class Steam Reserve in twelve hours. The loss of B Magazine through Colonel Boxer's injunction of 1856 was a further hindrance – it was now used as an empty barrel and case store, there being no buildings specifically designed for that purpose – and the Storekeeper asked that this be rescinded and powder in metallic cases allowed to be stored there. Colonel Foster, the CRE, suggested that the building could be made secure by the provision of a splinter-proof roof, replacing the existing tiled one by a flat roof of asphalted timber, protected by two feet of earth. Two earthen traverses would be provided, one to protect B Magazine from any explosion in the Examining Room for returned ammunition and the other to separate it from the laboratory. A committee was appointed to consider the matter and it was decided that the traverses might be dispensed with if the examining room was used as a store; it was thought that the office block served to traverse the laboratory. The traverses were accordingly abandoned, and tenders called for two sheds for empty barrels and cases, an extension to the rolling stage and the alterations to the roof of B Magazine. Bellingham & King's tender to complete the work in four months was accepted in November 1858. The provision of the empty barrel and case stores was the first step in bringing the facilities of Priddy's Hard into line with Bull Point, though there was no attempt here to match it in architectural distinction, the buildings being mere wooden sheds. These stores had to be completed to take the contents of B Magazine before the roof could be taken off. It does not appear that the flat roof was ever applied; the earth protection certainly was, and the fabric of the building shows clear evidence of alterations to the roof level. Even with B Magazine now made safe

to hold powder in metallic cases, the accommodation was still inadequate and the Storekeeper requested another bombproof magazine. As an immediate measure, one and a half million cartridges were sent from Tipner to Marchwood to enable it to house the ammunition for the Steam Reserve, and *Grampus* was brought back into use. Some of the workload was taken off the laboratory by the decision to supply ships with empty shells that could be filled on board as required, a feasible operation with the simple projectiles in use.[11]

In June 1859 Sidney Herbert became Secretary of State for War in Palmerston's new administration. Much has been written about his reforms and attempted reforms during his short tenure of office, but it has not been recognised that his resignation through ill health in July 1860 probably prevented Portsmouth being built up into a major arsenal, as recommended by the report of 1858. Soon after assuming office he was made aware of the immense concentration of gunpowder and warlike matériel on the Thames estuary; 50,000 barrels of powder were currently held at Purfleet and the Superintendent of the Government Powder Factory at Waltham Abbey was reported to have said that an explosion of the whole stock would be of such magnitude as to level the eastern side of London – providing, in the words of Colonel Asquith, Director of Waltham Abbey, a 'tabula rasa' to another Christopher Wren.[12] A new magazine of 12,000 barrels, for land service, was being built at Plumstead. Rumours were also circulating (true of course) that there was an even larger depot somewhere near Southampton. These matters had never been written about or raised in Parliament. His attention caught, Herbert wrote to

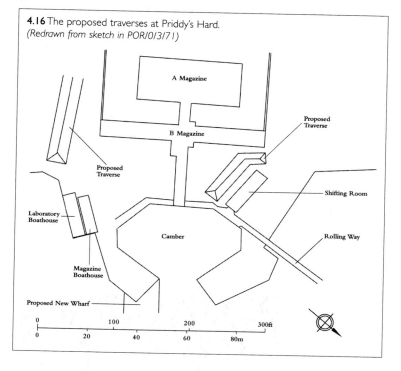

4.16 The proposed traverses at Priddy's Hard. *(Redrawn from sketch in POR/0/3/71)*

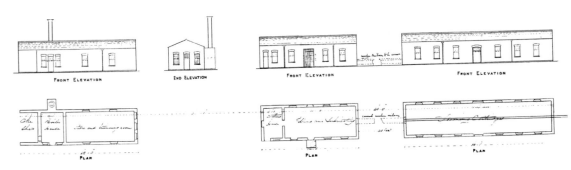

4.17 The Small Arms Cartridge Factory established by Herbert at Priddy's Hard. See figures 5.13 and 5.14 for illustrations of the later alterations to the buildings. *(From PTM/2852)*

Colonel Boxer at the Royal Laboratory, who replied: 'There can be but one opinion as regards Purfleet – It is in the highest degree objectionable to keep a large stock of Gunpowder in one locality … The question of Magazine accommodation generally, requires <u>serious</u> attention the present arrangements are by no means satisfactory.'

With such an authority to confirm his fears, Herbert set events in motion. A committee was appointed to investigate the safety of the transit of powder to and from the magazine and the laboratory at Priddy's Hard, which approved the existing double line of wooden railway between the landing place for shells and the laboratory, and its extension to the magazine. It was stressed that

returned powder cases should never be placed in the magazine before examination and that a special building or vessel should be provided to hold them until they could be inspected. The Secretary of State went into the matter in detail, wishing to know how many tumbrils of powder would be moved along the proposed railway when the establishment was working flat out.

Along with Herbert's interest in minutiae went a concern with the big picture; after years of public agitation on the subject, on 20 August he appointed the celebrated Royal Commission on the Defences of the United Kingdom, whose findings were to establish massive fortifications around the major dockyards. Within the defences

4.18 Section of C Magazine at Priddy's Hard, dated May 1860, showing the earth traverse built up against the elevation facing the depot. It was similar in design to contemporary fortress magazines, and comprised the northern terminus of the site's first tramway system which supplied the laboratory magazine and associated shell-filling rooms. It proved too small to play a key role in Priddy's Hard and had become an expense magazine for gunpowder and cordite by the 1890s. *(From PTM/3052)*

4.19 Priddy's Hard C Magazine today. *(Stephen Dent)*

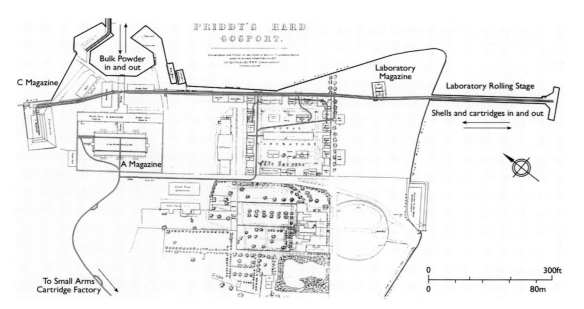

4.20 The communication system at Priddy's Hard in 1860. The relocation of the laboratory from Portsmouth marked the site's transformation from being solely a storage depot to one where explosives were manipulated. A tramway system was established for the first time. Bulk powder was transported straight to A Magazine, and then as required to the Small Arms Cartridge Factory. A tramway running across the site also transported powder returned from ships to C Magazine. Sufficient quantities for daily use in the laboratory, where shell filling was becoming more important, were then taken to its expense magazine. More stores for the storage of the empty cases in which shells were individually packed were added as a part of this process (see figure 5.11). Note also the location of the laboratory boat house and the laboratory workers' cottages, both designed in 1847. *(Adapted from MPHH 1/486)*

proposed by the Commission he proposed to establish new logistical bases. He noted that laboratories were established at Priddy's Hard and Bull Point, both making up cartridges for land and sea service. These he proposed to expand, as part of a programme of decentralisation of ordnance facilities, by establishing small arms cartridge making factories to be staffed by children. The provision of useful labour for children who might otherwise be thrown onto the streets showed his philanthropic nature (another concern of his was subsidising the emigration of impoverished seamstresses to Australia: 'All the change for these poor women must be for the better both physically and morally…'). As has been seen, part of the St Budeaux establishment was converted for this use (see page 69). A purpose-built factory was designed for Priddy's Hard, Boxer approving the plans in November. It was to be finished by the end of March 1860. The Director of Stores, Captain Caffin, RN, giving evidence to the Commissioners that month, stated that Woolwich could make up 1,250,000 rounds per week, and the two new factories were intended to have a capacity of 250,000 rounds per week each.

The Priddy's Hard Factory remains, though it has gone through a series of transformations. Priddy's Hard and Bull Point, though, could provide little relief for the bulk of stores accumulated at Woolwich, and one of the tasks Herbert set the Commissioners was to select a location for a great central depot, close to the great manufacturing areas. They condemned Weedon – no longer the clothing depot, which had been transferred to

Pimlico – for this purpose, being indefensible except at excessive cost, and its buildings were 'of very second-rate consideration'. Cannock Chase was the preferred site, and if a further arsenal was required on the western seaboard then Runcorn was ideally situated.

Nothing was to come of these plans for strategic dispersal, and any ideas Herbert may have entertained for the improvements of the laboratories and gunwharves were not pursued by his successor. The principal survival from his brief period as Secretary of State for War was C Magazine at Priddy's Hard. Herbert had recognised that the ammunition for the Steam Reserve needed additional magazine space, and at first he thought this could be managed by re-arrangements at Tipner and Priddy's Hard, with the aid of Marchwood. Enquiries Herbert initiated at the beginning of 1860 clearly showed that this would not suffice, and by March detailed drawings had been prepared for a building to hold ammunition returned from ships. It was debated whether this should be as light as possible – presumably on the model of Marchwood – or splinter proof. The latter was at first accepted, following the precedent of B Magazine, but in a total change of mind a bombproof design was adopted. This new magazine enabled a rationalised flow system to be established, based on a tramway layout (into which the Small Arms Cartridge Factory was incorporated) which, though far smaller than that which had been designed into Bull Point from the start, was to become a highly complex system by the end of the century.[13]

Guarding the Magazines

The security of the establishments and their stores was vital, in peacetime as well as war. This meant that quite apart from the storehouses, working buildings, offices and residences for the senior officers, extra buildings were required for accommodation for the men whose sole concern was security. Soldiers were the natural choice, and consequently barracks were an essential component of 18th- or 19th-century magazine establishments. The barracks, for two officers and sixty-four soldiers, built for the guard of Upnor Castle shortly after 1718 was one of the first to be built in England. Purfleet was provided with barracks, which have since been demolished, along with most of the buildings. The barracks established at Priddy's Hard in 1777 were later converted to a store, which was demolished to clear the site for the construction of E Magazine, and the two guardhouses that worked in conjunction with it have also long gone. The military made an inauspicious start there, as in August three sentries were found asleep. Two were sent as prisoners to their regiment, while the third deserted. Following this fiasco, labourers were briefly used as watchmen in their place. No barracks were provided for Keyham, detachments of soldiers presumably being sent from the barracks within the Devonport Lines. Barracks were completed for the new magazine at Tipner in 1801; these have

GM.1 Below left: Bull Point Barracks as completed. The defensible nature of the design is evident. *(From TNA WO 78/4484)*

GM.2 Below right: Bull Point Barracks, main gateway. *(Stephen Dent)*

GM.5 Opposite, bottom: Bull Point Barracks, exterior of eastern wall, showing ditch, gateway and loopholed bastion. *(Stephen Dent)*

GM.3 Above: Bull Point Barracks, detail of the main gateway, showing the date of construction on the keystone and the Ordnance Board coat of arms on the tympanum. *(Stephen Dent)*

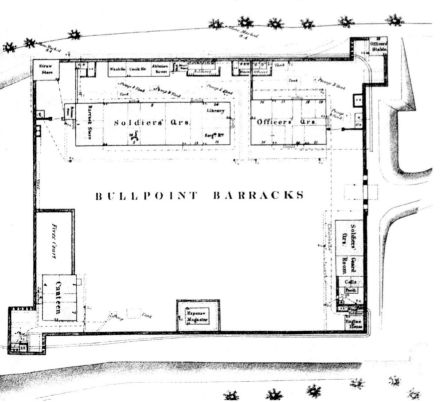

GM.4 Above: Bull Point Barracks from the air, showing the location of the barracks relative to the main magazines, the receipt and issue store, and the basin (all top left). The rough area in between is the site of now demolished police cottages. Also evident is the modern housing development now encroaching on the area around the barracks. (*Photograph by Frances Griffith, Devon County Council, 10 January 1992. Copyright reserved.*)

also been demolished. Of the other two principal magazines constructed during the Napoleonic War and subsequently retained, that at Upnor was already provided with accommodation, and a barracks for fifty men was built at Marchwood in 1815. This survives. In 1816, six sentries formed a patrol at Priddy's Hard, and the Marchwood garrison probably found time hanging heavy on their hands. A barracks of completely different design was begun in 1856 for the new Bull Point magazines. This was a defensible structure with caponiers to provide flanking fire at alternate corners, quite a different proposition from all previous barracks, including the so-called defensible barracks built in the previous decade at Pembroke Dock. While it was being constructed the guard of forty-eight men was accommodated in a pair of Longman's portable huts.[1]

Responsibility for guarding the magazines at Priddy's Hard shifted as a consequence of the abolition of the old locally recruited Dockyard Police in December 1860, to be replaced by the Metropolitan Police under their Chief Commissioner, Sir Richard Mayne. The military guard was maintained for a time, but in October 1864 Mayne suggested there was no need to maintain a military guard at Priddy's Hard, since by that time the Metropolitan Police from the Royal Clarence Victualling Yard (separated from Priddy's Hard by Forton Creek, across which most of the ordnance staff came to work on a ferry) patrolled the whole of the premises. However, the Storekeeper thought this distribution of personnel inadvisable should any fire or other emergency occur, as the ferry was closed at night. A range of police quarters had been provided at Bull Point, and probably Upnor, by 1866. By 1868 Mayne was asking for accommodation for a sergeant to be provided at Priddy's Hard, and the man was eventually given one of the cottages built in 1848 for key workers, though he did not stay there for long, as the cottages were converted to fuze and tube stores in 1878. The final residence was in the converted Small Arms Cartridge Factory. [2]

GM.6 Chattenden Barracks, photographed in 1930. Note the First World War pillbox, a type peculiar to Kent. *(Royal Engineers Library, E32-2/17-p.66)*

In contrast with the number of soldiers maintained in magazine barracks, in July 1882 there were only two Metropolitan policemen at Priddy's Hard, one at the ferry, the other at the gate leading to hardway. Two additional men were all that was required to patrol the unprotected parts. The new magazines at Chattenden, completed in 1875, were provided with a barracks for 8 officers and 120 soldiers; but this related to the military occupancy of the area rather than the magazines, and a terrace of police houses was also provided. Many detachments of troops occupied the barracks at Marchwood until 1891, when, on the depot being transferred to the Admiralty, a detachment of Royal Marines Light Infantry were stationed at Marchwood to supply working parties, although they were soon replaced by police. In March 1894 it was decided to increase the establishment at Bull Point by one sergeant and six constables, and additional accommodation was provided. Police also replaced the last of the civil watchmen, who had been responsible for the floating magazines at Upnor and Priddy's Hard. The state-of-the-art magazines at Lodge Hill and Bedenham were provided with extensive police accommodation from the start.[3]

The Admiralty, notoriously, for many years discounted the potential of air attack against surface ships under weigh (and for many years was quite right to do so), but when it came to land installations that was another matter. By 1912 it was clear that the Medway was within the range of Zeppelins at least, and at the end of the year it was decided to provide Lodge Hill with an anti-aircraft defence of four 3-inch QF guns of a new design and on special mountings, and by January 1913 materials for permanent concrete emplacements had been delivered. These were the first AA sites to be established in England, and remains of the installation may be seen today.[4]

After the First World War it was decided to withdraw the Metropolitan Police from all naval installations and replace them with Royal Marine Police. These were Marine Police pensioners whose income from that source formed a major component of their pay, and whose employment was consequently both agreeable to the Treasury and a source of aggravation to the men, who thought, quite rightly, that they were being exploited. The marines also used dogs. Curiously, to modern eyes, Airedales then appeared to be the favoured breed. They were not considered suitable for Crombie and Bandeath owing to large areas of

GM.7 Frobisher Court, the former barracks and flanking offices at Marchwood, built in 1816 and now converted into housing. (Stephen Dent)

the depots being let for grazing, and the dogs were thought liable both to bring claims for sheep worrying and spreading foot-and-mouth disease. However, the RMPs at Bedenham and Frater did not wish to take up the monetary allowances which had been given the Metropolitan Police, seeing the dogs as pets and preferring them to be entirely their own and not in any respect 'official'; and no wish for dogs had been expressed by the men at Holton Heath. By 1939 there were still very few dogs employed.[5]

The Abyssinian crisis of 1935 caused some – surely unnecessary – concern about the safety of the magazines. Fantasies about scores of Moscow-trained saboteurs were entertained at high level; though a note of sanity was struck by the thought that communists would be unlikely to aid fascists. The depots at Bandeath, Wrabness and Copperas Wood (the last two mine and depth charge depots in an exposed position on the Stour estuary close to Harwich) contained reserves of vitally important stocks of HE (see Glossary) particularly exposed to any form of raid, and it was considered essential that extra guards be provided. If the international situation should worsen, special measures would also be necessary in the event of sub-depots being established for storage of explosives at ports where naval auxiliaries services were fitting out. Special care was to be given to Crombie while the new underground magazines (see page 211) were being constructed, especially during the night shift when no departmental staff were present. The Admiralty had the power to call up any number of Royal Marine pensioners.[6]

The crisis came to nothing, and when the real thing came along in 1939, as will be seen in Chapter 10, it was to be air raids and not sabotage that posed the threat to the Ordnance Depots.

Chapter 5 New Ordnance, Fresh Challenges

The newly established small arms ammunition factories probably ceased work in August 1862 when the manufacture of 1853-type ammunition was suspended at Bull Point and Priddy's Hard, but appear to have been retained on a care and maintenance basis. By contrast, the gunwharf capabilities were greatly increased. The 1860s and 1870s were to see a sudden increase in the complexities of ordnance and consequently in the duties of the magazines and gunwharves, challenges matched by problems of funding and organisation.

New armament requires new ways of working

On 1 October 1860, the officials at Portsmouth Gunwharf were told that they were to supply armament to the first pair of British ironclads, *Warrior* and *Black Prince*. Initially each vessel would require four 40-pounder Armstrong guns (see Ordnance and Armament, pages 119–120) but this number was subsequently increased. The Armstrong guns were rifled breechloaders and, together with their carriages, were assembled from a far greater number of components than the old

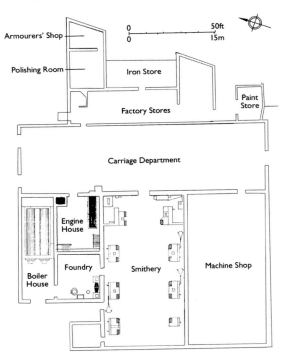

5.1 The Portsmouth Gunwharf Factory. *(Adapted from PTM/1845)*

smoothbores. The new magazine at the gunwharf housed the shells, fuzes and bursters for these pieces, and in February 1861 powder was sent from Purfleet to Priddy's Hard specifically for filling cartridges for them. During the following month the Assistant Firemaster was informed of the shells' bursting charges. Further laboratory work was created by the necessity to coat the interior of the shells with a mixture of asphalt, pitch, resin and tallow, and the edict that obsolete ammunition received from foreign stations was to be broken up at Priddy's Hard instead of being sent to Woolwich for disposal. Later that same year all the made-up ammunition at Marchwood was sent to the laboratory for examination. It was decided that Armstrong shells did not need to be stored in boxes, but could be stacked in the same way as other projectiles, boxes only being needed for transit. This reduced the packaging time, as earlier shells each had individual boxes, from which they were only removed just prior to firing. The workload on the ordnance staff may be judged by the proportion of ammunition stores required for a 100-pounder Armstrong-built muzzle loader: 250 filled cartridges and 50 empty; 50 filled common shell and 50 filled segment shell; 50 empty common shell and 50 empty segment shell; 50 solid shot; 280 lubricating wads; 150 concussion fuzes and 150 time fuzes; 150 adapters for fuzes; 300 priming tubes; 250 friction tubes; 250 detonating tubes; and sufficient powder to fill the empty cartridges and shells. The powder, filled cartridges and empty shells were the responsibility of the Storekeeper at Priddy's Hard, the remainder being gunwharf stores.[1]

In a continuation of Sidney Herbert's policy of 1859, a Gunwharf Factory was designed, for completion by the end of the year, and equipped with machinery by the celebrated engineer James Nasmyth. This was to be operated by a staff of 64 men, and gun carriages were envisaged as the principal manufacture. The factory was to prove a bone of contention between the various departments concerned with ordnance from the day it commenced work on 31 January 1863, when the artificers were transferred from the Military Store Department to the Royal Ordnance Factory, under the direction of an Artillery officer. Priddy's Hard Laboratory was amalgamated with the factory in the reorganisation, with Major Bayley operating as Assistant Inspector of the Royal Ordnance Factories at Portsmouth. However, the arrangements were made as difficult as possible by the Military Store Department, who resented the interloper and contrived to retain charge of the armourers, collar-makers (see Glossary), painters, labourers and the leading hand of carpenters. No documentation appears to survive from the parallel establishment at Devonport, built in 1867 at a cost of £6,982, though it is known that the Director of Stores somehow managed to retain control of it.

The Director of Ordnance, who had controlled the ordnance factories since 1861, noted in his first report that, since the establishment of small arsenals at the dockyards, their working had been the subject of continuous criticism by the Store Department, but 'as every representation made by their officers to the discredit of the present method has been easily controverted' he had hoped – in vain – that opposition would have died away. Far from it. As Major Bayley reported after the first two years' work, the masters of trades (who had been the sole judges of work under the old regime) resented the new rules imposed by him, and practised a system of passive resistance while supplying information to Bayley's enemies in the Store Department. He wrote that the men had lacked the ability to work to fine tolerances and also been obstructive, but their attitude improved as their skills developed. Skilled men had to be hired to work on rifled ordnance and projectiles and to maintain the new machinery, and wages were increased as a consequence, causing further problems with the Superintendent of Stores. That officer had,

'often, in his complaints, picked out a particular nature of repair, for instance, carriages, which was carried on by him, and by a comparison with the number repaired by me, tried to throw discredit on these Factories; but it will be seen how erroneous and false these charges are when it is considered that this kind of work was the only one performed by him, and he sent away those requiring much work, and also, when necessary, he was supplied with brackets, axletrees, &c., from Woolwich; whereas we can manufacture these for ourselves, and are given those carriages which require most labour...'.

Another grievance of Major Bayley was the way in which his department was, as he saw it, starved of work. The factory and Priddy's Hard had the capacity to make every munition of war (with the exception of guns, shot, shell, rockets and fuzes), but much of the machinery, including that of the Small Arms Factory at Priddy's Hard, was standing idle. An advantage of the new arrangements was that staff could now be transferred from the factory to the laboratory as the need arose, with economies being made at the latter establishment as a consequence. By 1866 Bayley had been replaced by Colonel Fraser, who was to be a feisty defender of his factories.[2]

The 1865 Committee on Government Magazines and Depots of Gunpowder

Over the same period, the safety of magazines had become a subject of popular concern, not through any accidents at the Ordnance Yards but by the spectacular detonation on 1 October 1864 of a civilian magazine at Erith, through gross negligence. Thirteen people were killed on the spot, and an unknown number subsequently died. Window glass was broken at up to 10 miles away, buildings close at hand were demolished, a building on the brow of a hill one and a half miles off was seriously damaged and ten unfinished cottages nearby fell down the following day. *The Times* despatched a reporter to Portsmouth who was allowed to visit all the magazines and ordnance stores in the area, and reassuringly told his readers that 'All that the skill of man, guided by experience over a long series of years, can do ... is done here.' The War Office set up a Committee on Government Magazines and Depots of Gunpowder under the presidency of the veteran Royal Engineer General Sir John Fox Burgoyne, and the committee visited all the sites. The general feeling was that most of the existing magazines were too large; in January 1865 the CRE at Portsmouth suggested long, low magazines with a capacity of only 2,000 barrels and separated by traverses. The Storekeeper at Purfleet, perhaps influenced by the enormous stock of powder he was living beside, suggested that the size could be reduced still further. By March 1865 the committee had come to a drastic decision; the members proposed to abandon the Priddy's Hard site altogether.[3]

Recommendations for the new site stated that it should be about 50 acres, with good water communications, be free from roads or buildings and with no valuable properties nearby. The CRE and the Superintendents of Stores had suggestions, as did the committee; Great Horsea Island could not possibly have much financial value, which meant that it was a possibility, but a channel would have to be cut to allow access at all times of tide. At Little Horsea the old powder pier was still serviceable, but the useable portion of the site was restricted. A location at the foot of Portsdown Hill had no adequate access by water. However, all these sites were only suitable for depot magazines; an establishment where daily receipts and issues were to be made needed to be closer to the dock-

5.2 The small
heavily traversed
magazines
recommended in
1865. (From TNA
WO 33/15)

yard and gunwharf. The Superintendent of Stores at Portsmouth suggested two small magazines of 600 barrels capacity each should be provided for lodged ammunition at Priddy's Hard, the bulk of the powder to be placed in the resurrected *Grampus*, to be moored off Frater Point. As *Grampus* had been cleared in December 1862 and returned to the Admiralty, it was available. The Deputy Superintendent of Stores at Priddy's Hard also recommended Frater Point, though as the site of a land magazine. (That would come about, although not during the 19th century.)

The committee made its report in July 1865. Its principal recommendation was that future magazine establishments should be composed of small units placed well apart and traversed, holding some 2,000 barrels each. The buildings were to be about 100 feet long, 18 feet wide, given arched roofs of light construction, and their ideal situation would be on a gentle slope, which could be partially excavated to inset the magazines. The excavated earth would be used to form traverses not less than 30 feet thick at the top. It was thought that this would suffice to contain the explosion of a single unit, the material of the roof being blown to harmless fragments. If the site were to permit it, natural heights of ground would be the best protection, but massive artificial traverses were the next best thing, and shelter belts of trees would have a noticeable effect. These recommendations, as will be seen, were to be carried into effect during the next decade at Chattenden.

All this was an ideal solution. Despite there being little prospect of money being available for a new building programme, the committee wanted to draw the Government's attention to the risks, and made immediate recommendations to lessen the dangers of the existing establishments. At Purfleet it was

'fearful to consider that the arrangements of this station are such that the accidental ignition of any portion of the powder, either in a barge at the wharf, or within the precincts of the Magazines, would entail the explosion of the whole mass of 52,000 barrels, and that this mass has not the security of an enclosed depôt rarely touched, but is dealt with daily to an extent requiring 30 or 40 men permanently employed …'.

The committee recommended that powder be stored away from the proof establishment, and that a new set of magazines be built in the rear. Powder to be proved could then be held in the original magazines, with a capacity reduced to 2,000 barrels each and alternate magazines converted into traverses. The situation of Upnor was even more objectionable than that of Priddy's Hard. The committee recommended that the magazines be moved further down the Medway; the cost being recouped by using the present magazines for storing saltpetre instead of renting warehouse space from dock companies. Marchwood held far too much, too close together, and the traverses were thought to be ineffectual. It was decided to reduce the store to 40,000 barrels. In the case of an accident, improved traversing (never carried out) would then limit the damage to Southampton to the breaking of windows and 'the overthrow of anything that a slight shaking would disturb'. Tipner posed little or no risk, but the committee members confirmed their earlier opinion that the magazines should be moved from Priddy's Hard, probably to Frater, but that if difficulties arose in procuring a site, purpose-built floating magazines would serve. The old magazines could be used for storing powder from docked ships, and the live shells moved there from the gunwharf. Weedon only required the provision of a store for small arms ammunition, and Bull Point came very close to the committee's idea of a perfect establishment, except that the capacity of the magazines, being for 10,000 barrels each, was not in line with current opinion. Colonel Boxer (see Chapter 4) considered the recommendations too weak, and stiffened them up in his own addendum to the report. The implementation of all these measures would come to £161,000.[4]

In time most of these recommendations were to come to pass. Immediate measures had to be taken at Portsmouth, where a crisis of ammunition storage was building up. The cause of this was the rapid introduction of the ironclad warship as the principal arm of naval power. The increased size and weight of the projectiles and cartridges for the rifled muzzle-loaders (see Ordnance and Armament, pages 120–121), now the chosen form of armament, were only partly the cause of this. The ships needed to be docked far more often than their wooden predecessors because of the need to keep their bottoms free from fouling, in spite of the Admiralty's experiments with a variety of supposedly curative paints, and explosives were not permitted on a docked ship. When several of these ships were in port at once, as was now constantly the case, C Magazine of 1860 was not large enough to contain their stores. Following Boxer's ruling of the previous decade, no other building at Priddy's Hard or Tipner could be used for this purpose without special authority being obtained – and there was rarely enough prior warning for this to be done. In the circumstances permission was granted for the shifting house to be used, and in February 1866 the Director of Stores, Admiral Caffin, gave verbal directions for *Grampus* to be fitted up again as a floating magazine, with written orders arriving in July. Mr King, the Deputy Superintendent of Stores at Priddy's Hard, investigated the possibility of implementing the committee's recommendation that the filled shells should be transferred to the Hard from the gunwharf; the Superintendent of Factories added his voice in support of this. King considered that the amount of powder that would remain at

Priddy's Hard could easily be stored in C Magazine and the small arms ammunition in the south wing of B Magazine, leaving the whole of A Magazine available for use as a filled shell store. This would be given a new tramway connecting it with the rolling stage which would then be reserved for loading and shipping shells, leaving the Camber for powder alone. Rowland, the Superintendent of Stores at the gunwharf, believed there was no danger at all at his site, and thought it unnecessary to transport shells to Priddy's Hard. The danger was not in storage but in extracting fuzes. He had seen a shell explode in the shell room at Hong Kong caused by such an operation and no shell fragments escaped from the room, which suffered no damage. In any case, the

Anonymous letters

As can be seen in the main chapters of this book, safety was a primary concern at most of the depots for much of the time, particularly after a disaster had occurred. The position of some of the depots close to human habitation caused considerable local disquiet. The traditional means of airing local concerns about the safety of magazines, or settling personal scores with employees, was the anonymous letter directed to the Board of Ordnance. These cast light on the way that the arsenals were seen by the public and on the lifestyles of the men concerned, which provide an insight in to the human face of ordnance storage. The following selection shows some of the recurring themes.

January 28 1777. 'The Inhabitants of the Borough of Portsmouth having represented in their Letter of 25 inst. that it is about 7 Years ago, the King on consequence of a Petition presented to him from the Inhabitants of the said Town was pleased to give directions for the Building Powder Magazines up the Harbour that the Old One (which is Situated in the Town) might be removed they therefore desired that the Board will be pleased to take the same into Consideration & give directions for the immediate removal of the said Magazine to prevent any Accident happening as the many recent Attempts of Villainous Incendiaries at that Port & other places have given them great alarm & filled them with great Dread & Apprehension for their Lives & every thing that is dear to them.'

May 14 1777. Letter sent to Board by Portsmouth resident [all sic]: 'Whereas this is to set forth a Conversation that wase between two Gentlemen in Portsmouth some time since one of the Gentlemen wase Mr Parise Taylor wharein He said great deal about the new Magazine not being Ready to receive the Powder the other Gentleman said to Mr Taylor that there was a Place in Portsmouth Allmost as dangerous as the Magazine Mr Taylor said whare is that why Sir it's the Old Armoury Pray Sir what is keep their? Garrison Stores What are they composed off Why there is some Thousands of live Shelles some thousands of Infuses Meal Powder &c And in case of a fire there is no Water but what Runs from the Storehouses into two or three tubs ... [The Master General, Lord Townshend, had placed his footman – Peter Guilett according to this letter, actually Henry Gillett – as overseer of the new works at Portsmouth; he

had been raising flowers in the Armoury Yard which had attracted the public] ... So that All the last Summer The Armoury was as Publick as the Market from Six a Clock in the Morning often till Nine at Night.'

April 2 1846. Anonymous letter complains of dangerous situation of Portsmouth Laboratory. Apart from its proximity 'not 20 Yards from the flames of our Chimneys' a powder vessel has been lying by the laboratory for many weeks, 'a great portion of that time aground, thereby rendering her removal absolutely impossible in case of Fire, and also the great danger there is of an accident surrounded as she is with an 100 Men [Excavators] the most depraved who in a moment of their insane drunkenness might be the means of hurrying hundreds of lives into another world and a severe loss of property...'

October 3 1853. 'A friend to Sobriety' writes to the Master General: 'I being a resident of the village of Upnor feel I can live no longer in safety without apprising you of the conduct of a person of the name of Ward who has charge of a Powder Magazine at that place he is continually in a state of stupor from Drink Opium &c the quantity of Gin being from 3 Pints to 2 Quarts a day Porter into the bargain – 3 weeks back lying 4 days dead Drunk from the effects. Do for Mercy sake keep such a dangerous character as this clear of the Powder Magazine as we shall all be blown up – The same game has been carried on ever since he first came to Upnor.'

August 23 1856. Anonymous letter from a labourer at Priddy's Hard denouncing the Assistant Firemaster. For a long time there has been a bad feeling on the part of the Firemaster towards the Storekeeper: '... it is a great pity Captain Yates and Family ever went to Priddy's Hard as they have caused a great disturbance in many quarters since they have been there, as for their Son, he is a Drunken worthless Little Blackguard and he ought to be sent about his business. Mr Jenkins with all his faults he was Master he kept them all in their proper places, it would not do for Captain Romer to play the fool with Mr Jenkins.... I hope ... you will see into it and not suffer the Fire master tyrannise over every one, you would think we were nothing but Dogs under him... '

WO 47/89, WO 55/2010, WO 55/2100, ADM 160/100, WO 55/2114

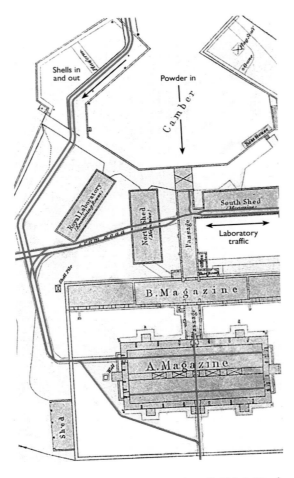

ask permission to use the vacant A Magazine. The practice of restoving was abolished in the spring of 1867, which meant that there was at least one less storage problem to deal with. [5]

Cutting costs

A new reorganisation at the War Office, however, ensured that economic arguments became the most important. In November 1866, Lord Strathnairn's Committee on Army Transport agreed that the administration of army transport and supply should be unified. Consequently, in December 1867, Lieutenant General Sir Henry Storks (see Appendix B) was appointed Controller-in-Chief in charge of all stores except ordnance. The Control Department was not formally set up until November 1869, but had a *de facto* existence from the time of Storks' appointment. Storks had been in charge of the British establishments in Turkey during the Russian War and had lately been Governor of Jamaica following the unsavoury suppression of a revolt. Major General Balfour was appointed as his assistant in January 1868; he had made his name in reforming the military administration of India. Under these two men, Controllers were appointed to each military district. Their duties were extensive; out of 154 clauses outlining them the following are perhaps the most relevant.

'The Controller will be bound to investigate minutely the sources of expense in all branches of the military service, and will, with the concurrence of the officer commanding, bring to the notice of the Controller in Chief every opportunity of reducing the expenditure in money or stores, consistent with the maintenance of efficiency.

The Controller will not submit any application for outlay on a new service unless accompanied by an estimate of the cost, and then only if convinced that the additional cost is justified by absolute necessity.

The Controller is the financial adviser and agent of the officer commanding in all matters connected with the raising or issue of money, the supply of provisions, stores, and clothing ... and with the provision of transport. He will assist the officer commanding in economising public expenditure, and will relieve him, as far as possible, from all details connected therewith.'

The new department immediately aroused the enmity of almost all who had to deal with it. Part of the trouble was a matter of linguistic nuance; had the term Comptroller (originally applied to Storks but rapidly altered) been used much less offence would have been given. As it was, the word control implied, and the behaviour of some

gunwharf was a safer location than Priddy's Hard, which could be – and, incredibly, had been – hit by fire from the navy's centre of gunnery expertise, HMS *Excellent*. He also had other, perhaps more convincing arguments. The gunwharf was better placed to catch the tide in despatching and receiving ammunition at short notice. Orders were often received too late in the evening to send a hoy out to Spithead to take the shell from a ship that would dock the next morning; if the tide was missed, a day would be wasted with all the consequent expense. An additional labour force would also be required at Priddy's Hard. Shells of a calibre greater than 7 inches were about to enter service, which would need four men to lift them, six to push the trucks on the tramway, eight in the magazine to work the travelling crane and stack the shell, six men to work the crane and two to work in the hold of the ship. He calculated that the increased cost would be £1,337 a year. The financial argument proved decisive for a time. King did not see his responsibilities enlarged; he was transferred to Dover and his replacement Mr Cleeve oversaw the removal of all the powder and cannon cartridges to *Grampus*. Although the committee's recommendations on shell storage were not immediately carried out, the decision to reduce the stores at Marchwood was implemented by an order of October 1867, and there was no space at Tipner or on *Grampus* to take any. Cleeve had to

Controllers demonstrated, that the department were top dogs. Part of the problem seems to have been in the type of men recruited and their attitude to the work. Henry Tatum, Controller at the War Office and a man of great practical experience, found that the younger officers despised what they termed 'clerk's work' or 'Storeholder's work' and thought they were cut out for higher things. In 1875, a senior member of the organisation was to state: 'The military believe that the civil officers attached to the Army have no feelings in common with them; that they exist rather for the purpose of checking the Army in every possible way, than to aid and assist it…'. However, when Edward Cardwell became Secretary of State for War in December 1868 he saw the matter in a different light. Self-styled reformers had quite another perspective from men who actually did the work. Lord Northbrook, his Under-Secretary of State, wrote to him: 'I think the Control System is the only gleam of light which has ever yet been thrown upon Army Administration and … it is

opposed by certain Military authorities, because they see in it the first step towards a simplification of the staff & a reduction of appointments of one kind or another…'. Indeed it was, for by September 1869 Northbrook could report that the number of Military Store Officers had been reduced from 184 in 1868–9 to 154 in 1869–70.

5.4 HMS *Warrior*, the revolutionary ironclad warship (see page 80), laid down in 1859 and completed two years later. *(Conway Maritime Press)*

Rethinking the decisions of 1865

In September 1871, a committee was set up to determine the location and design of a large new magazine establishment on the Medway. It effectively overturned the decisions made only six years earlier, with new calculations of the blast effect underpinning this turnaround. The committee concluded:

'The objects proposed by storing Powder in such quantities are to limit the effects of explosion both with respect to loss of Powder to the Government and injury to property in the vicinity. With due precautions the risk of accidental explosion of Powder in a Magazine, and of which the keeping qualities are known, may practically be disregarded, and the same security on this head may be assumed for large & small Magazines.

'The fewer the Magazines the more easily could they be protected against being fired by evil disposed persons, and the advantage would, therefore be with large Magazines.

'The risk of explosion from an enemy's fire would be proportionate to the amount of roof & wall exposed, this would be greater in the small than in large Magazine, & the latter, therefore would be preferable.

'With regard to the liability of one Magazine being fired by the explosion of another adjacent to it, there appears to be no data as to the interval or nature of obstacle which will ensure perfect immunity, but the radii of the spheres of equal effect of explosions of powder vary not in direct proportion to the quantity exploded, but in proportion to the cube root of those quantities, that is if Magazines containing 2000 barrels are spaced at 40 yards as proposed by the Committee of 1865, the intervals to provide the same security for Magazines containing double, or four times that quantity need not be double or four times 40 yards, but $40\sqrt[3]{2}$ or 50.4 yards and $40\sqrt[3]{4}$ or 57.7 yards respectively instead of 80 & 160 yards. Hence it may be assumed that on a given area a definite quantity of powder could be stored in large Magazines in greater safety than in small Magazines because they may be placed at intervals greater than the radii of equal effect.

'There is no doubt that the loss of powder, the injury to adjacent property would be less with small Magazines than with large, provided the explosion could be confined to one Magazine, but taking into consideration the points before adverted to & the economy that will result from adopting large Magazines, the Committee recommend that 5 Magazines for 8000 barrels should be constructed at as great intervals apart as the site will allow…

'The Committee are of opinion,
1st. The barrels should be placed in stacks 4 barrels wide and 9 high; the bays being constructed so as to admit of the stacks being increased to 12 barrels high on emergency.
2. That the space between the stacks & the wall should be 2 feet wide & the central passage 5 feet wide.
3. The roof of the Magazine should not be bomb proof but of a medium construction, which while offering considerable strength against external injury should admit of being easily lifted by an explosion, & that should not contain any inflammable matter.
4. The space between the wall of each Magazine & the foot of the adjoining Traverse should be 10 feet.
5. The Magazine should be sunk into the side of the hill so as to obtain traverses about 50 feet in height and the sides of the traverses should be left at as steep an angle as the soil will admit.
6. That the limit of 200 yards round the Magazine enclosure should be secured by absolute purchase & not by clearance rights. The rental of the land will offer a fair interest for the outlay & the necessary powers over the land will be more effectually secured.'

WO 32/18196

By 1869 the Controller-in-Chief had increased the scope of his activities to include ordnance, and Cardwell attempted to mark out his boundaries:

'I have found the Supply Votes, by far the larger part of which relates to the manufacture, purchase, storing, & issue of Munitions of War, in the hands of the Controller in Chief; under whom had also been placed the custody of all the Stores, whether appertaining to the Munitions of War, – or to other articles of Supply … The principle, I think, is that whatever relates to economy in respect of manufacture & supply belongs to … [the Controller-in-Chief] – & whatever is scientific or strictly professional, to … the Director General of Ordnance.'[6]

How did all this appear to men not inhabiting the rarefied world of Cardwell and Northbrook? The records of the Portsmouth Ordnance Office show what it meant in that area, and the tale was probably repeated elsewhere. In January 1869 General Balfour informed Mr Young, Superintendent of Stores, that the expenditure in the Manufacturing and Store Departments was to be reduced in the next year from £1,491,000 to £1,000,000. It seemed obvious to him that the War Department could dispense with many of its vessels, as the great increase in the size of guns had so reduced the numbers carried on warships; instead of a fleet of 80 ships armed with 4,500 guns, a fleet carrying 250 guns would suffice. Young was told to confer with Colonel Fraser about the best means of running the service efficiently with half the number of boats – the work at the Ordnance Factory and the laboratory was to be 'entirely reduced'. This news was accompanied by a threat: 'A cordial Co-operation on the part of every one can make this reduction fall on useless Establishments, but failing obtaining that Aid which thoroughly practical Knowledge can afford, as to what is unnecessary or useless, the reductions will fall where they can be easiest effected, and necessarily cutting off some useful Establishments.' Deputy Superintendent Cleeve wrote from Priddy's Hard to Storks outlining the duties of the five vessels under his orders. They carried ammunition to and from the ships in harbour and at Spithead, the coastguard ships at Southampton and Weymouth, to Tipner and Marchwood, and the most demanding duty of all, the nearly daily trips to *Grampus* two miles away, vital as the only powder held at Priddy's Hard was for laboratory use, the magazines holding only small arms ammunition. It was necessary to have ships available at short notice; unavailability would entail increased costs. He pointed out that the reduction in the number of guns had not proportionately reduced the ammunition carried. *Duke of Wellington* had borne the largest number of guns ever placed on a

Royal Navy ship: 131 guns, requiring 70 tons of ammunition; the most powerful ironclad, *Hercules*, with 12 guns, required 57 tons of ammunition.

Balfour's misconstruing of the situation was far from unique; ignorance of ordnance matters was general throughout the Control Department, most of the senior officers having been drawn from the former Commissariat (a department thought to have emerged with little distinction from the Crimea). A committee on the education of artillery officers was surprised to find that no officers who had passed through the Firemaster's course or the Advanced Class at Woolwich had been selected for any of the higher posts in the Control Department, and that their specialist knowledge was not considered any qualification for such an appointment. Colonel Fraser defended his factory stoutly, and was prepared to justify all the work done and the need for all his boats, but the establishment's fate was sealed, the Ordnance Factories at Portsmouth Gunwharf and Devonport both closing in August 1869. Balfour was even reluctant to allow Young to take on a tinman and a carpenter for repairing powder cases, suspecting that another factory was in embryo, telling Young 'of the distrust which his increases create. I see no reason for having an Establishment larger or more expensive than that which existed prior to the war with Russia.' Young, though not displeased that the interloping factory was closed and that his piece of turf was returned to him, had to point out to the bean-counters that a steam engine was required to keep pace with the navy's demands, and to enable the artificers of his Store Department to be profitably worked; Balfour had hoped that much of this work could be farmed out to the dockyard, but the Admiralty did not see things in the same light and on enquiry their proposed charges were considered to be exorbitant.[7]

Despite the recent additions to Upnor during 1856–7 (see chapter 4), powder was still being kept in the castle, the most objectionable building to use as a magazine from the point of view of safety. Following public concerns after the Erith explosion of 1865, and probably more influentially naval concerns about the situation of the magazines opposite the main caisson of the dockyard extension, the decision was taken in July 1869 to remove it. After 1870 the logistical situation at Upnor became somewhat complicated, as the War Office, seconded by the Admiralty, then decided to virtually institute Purfleet as the Powder Depot for ships in the Medway District. Marchwood had room for 2,000 barrels and if the filled cartridge bags for mortars (a relic of the armament prepared for the assault on Kronstadt during the Russian War) were disposed of, room would be made for another 2,580. The forts and batteries around Portsmouth could lodge 2,800, and the lack of accommodation enabled the Acting Controller for the district to speculate that '... if enquiry be made as to the quantities and descriptions of Lodged Stores for Royal Artillery at Priddy's Hard and Portsmouth it would exceed belief. Here indeed control is required...'. The Deputy Storekeeper at Marchwood noted that public feeling in Southampton about his magazines matched that at Chatham, and would not ask to exceed the recently laid down limit of 40,000 barrels; he was also uneasy about the presence of rockets, fuzes, lights and other pyrotechnics in his depot, and these were transferred to Priddy's Hard. That depot had been reduced effectively to a laboratory (where, in accordance with Control's injunctions, very little work was being done and many men laid off) and small arms ammunition store. However, in accordance with the Magazine Committee's recommendation for storing filled shells, the site was about to be redeveloped: in September 1869 an estimate was prepared for altering A Magazine and making additional tramways. The inconvenience of the arrangements by which shells and fuzes were sent from the gunwharf to Priddy's Hard to be filled and then returned, was evident to the Deputy Controller, who told Balfour that he was also concerned about the possible dangers of landing fuzed and filled shell. The various kinds of Armstrong fuze in particular appeared to be deteriorating rapidly. Colonel Boxer found the condition of the Pettman general service fuzes to be alarming. Some held in store were liable to detonate at a blow and if fixed in a filled shell would produce a premature explosion in the bore. He ordered that all those in a condition to resist moisture were to

be returned to Woolwich at once.

This was to be Boxer's last intervention as Superintendent of the Royal Laboratory. He harboured a long-standing grievance that his many inventions in the field of ordnance had gone unrewarded. They were, however, appreciated by some: French gunners who asked for fuzes before Sebastopol had been supplied with a type equivalent to their own, but brought them back with the words "nous voulons la fuzée de Boxer" ['we want the Boxer fuze']. In 1859 Boxer had approached Sidney Herbert about the matter. Herbert regretted that Boxer felt his services had not been properly appreciated, but declined to reward him – he probably felt that Boxer should have been as high-minded as himself and been above such matters. In 1867 the Colonel tried again, with the words: 'I must express the disappointment I feel in being obliged to seek for that which I have long hoped would be granted spontaneously.' This request opened a can of worms. Boxer had assigned his patents for cartridge cases to the Eley firm, which had received a large War Office contract. This contract was brought to the attention of the Secretary of State for War, Sir John Pakington, who 'much regretted' the fact, and thought that Boxer's contributions were only what could be expected of a public servant. Pakington also stated that although he 'regretted' the Eley business, he thought that it was appropriate for Boxer to be rewarded through his patents rather than by the state. The Colonel felt, not unreasonably, that running the laboratory was a full-time job and nobody could be expected to do over and above this, and that he was being placed in an impossible

5.5 The gatehouse of Portsmouth Gunwharf, pictured in 1905 dressed overall. (Priddy's Hard Archive, 1998.3.123)

position by the War Office, which now asked him not to undertake any personal agreement with Government contractors 'or others with whom I may *possibly* be brought into communication with in my official capacity. *These instructions practically amount to this, that I am to make no arrangements at all with the private manufacturers to work my patents. But now I am told I must look for reward from the very royalties or other remunerations I may receive as a patentee from private manufacturers.*' [Boxer's italics] Pakington offered to raise his salary from £500 to £800, but Boxer scorned the offer as altogether insufficient, and the pot was stirred by another inventor in the same field, George Daw, denouncing the financial arrangements with Eleys to Sir Henry Storks. Boxer flatly refused to give any information on the royalties he had received. When Cardwell took over the role of Secretary of State for War, he appears to have taken a different attitude from his predecessor Pakington, and Boxer was informed that if he wished to keep his job he would have to comply. He refused to do so and resigned on 22 November 1869.

Boxer went, but Colonel Fraser, now with only Priddy's Hard Laboratory under his control, remained. He attempted to install heating in the laboratory rooms and, although at first thwarted by the Control, succeeded in the autumn of 1870. By that date his services had been found to be useful in an emergency. There was a shortage of small arms ammunition and the factory established by Herbert had been lying unused. Fraser proposed to recruit eighty-eight boys to manufacture the 350,000 ball carbine cartridges and 2,000,000 blank required, to be supervised and assisted by three of the men recently made redundant there. In store were 400,000 cartridges of 1853 pattern, and these were to be broken up and the bullets re-used. It would take about four months for the whole job to be done. This appears to have been the final use made of the Small Arms Cartridge Factory, which was soon converted into storehouses and known as the West Stores.[8]

It is appropriate here to outline the rest of the life of the Control Department. In its pristine form it had a very short life. It was decided in 1870 that the charge of warlike stores should be given to a sub-department under the Director of Artillery, which with the other supply and transport services would be under an official bearing the revived title of Surveyor-General of the Ordnance. Storks took up this appointment in June 1870, holding it until his death four years later, and the title of Controller-in-Chief lapsed. The Control Establishments Subdivision lived on, but the Portsmouth records from this point show little evidence of the interference that had been such a feature in 1869. However, there is no evidence that the easing of its hold on operations made it any more popular; in 1875 the Assistant Director of Supplies and Transport wrote: 'We have now redivided the Control Department into two branches, and have got rid of the obnoxious and objectionable title of Controller; but in other respects we have made no change whatever, and there is no reason to expect that the divided Department will be more popular with the Army, or more successful in its operation, than it was under the organisation of 1859 or 1870…'. In 1876 The Control Department was renamed the Commissariat and Transport Establishments Division.[9]

Storage of new ammunition

By 1870, the massive rifled muzzle-loaders (RMLs) built at Woolwich were the standard weapons both for warships and coastal defence fortifications. These weapons were theoretically much more accurate than the smoothbores and consequently the propellants required precise weighing. Rifled guns were subjected to a greater strain on firing because of the rotation of the projectile. The difficulty was overcome, apart from increasing the strength of the gun, through the use of new, slower-burning powders, which were denser and of increased grain. As the size of the guns increased, so did the size of the grain. By December 1870 pebble powder (see Glossary) had been developed and was sent to Priddy's Hard for issue and trials with full battering charges aboard ship. It was discovered that the larger grains of powder could not be repaired once affected by damp, and in the summer of 1867 it was decided that the practice of restoving be discontinued. At this same time, the Harvey torpedo (see Glossary) was developed, which required storage at the gunwharves. This torpedo was to be towed by warships in the hope that it would strike an enemy ship. After a few years of use the Admiralty asked the captains of the Mediterranean Squadron for their views on the weapon; they were virtually unanimous that it was more of a menace to the user than a threat to the enemy, although one officer thought it should not be removed from the ships as the knowledge that it was Royal Navy equipment might induce potentially hostile navies to waste money on it.

During the 1870s a new explosive first appeared. In March 1871 experiments had

5.6 Pebble powder, actual size. (From Lynal Thomas, 'The Action of Fired Gunpowder in Guns' in the Illustrated Naval and Military Magazine, Vol. I, 1884)

5.7 The ironclad is being menaced by a smaller ship towing two Harvey torpedoes.
(From Instructions for the Management of Harvey's Sea Torpedo, London, 1871)

demonstrated that guncotton (see Glossary), in the form developed by the War Department Chemist Professor Abel, could be stored safely: it was not liable to explode by accidental ignition when stored in specially designed boxes in the magazines; and when stored in a wet condition it was perfectly safe. However, despite much effort, it was found that this explosive could never be used in guns, but it was admirably suited to fill mines and for demolition work. The first delivery of 10 tons of guncotton was made at Upnor Castle in July 1871, and was being examined when the manufacturer's magazines at Stowmarket exploded with serious loss of life. To ensure safety, the guncotton at Upnor (now 20 tons after a second delivery) was made safe by wetting. On examination it was found that the second batch contained serious impurities, the verdict of the subsequent inquest being that it had been tampered with after manufacture. The Committee of Inquiry set up by the War Office gave this new explosive a clean bill of health and it was decided that Government production at Waltham Abbey was to go ahead, at an initial rate of 4 tons a week.[10]

During this period Portsmouth New Gunwharf was considerably expanded (see Fig 9.30). Quite apart from the demands of the navy, the gunwharf also served the enormous programme of fortifications and gun batteries (whose armament was in constant flux) at Gosport, Portsdown Hill, Spithead, the Isle of Wight and Portland. It was also the reserve for all barrack and hospital stores, and a depot for harness and saddlery. The former Royal Ordnance Factory at the gunwharf, now returned to the Store Department, became the gun carriage department, and had been supplied with a steam engine as a result of Young's representations, as Superintendent of Stores, in 1869. In 1872 plans were drawn up to supplement this with a new armoury with a capacity of nearly 20,000 rifles, offices, gun carriage stores, gun shed, collar-makers' shop, sea service store, transit stores and shell magazines. This increased accommodation for shells at the gunwharf was caused by the inadequate landing facilities at Priddy's Hard, where vessels could not be loaded and unloaded at the

rate required, only one vessel at a time being able to lie alongside the stage. Plans for converting part of the Small Arms Cartridge Factory to a shell room were consequently not implemented and the recommendations by the Committee on Government Magazines and Depots of Gunpowder concerning shell storage (see Chapter 5) remained largely unanswered, with space for over 6,000,000 rounds of small arms ammunition remaining in A Magazine. Reductions in the senior staff further hampered the work there.[11]

Apart from all this, *Grampus* was in a bad state, with any money being spent on her a waste; but any replacement would need a capacity of between 15,000 and 20,000 barrels. The Deputy Controller thought provision for this should be made in the 1874–5 Estimates. Given the condition of the ship, the only course that Captain Moloney, the Assistant Controller at Priddy's Hard, could see was to remove the restrictions on the use of the magazines there. If A Magazine were cleared of its contents of small arms ammunition and shells, about 7,500 barrels of the 10,000 currently afloat could go there, with the remainder going to Tipner. In case of urgent need then the restrictions on the use of Marchwood would have to be lifted also. The matter was settled by the fact that no money was available for a new floating magazine, and in November 1873 arrangements were made to clear the contents of *Grampus*. However, once the barrels were distributed, Priddy's Hard and Tipner would be full. None of the magazines in the new ring of fortifications were ready to be used although their availability would have solved many difficulties. *Grampus* was docked and inspected, and the fears about her condition confirmed; she was far from finished, however, and her continuing career is a vital part of the story of explosive stores (see Chapters 6 and 7). The recycling or disposal of obsolete stores was an obvious way by which magazine space could be created, and smoothbore cartridges were broken up. In addition, the issue of the new Martini-Henry rifles (see Glossary) to troops, beginning in October 1874, meant that further stocks of ammunition were made redundant.[12]

NEW ORDNANCE, FRESH CHALLENGES

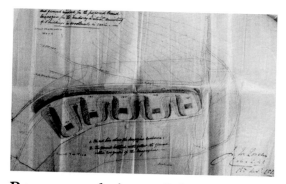

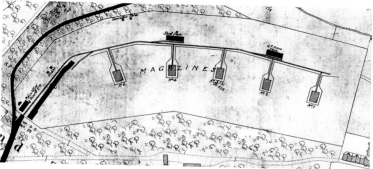

Recommendations of the Magazine Committee

It was high time for some joined-up thinking to be done, by serving officers rather than bureaucrats. During 1875, a Magazine Committee appointed to consider the transport and storage of gunpowder and guncotton, reassessed the conditions at the various Ordnance Depots. As may be imagined, Priddy's Hard was considered far from satisfactory. Stored in the various magazines were 7,943 barrels of powder or made-up cartridges, with A Magazine having been brought back into use; the total capacity was reckoned to be 12,348, so a working space was available for powder landed from ships. But in order to make the establishment function, the regulations for laboratory operations, as laid down in Queen's Regulations of 1868 and reiterated by an 1874 report made by a Select Committee on Explosive Substances, had been disregarded. These ordered that no laboratory operation with a risk of explosion should be carried out within 400 yards of a magazine in which large quantities of powder were stored – and at Priddy's Hard the distance from A Magazine was less than 100 yards. The planked way connecting C Magazine with the other magazines was liable to be scattered with dirt and shingles, and the buildings (mostly case stores) around the camber and the covered rolling ways were largely wooden, forming a mass of inflammable material in close proximity to the magazines. Cottages for key members of staff were only 40 yards from A Magazine, and there was no shifting room dedicated to changing civilian dress for laboratory clothes. All this needed to be addressed. A replacement for *Grampus* was the first priority, with only C Magazine being allowed to store powder or filled cartridges, the others storing filled shells, rockets and small arm ammunition. For Marchwood, where the only action taken since 1865 had been the reduction of its capacity, the recommendations of the Magazine Committee were largely the same. The traverses needed to be extended and new ones added to protect the accommodation buildings; powder should be removed from A and B Magazines, with A Magazine becoming an examining room. A single shifting room for the whole establishment should

replace the shoe rooms (see Glossary) at each individual magazine, and C and E Magazines ought to be divided by a central traverse.

Bull Point was much more up to the mark, though the passing of twenty years since its completion had ensured that it now fell short of the ideal. Part of the criticism centred on the extensive and pioneering internal communications system. The 3-foot 8-inch gauge track was partly gunmetal, partly iron laid on cement ways, which crumbled and was a constant dangerous source of grit. The committee recommended that boards should replace this and the gauge reduced (trucks carrying four barrels would be quite adequate and do away with the need for turntables), and the rails should be all gunmetal except where they entered magazines and examining and cartridge-filling rooms. There they should be wooden, and the stone sills at the entrances to the magazines similarly replaced. The passage of filled shells from the laboratory area to the basin area past the magazines was now seen as objectionable. There was no provision on the powder jetty for examining or repairing damaged barrels, which had to be despatched as found to the laboratory area. The other main area for complaint was a matter that had probably been one of congratulation when the site was new; some of the buildings were far too substantially constructed. This was a real disadvantage when they were employed as danger buildings. The two examining rooms were in use for the inspection of small combustibles, the examining of powder and the examining and breaking down of returned cartridges. The latter work was undertaken only 200 yards from No.1 Magazine, which violated the regulations, and even worse, the former carpenters' shop, 300 yards distant, was now employed for making up cartridges with up to twenty barrels of powder in use at one time. It was recommended that arrangements should be made at once to stop manipulation of powder in all stone buildings; the two wooden filling rooms at St Budeaux, which were then disused, were suggested as suitable replacements although inconveniently far away. Regulations were also broken in *Conquestador*, where powder, loose and in cartridges, was stored with shells and combustibles. The provision of a second floating magazine would enable the two classes of explosives to be separated.[13]

5.8 Left: the original 1871 sketch for the Chattenden Magazines, showing the traverses. *(TNA WO 32 18196).* Right: the Chattenden magazine enclosure around 1905. The dark buildlings are, from left to right, a shifting house, cooperage and empty barrel stores in one long line, a shell store to the centre, and a QF ammunition store to the right. *(From TNA T1/10674B)*

5.9 Opposite: An aerial photograph of the Chattenden magazines taken in 2004. The valley slope acted as a natural traverse, the excavations for the magazines enabling them to be further heightened. The railway connected the site to Upnor. *(NMR 23189)*

In the Medway, Purfleet had been the main Powder Depot since 1870, which had generated both logistical problems and shown the inadequacy of Purfleet's accommodation to perform this additional role. However, this was about to be eased by the completion in June 1875 of a set of five magazines inland at Chattenden, whose design (set into a traversed hillside) and size (4,000 barrels each) was in line with the current ideal. Unfortunately the hillside situation was to prove a liability, as the geology almost immediately caused slippages to occur which have plagued the site ever since.[14]

The 1875 Magazine Committee made some key amendments to the conclusions made by its 1865 predecessor. The optimal capacity for a magazine was no longer considered as 2,000 barrels. This was partly for financial reasons: the greater number of magazines required would increase the area of land required. The greater distances over which the powder would have to be transported would add dangers of its own, and necessitate a larger staff. Accordingly an upper limit of 8,000 barrels per magazine was recommended, with the actual size determined partly by the topography of the site and partly by the nature of work the building was called on to perform. Each bay of these magazines was to take 240

barrels, stacked eight high and three deep, and travellers were to be provided for handling them. When powder was transported by water (as in the majority of cases) a lightly built examining room was to be erected on the wharf or jetty. The work carried out there was to be of a strictly limited nature, no operation apart from the replacement of damaged barrel hoops being permitted, the container being sent in a special truck to the regular examining room. The wharf or jetty ought not to lead directly into the magazine enclosure (as was the case at Bull Point) and where possible a traverse should be interposed. The most influential recommendation was that all employees should enter a magazine enclosure through a shifting room, divided internally into two sections by a physical barrier, one side to contain the men's outdoor clothing, the other, whose floor was kept scrupulously clean, their magazine shoes and clothes. These were to become known respectively as the 'dirty' and 'clean' sides of the room, and this terminology was extended to apply to walkways or platforms (see figure 7.26). The term 'shifting room' was in future to be applied solely to this changing room, the former usage of the term being abolished (see Glossary). New examining rooms were to take on the role of the previous

5.10 One of the Chattenden magazines, pictured in 1930. (*Royal Engineers. Library. E32-2/17*)

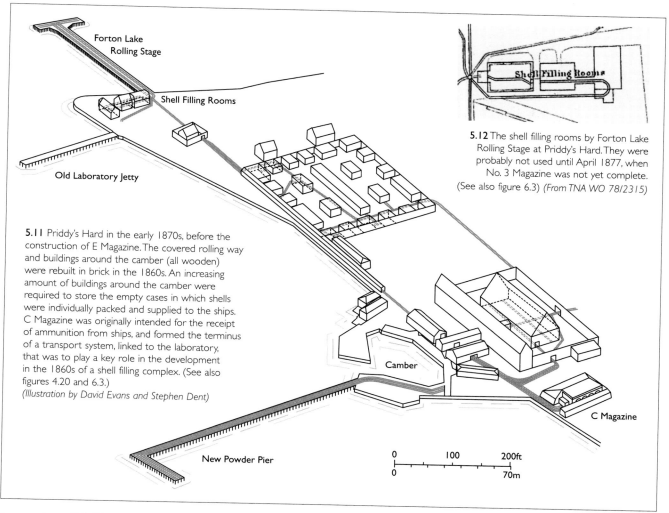

Forton Lake
Rolling Stage

Shell Filling Rooms

Old Laboratory Jetty

5.11 Priddy's Hard in the early 1870s, before the construction of E Magazine. The covered rolling way and buildings around the camber (all wooden) were rebuilt in brick in the 1860s. An increasing amount of buildings around the camber were required to store the empty cases in which shells were individually packed and supplied to the ships. C Magazine was originally intended for the receipt of ammunition from ships, and formed the terminus of a transport system, linked to the laboratory, that was to play a key role in the development in the 1860s of a shell filling complex. (See also figures 4.20 and 6.3.) (Illustration by David Evans and Stephen Dent)

Camber

C Magazine

New Powder Pier

0   100   200ft
0   70m

5.12 The shell filling rooms by Forton Lake Rolling Stage at Priddy's Hard. They were probably not used until April 1877, when No. 3 Magazine was not yet complete. (See also figure 6.3) (From TNA WO 78/2315)

incarnation of shifting rooms (where barrels were unheaded for the examination of powder), and were if at all possible to be placed outside the magazine enclosure. An army circular of 1877 officially imposed these new terms.[15]

Following the Magazine Committee's recommendations the War Office initiated enquiries with the Admiralty about the provision of a suitable floating magazine at Priddy's Hard. It was thought that a capacity of 24,000 barrels would be required to store the powder for the ships of the First Reserve, for a quarter of that provided for in the Estimates, a quarter of the reserve for the Channel and Mediterranean Squadrons, and ammunition lodged from ships. Land Service demands were only expected to account for 300 barrels. However, a suitable hulk could not be found and it was decided instead to build a land magazine – the new E Magazine (see page 94) – with a capacity of 7,000 barrels, the requirements for the establishment having been recalculated at 14,000 barrels (apart from that temporarily deposited in C Magazine). A new powder pier was designed in the summer of 1876 to serve this magazine, replacing the old rolling stage; connected to the northern arm of the camber, its construction featured iron screw piles, which supported a wooden staging

carrying a tramway. Many drawings for this have been preserved, which show also that a small examining shed was provided at the head of the pier. The laboratory was clearly now incapable of sustaining shell filling at the required rate, and a set of three shell filling rooms were added (see above). No original drawings survive for these buildings and they are the least documented section of the whole Priddy's Hard complex. Although shown on a site plan of 1873, the only located reference is from April 1877 when 144 hides were required as floor coverings to complete No.2 Shell Room. An extensive building campaign was now initiated to bring the establishment up to the desired standards.[16]

Developments at Portsmouth

The sequence of this construction had its own logic. The site selected for the new magazine was within the eastern demi-bastion – the spot occupied by the old barracks, now in use as a fuze and tube store. Before this could be pulled down accommodation would have to be found for its contents. The cottages were selected for this purpose – it has been seen that these were thought to be dangerously close to A Magazine – which

5.13 The Small Arms Cartridge Factory converted to cottages for key workers. The building to the left was converted into a cookhouse after 1877, and twenty years later became a proof house for the testing of explosives. *(From PTM/2943)*

5.14 The Small Arms Cartridge Factory, photographed in 1994. The long range shown in figure 5.13, with its flat roof for protection against incendiary bombs added in 1940. It has recently been demolished. *(NMR BB94/10313)*

meant the rehousing of all their inhabitants: the Foreman of the laboratory, Office Keeper and Police Sergeant. The old Small Arms Cartridge Factory buildings, renamed the Western Storehouses to reflect their new use, were initially selected for conversion, but the original proposals provided for accommodation far inferior to that the men and their families were leaving. Deputy Commissioner Booth at Priddy's Hard (titles changed once again after the abolition of the Control system in 1876) and the CRE at Portsmouth both strongly urged that this be improved:

'The three men for whom accommodation is to be provided are the only subordinates of the Department of the Commissary of the Ordnance who reside at Priddy's Hard and considering the immense quantity of Gunpowder and combustible materials stored there, and the very serious consequences which would result from Carelessness or unsteadiness on the part of these men it is evidently most important that they should be of a superior class and thoroughly to be depended upon … the extra expenditure … will be in reality a very cheap insurance of the government property at Priddy's Hard and of the

lives of the residents there & in the neighbourhood rendering it easy to secure the Services of thoroughly trustworthy men to fill these very responsible posts.'

The point was taken and the plans were revised. With the men rehoused, the changes could go ahead. The fireplaces of the cottages were bricked up and the porches altered, and by December 1877 plans were completed for the new magazine. The design of E Magazine, as it was to be known, originally provided for the building to be earthed up to roof level, but on the surviving drawing this is annotated 'omit from present contract' and it was never done.[17]

The gunwharf was being developed in parallel with Priddy's Hard. The increasing weights of ordnance (*Devastation*, completed in 1873, carried 35-ton guns and 81-ton guns were in the offing) meant that superior lifting gear was required. A pair of sheerlegs was taken from Woolwich and re-erected at the New Gunwharf, and by the summer of 1876 a dedicated fuze and rocket store had been provided. In keeping with the status of the gunwharf as the premier ordnance establishment, the building was provided with smart facades giving no indication of its function, but its

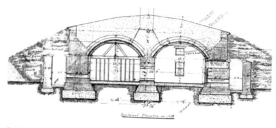

5.15 A drawing of E Magazine from December 1877, showing its earth protection, which was never applied. *(From PTM/3056)*

construction was determined by its intended contents. The Pettman general service fuzes, which Colonel Boxer had complained about, were still potentially lethal (those returned to Priddy's Hard by *Monarch* in December 1872 being in a dangerous condition), but those of his own design may have been little better: in April 1876, 29,638 Boxer Mark 1 fuzes were condemned – but in fairness they may have been past their sell-by date. Taking no chances, the new Store was of fireproof construction.

As has been seen, gunwharf officers had tended to resent any suggestion of shell storage being transferred to Priddy's Hard, but Commissary Tatum (see page 85 for his earlier incarnation as Controller at Woolwich) now strongly urged that a dedicated shell store be provided there. He had,

'in former reports pointed out the great loss of time & inconvenience caused by the detention at Priddy's Hard of the WD Vessels having filled shell

5.17 Right: A side elevation of E Magazine as completed, showing its ventilation hatches and the brick wall to the earth traverse. *(NMR BB95/11056)*
5.18 Below: E Magazine from the west, showing the police post of 1939 on the roof. *(NMR BB95/11060)*

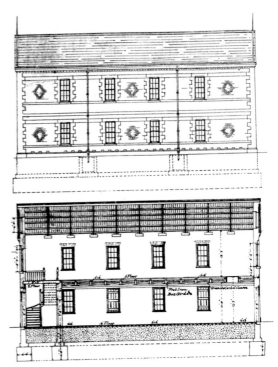

5.22 A drawing, dated April 1877, of the Portsmouth New Gunwharf fuze and rocket store. (*Adapted from PTM/1830*)

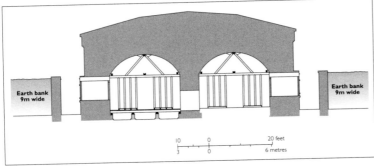

5.19 Top: One of the interior traveller cranes in E Magazine. (*NMR BB95/11049*)

5.20 Above: Cross-section of E Magazine as completed. Compare with figure 5.15. (*Drawing by Stephen Dent, based on cross-sectional drawing of 1877 in PTM/3056*)

5.21 Interior of Priddy's Hard E Magazine, built in 1878/9, showing the construction of the partitions for the gunpowder barrels. By 1913 it was reclassified as a cordite magazine. (*Priddy's Hard Archive NAM1434*)

on board for examination &c; and I am thoroughly convinced that in any time of pressure very serious inconvenience and delay would arise in operations connected with the examination of filled Shells, from the want of a proper Magazine at Priddy's Hard for their reception. During the recent examination of Shells for HMS *Shah*, *Danae* and *Lord Warden*, it was with the utmost difficulty that the examination could be completed in time to prevent the detention of the Ships. The Inspector of Warlike Store fully agrees with me that the want of a proper Shell Magazine is not only inconvenient – but is really a source of danger, because there is no proper place in which the shells can be deposited during the course of their examination.'

As an immediate consequence, plans were prepared in 1879 to adapt A Magazine as a shell store, the building being surrounded on three sides by a massive earthen traverse, but this project never came to fruition. Tatum also wanted the objectionable wooden storehouses by the camber rebuilt in brick, which, as will be seen, was done. The ignorance of practical matters that had dogged the previous decade still persisted in some quarters at the highest level: Booth was asked to supply a list of all shells filled and emptied at Priddy's Hard, apparently with a view to his superiors being able to judge the amount of work on hand. He replied that this would give no idea of the amount of powder involved. Different marks of shell of the same calibre held different bursting charges, and so absorbed differing degrees of labour in filling or emptying. Should 1,000 64-pounder shells be sent from the gunwharf to be emptied, they would hold 4,500 lbs if they were Mark I, 7,000 lbs if Mark II, and 7,125 lbs if Mark V.[18]

No facilities for storing guncotton were provided at Priddy's Hard or the gunwharf, and initially it was stored in the Hilsea artillery stores, quickly supplemented in 1876 by the abandoned fort at Browndown, part of the Gosport defences of the 1850s and now adapted for the purpose. Apart from its use as a filling for mines, guncotton was also required for torpedo warheads, and great delays were caused in bringing it to HMS *Vernon*, the hulk commissioned as a Torpedo School some six months before Browndown was brought into service. Tatum thought that Priddy's Hard would be a much more convenient location, and asked for a guncotton store to be included in the 1878–9 Estimates. That was turned down, but six tanks to hold wet guncotton were issued to Fort Monckton. Those, however, were not for naval use. The army, in the shape of the Royal Engineers, had taken an active interest in submarine mining for harbour defence purposes since the late 1860s, which took practical shape following the report of the Torpedo Committee in October 1870. The first Royal Engineer Submarine Mining Companies were accommodated in 1873 in the hulk *Hood* at Chatham, soon moving ashore to St Mary's Barracks in Chatham Lines. In the Portsmouth area, the facilities were all on the Gosport side. A test room was built at Fort Gilkicker in 1873, and Forts Blockhouse and Monckton were taken over for mining purposes. Later on, as will be seen, a purpose-built Mining Depot was built at Stokes Bay (see page 122). The storage of guncotton at Priddy's Hard continued to be mooted, and in 1880 drawings were prepared. It is not known if these were worked to, but some kind of building was provided, though Browndown was to remain the principal storehouse for this explosive for nearly twenty years.[19]

Work on improving the facilities for shell filling and storage continued at Priddy's Hard. It has been seen that a major obstacle to the development of the depot for this purpose was the inadequacy of the berthing arrangements for ordnance vessels, and the consequential ad hoc arrangements required remedy before the proposed transfer of shell storage from the gunwharf could take place. A new shell pier was begun in March 1879 and finished in October. Equipped with a 3½ ton crane, this provided a completely independent flow line for the issue and receipt of shells; together with the slightly earlier powder pier it replaced the earlier jetties. The old laboratory pier at Forton Lake was abandoned, though the camber still had a limited role to play. As the new pier was finished designs were prepared for a pair of new

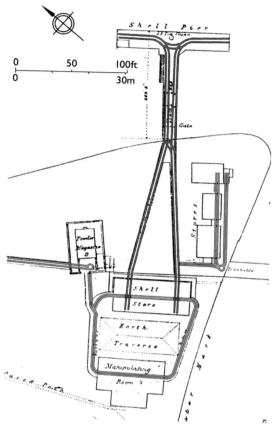

5.23 The dual gauges of the shell filling system at Priddy's Hard in 1883. The paler powder line is 1ft 6in, the darker shell line is 2ft 6in. *(Adapted from MPHH 1/486)*

laboratory buildings, separated by an earthen traverse, to work in conjunction with it; these were a shell store and a manipulating room, for filling and emptying shells, although cartographic evidence suggests that both buildings were intended to be dual-purpose. A dual system of gauges was to be used for the tramways from now on – shells were sent on a 2-foot 6-inch gauge track and powder on a 1-foot 6-inch track. The importance of flow lines, which had been initiated at Bull Point (though, as has been seen, with a choke point) was clearly recognised. E Magazine had been completed the previous year and handed over to the Ordnance Store Department in September 1882. Booth reported on the current

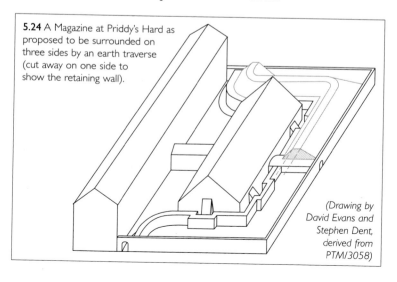

5.24 A Magazine at Priddy's Hard as proposed to be surrounded on three sides by an earth traverse (cut away on one side to show the retaining wall).

(Drawing by David Evans and Stephen Dent, derived from PTM/3058)

5.25 The New Gunwharf, Portsmouth, as it appeared in 1979, when part of HMS Vernon (the navy's torpedo and mine warfare establishment), with eight of the numerous and long-lived 'Ton' class minesweepers tied up at the quayside. Vernon was closed in 1991 and the site sold five years later for redevelopment. The principal surviving building is now the Grand Storehouse of 1800–14, the left-hand wing comprising a rebuild after bomb damage in the Second World War. See figure 9.30 for a plan of the site. (Portsmouth Dockyard Historical Trust, 79-124)

state of the depot at the beginning of 1883, noting the changes instigated by the recommendations of 1875. A and E Magazines were in use; the upper floors and sand protection inserted in the roof of B Magazine during the 1858 alterations had been removed and the storehouses around the camber rebuilt in brick (it is evident from the buildings as they are today that the wrought iron roof trusses were re-used: see Appendix A, pages 236-244). The recommendation that the entrance road near the planked way should be of asphalt or some other non-gritty substance had been placed in the Estimates every year, but always struck out as inessential, though all ground at the camber wharf likely to be used by men wearing magazine shoes had been planked. The chief omission had been the continued failure to provide a shifting room. The new shell buildings were completed on time and inspected by the Superintendent of the Royal Laboratory, and Booth could write: 'There is a good large room here for the examination of Gunpowder, the Service can be carried on without difficulty …'.

Priddy's Hard now appeared to have been satisfactorily modernised – but all was to be undone.[20]

5.24 A photograph of circa 1900 (around the same time as figure 2.3) of guns stored outside the Grand Storehouse at the New Gunwharf. (Portsmouth City Museums and Records Service)

6 NAVAL ORDNANCE, H. M. GUNWHARF   COPYRIGHT

Chapter 6 **A Modern Magazine System**

On 5 May 1883, a shell exploded in the manipulating room at Priddy's Hard, demolishing the building and killing a naval pensioner and five artillerymen engaged in shell filling. The traverse did its job, though, and the shell store was undamaged. The projectiles being filled at the time were 40-pounder RBL common shell. Of an old pattern, they were coated internally with a rough black lacquer, which contained portions of the sharp sand retained from the core used in casting the shell. In addition, the shell had a rough iron screw-bottom plug projecting into the interior. It was an accident waiting to happen. It was assumed by the investigators that one of the men had applied undue force to the copper rod with which he was forcing the powder down into the body of the shell, and the friction between the grit and iron caused the explosion. Though the major building for shell filling was gone, the business of the depot had to continue with marquees erected on the gunwharf for shell examination. Alterations were hastily made to the old laboratory to enable it to take on some of the burden, and the complex of buildings and tramways there probably attained its final layout at this time. A covered rolling way, which survives today in truncated form (see page 240, Appendix A), shows all the signs of hasty construction. These arrangements plainly would not do for long and the shell filling facility would have to be rebuilt on another site. Its eventual design and arrangement was to make Priddy's Hard, for the first time, a pace setter for ordnance buildings.[1]

The explosion completely undid all the recent developments at Priddy's Hard. Everything had to be rethought, and for this purpose a Committee on Laboratories was set up under Colonel Henry, the CRA of the Southern District. The transfer of filled shells from the gunwharf was still considered imminent by the Director of Artillery on 13 November 1883, when he directed the committee to go there and report on the necessary arrangements, but by 27 November that project had been abandoned. *Hecla*, the depot ship for naval mining work, had been docked in the summer, and her mines placed in the shell store at Priddy's Hard, so making it unavailable for shells; indeed, Booth thought no shell filling could be carried out while they were stored, and the ship was expected to

remain in harbour for some time. The need for a dedicated mine store now became apparent, and it was proposed that *Grampus* be resurrected for that purpose. Her upper decks were very leaky and her hatches needed renewing, but it was thought that by the use of tarpaulins she could be made usable as a mine store, so early in December a foreman and three labourers were appointed to her. However, although *Grampus* might serve at a pinch as a mine store, it was very doubtful that she would be capable of taking shells. Living conditions on the ship had been abominable in the past, particularly in winter, but were now to be mitigated by the provision of a coke stove for cooking. Quite apart from the shell store being temporarily unavailable and the dislocation to the working of Priddy's Hard, the committee were opposed to the storage of filled shell – or indeed any explosives in bulk – at the site. They wanted the store establishment to be removed entirely to floating magazines, with the depot serving only as a laboratory.[2]

Report from the Laboratory Committee

Pending the committee's final report no decision could be made locally concerning the rebuilding of the shell filling facility. Deputy Commissioner Booth was transferred from Priddy's Hard to Halifax, Nova Scotia, at the beginning of 1884; his replacement was Assistant Commissary Pridham.

6.1 Two views of the demolished manipulating rooms. Above: note the laboratory magazine on the left; Below: on the right, the original set of shell filling rooms. *(From H.W.Semark, The RNADs of Priddy's Hard)*

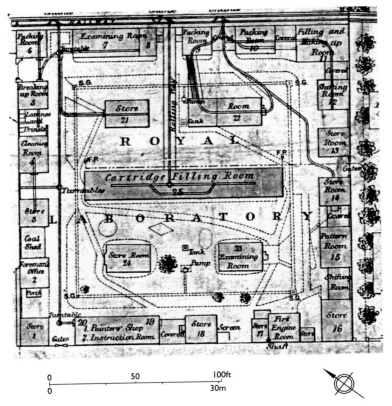

6.2 The laboratory at Priddy's Hard in its final form, 1896. *(From PTM/3027)*

improvement of the shell filling facilities would have to be undertaken, and £3,000 was inserted into the 1884–5 estimates for this purpose.

Colonel Henry delivered his report on 1 July 1884. The recommendations concerning the storage of powder were drastic. No more than 15 tons of powder, loose or in cartridges, was to be kept at the depot, and this edict was enforced at once. On 5 July the Director of Artillery ordered that the powder in E Magazine (some 700 tons) was to be moved to Tipner, and the rockets to any convenient magazine in the forts, maintaining a small store of them on *Grampus*.

The importance of the remaining services at Priddy's Hard was stressed by the recommendation that a Laboratory Manager be appointed, and the post was given to a nominee of the Superintendent of the Royal Laboratory. The number of laboratory buildings required was not stated, nor their dimensions or location. The committee took on board suggestions made by the Commander of the Southern District, Lieutenant General Willis. He wished hulks to be used for ammunition issued to and received from ships, with Marchwood and Tipner storing all other explosives except those required for laboratory use. Willis determined that guncotton, torpedoes and rockets ought to be held in detached land magazines, but when required afloat should be stored in floating magazines. Above all, he wanted Priddy's Hard to house all the filled shell at the gunwharf, and all the small arms and machine-gun ammunition at Marchwood.[3]

Financial considerations, as always, played a part in reducing the scale of the proposed arrangements. The provision of the floating magazines would involve a considerable expense, and it

The ruins from the explosion were left where they stood until the early summer, when it was found that most of the materials were only fit for road making. The shell filling rooms of the early 1870s were renovated to assist the laboratory, but were found to be 'very small and contracted' compared with their transient replacement. Continued heavy demands for filled shells placed a strain on the available facilities. Demands did indeed increase, and some temporary labourers had to be retained. Whatever the committee's final decisions,

Laboratory Committee Recommendations for 1884

- New Shell Filling buildings to be erected. Tramway to connect E Magazine with Shell Filling rooms & pier. Tramway to be laid along Southern Boundary to connect Shell Filling Rooms with existing Tramway on the pier.
- Small expense magazines to be built alongside proposed Tramway.
- Instruction rooms to be built.

Suggestions for Laboratory Buildings:

- Interiors to be lined with wood and to avoid places where dust can accumulate.
- Floors to be covered with leather.
- Doors to open outwards.
- Closed porches at every entrance.
- Cartridge filling buildings to be artificially warmed by pipes fixed to the walls.
- Compartment in Cartridge filling building for drying serge bags in which spare powder was issued.
- Thermometer for Cartridge filling buildings and a book to keep records of the temperatures.

- Exteriors of buildings to be adequately illuminated at night.
- Notice boards stating the quantities of powder and other explosives permitted in a building at any one time.
- Apparatus capable of lifting 1 ton to be fixed where heavy shells have to be manipulated.
- Buckets of water to be kept in each room.
- Building for Signal Rockets? *[Query on original document]*
- Additional magazine at Browndown to hold 1 ton dry guncotton. Storeroom at Browndown for war & Life-saving Rockets. Tramway over the shingle to connect Guncotton Stores with Military Road.
- Pier at Browndown to be built.

Recommendations not involving works:

- Floating magazine in addition to *Grampus* for filled shell.
- Floating magazine accommodation for ships' proportions of ammunition – an urgent necessity.
- Steam launch & powder barges.

WO 55/2226

seemed to the General by November that it would be best to spend the £3,000 on deepening the channel to Tipner and extending the pier there to improve its availability. If it were possible to leave ammunition of warships in harbour for only a short time then Tipner might prove adequate to solve the storage problem. By the end of 1884 it was hoped that all the transfers would have been carried out, with all the small arms and machine-gun ammunition in the area then being held at Priddy's Hard. Additional requirements continued to appear without let-up. Browndown Fort was now thought to be insecure and a better location for the guncotton was required; a much greater necessity was a range for testing and adjusting torpedoes, at the time being done in the hopelessly inadequate canal at Woolwich. The new fitting-out basin at Chatham was shortly to be used instead, but the certainty of interference with the operations of the dockyard was plain to see. The relentless increase in size of naval ordnance meant that the facilities at Tipner were now inadequate, for its travelling cranes were not strong enough to hoist the cartridges for *Inflexible*'s monster guns (see figures OA.3 and OA.4). Although nothing had been done at Priddy's Hard to replace the destroyed building, the increasing workload meant that by the spring of 1885, twenty-five additional men and boys had been taken on at the laboratory, and Pridham could turn out 80 quarter charges of 52½ lbs for 12.5-inch RML daily, for four days in succession. After that the rate of filling would fall to 28 a day, because of pressure to turn out other cartridges for sea service, particularly for *Inflexible*. As always, the need for this extra labour was questioned, but Pridham replied that the naval work alone was overwhelming, quite apart from the requirements of the army. Further expenses were incurred through the new arrangements. To prevent any accumulation at Priddy's Hard daily transits were required to Tipner, and to expedite this a steam launch had to be hired for towing an ordnance barge.[4]

The new shell filling facility

New developments in weapons and explosives added another layer of complexity to this situation. At least £3,000 was needed for the works recommended by the Laboratory Committee, but bureaucratic inertia ensured that no money had been budgeted for the year 1885–6. The situation was becoming more pressing at Priddy's Hard, with the imminent introduction of the new heavy breech-loading (BL) guns, so yet another committee was set up to determine the way forward for the hard-pressed depot. This was at a high level, with members comprising the Director of Artillery Stores, Assistant Director of Artillery Stores, Commissary General of Ordnance and the Director of Works for Fortifications. After deliberating they felt it might be necessary to make changes to the recommendations of the Laboratory Committee. Meeting at the end of September 1885, they fixed on a location for the replacement buildings beyond the caponier (see Glossary) by Forton Creek. This was indeed to be the site of a new shell filling facility, but what the new committee envisaged was a duplication of the arrangement of a paired shell filling room and filled shell store separated by a traverse. The multiplication of risks caused by several people performing potentially hazardous operations within one large space was still apparently not recognised, although if the accident of 1883 had been limited to the shell under manipulation, only 2½ lbs of powder would have detonated, instead of the explosion spreading to other shells and a nearly full barrel of powder. The proposed protection was to be effected by a ready-made traverse using the ramparts, with another traverse between the buildings, rather than through a number of separated and individually traversed units. The surviving

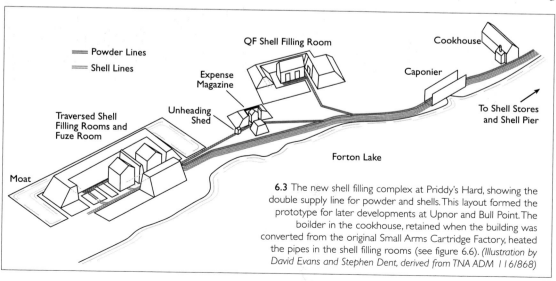

6.3 The new shell filling complex at Priddy's Hard, showing the double supply line for powder and shells. This layout formed the prototype for later developments at Upnor and Bull Point. The boilder in the cookhouse, retained when the building was converted from the original Small Arms Cartridge Factory, heated the pipes in the shell filling rooms (see figure 6.6). *(Illustration by David Evans and Stephen Dent, derived from TNA ADM 116/868)*

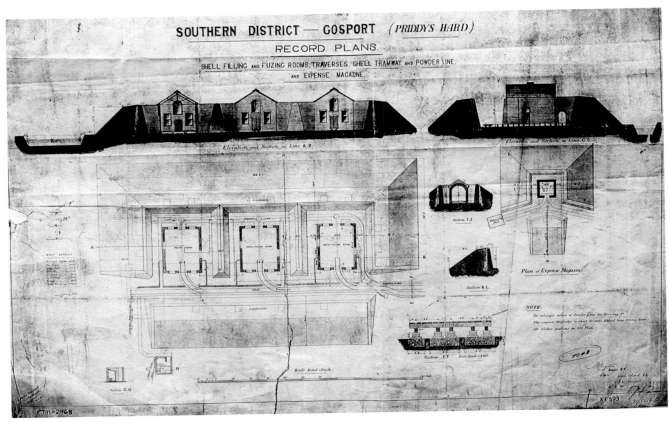

6.4 Above: Plan, sections and elevations showing, from left, the fuzing room, two shell filling rooms, and the expense magazine, all with their traverses, in the new shell filling complex at Priddy's Hard. *(PTM/2968)*

6.5 Below: 'The Straight' at Priddy's Hard; the fuzing room and two shell filling rooms looking east. Prominent are the massive brick-faced traverses. (See also figure 6.4, above and title page.) *(Stephen Dent)*

6.6 Interior view of a shell filling room, showing the piped heating system, supplied from a boiler housed in the former Small Arms Cartridge Factory, that ensured a warm and dry environment for the powder. (See also figure 6.3 and front cover.) (Explosion! Museum of Naval Firepower)

6.7 The shell filling complex from the east, showing the former powder tramway leading to the expense magazine (to the right) and the shell filling rooms (in the distance). To the left of the picture is all that remains of the trotyl melting rooms of 1915 (see figure 9.10), with its distinctive clerestory roof. Trotyl, a nitro-compound, was first used as a shell filling in Britain in 1914. (Jeremy Lake)

shell store was to be used for receiving shells landed at the shell pier and, after examination in the nearby examining room (probably part of the shell filling buildings of some ten years previous), they were to be sent beyond the ramparts to the proposed buildings. The Laboratory Magazine, D, should hold the powder required for filling, and the suggested functions of the other magazines were to be: A, to house small arms ammunition; B, not mentioned; C, to be an expense magazine; and E, to be traversed and used to store ammunition returned from ships. The entrance to E Magazine was altered to conform to this. It was suggested that Tipner would need to be enlarged

to take a further 10–15,000 barrels. However, the committee were determined that a second floating magazine about the size of *Grampus* would be far preferable, *Carnatic* being the final choice.[5]

It may well have seemed that the ordnance store situation at Portsmouth was both inextricably complicated and insoluble. But in April 1886, the CRE Gosport, Lieutenant Colonel Ovey, provided the answer. A sum of £3,950 had been set aside in the Estimates for the still undesigned shell filling facility, and in consultation with Pridham he drew up plans for a set of three rooms, one for fuze filling and two for shell filling. They would be brick built but not of very substantial construction, with slated roofs on wooden trusses and traversed on all sides. Forton Lake lay before the front of the complex and further protection was given behind the buildings in the form of a moat similar to that used in the rear of the restoving establishment at St Budeaux. Instead of using the old Laboratory Magazine some distance away, as suggested, an expense magazine now formed part of the plan. The dual system of gauges recently introduced was employed. The first drawings to survive, produced in June 1886, incorporated the recommendations of the reconstituted Committee on the Transport and Storage of Gunpowder and Guncotton (see below). This committee had been dissolved in 1881 but reformed at the end of 1884, probably partly because of the continuing indecision about what to do at Priddy's Hard.

Almost all their recommendations were adopted, though heating had still not been provided for the shell filling rooms by the beginning of 1889. Ovey's original scheme was almost immediately supplemented by a further filling room, of different design, for another new weapons system, the quick-firing gun.[6]

The impact of a new weapon

The first quick-firing (QF) guns, then on the point of introduction into service, featured the shell and cartridge (which was contained in a brass case) made up into a fixed unit, like an enlarged version of a rifle bullet. They were fed into the breech of the gun by hand; after firing the cartridge case was ejected and a new round inserted. A skilled gun crew could attain a rate of fire of twenty-five to thirty unaimed shots per minute, and fifteen aimed shots. For obvious reasons this was only practicable with projectiles that were light enough to be easily manhandled. Two versions were originally procured, firing 6-pound and 3-pound shells, and made by the firms of Nordenfelt and Hotchkiss. They were introduced into service in large numbers as anti-torpedo boat defences for capital ships and coastal fortifications, and as the primary gun armament for torpedo boats and their successors. It is evident

---

Recommendations from the Committee on the Transport and Storage of Gunpowder and Guncotton

- In places classed as 'clean' all rails and their fastenings, as also the fastenings of floors, all hinges, bolts, locks, keys, and window fastenings, should be of wood, copper, or copper alloy.
- Trucks when used in such places should have the wheels and their fastenings of copper or copper alloy.
- Precautions should be taken to prevent metal fastenings of the roof from falling accidentally into the buildings.
- Travellers or cranes: inside – standing parts might be made of iron, but all working parts should, if possible, be of copper or copper alloy, or of wood or rope; outside – on piers, wharves, etc, iron might be used for both standing and working parts.
- Low-pressure steam or hot water warming apparatus could be used in magazines and laboratories. The pipes might be of iron, but should, if possible, be fixed at a height of not less than 6 feet 6 inches above the floor. They need not be galvanised nor otherwise coated, nor boxed in with wood, but should be quite detached from the walls and not less than 6 inches from any timber work. They should be frequently wiped so as to prevent an accumulation of dust.
- Copper sheeting for magazine doors and windows might be discontinued, provided that the outside platforms were disconnected from magazine floors by making a portion of the platform 6 feet in length removable.

WO 33/46

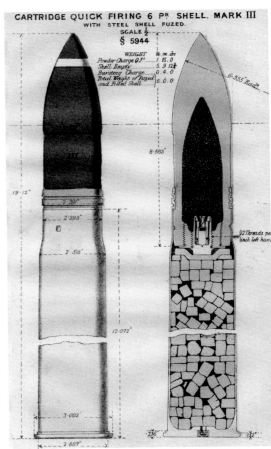

6.8 A 6-pounder QF shell.
(*From Treatise on Ammunition, 5th ed., London, 1892*)

that the assembly of one of these pieces of ammunition was of a different order – particularly when the shell was fuzed – from the simple operations that had gone so wrong at Priddy's Hard. All this ammunition was supplied by outside makers, the cartridge cases being filled at Woolwich, and a QF-shell filling room was designed in the spring of 1887 as an addition to the new complex. There is no evidence that the 6- and 3-pounder ammunition was ever prepared there; the building was intended to prepare shells for the 4.7-inch QF, which had separate shells and cartridges.

Great things were expected of this gun (see Ordnance and Armament, pages 128–134). Lord George Hamilton, the First Lord, in his speech on the Navy Estimates for 1888–9, announced that it would supersede the 4-inch and 5-inch BL guns in all new warships. The gun had been adopted for service in November 1887, and could be worked at a rate of about 12 rounds per minute. As an intended key element in the future armament of the navy, facilities for its ammunition were an important part of the revamping of Priddy's Hard, and were naturally also provided at Bull Point. No such facilities seem to have been provided on the Medway, which was supplied with the ammunition by Woolwich. Unlike the shell filling rooms and the fuze filling room, the QF building was subdivided into four cells, in each of which a single shell was manipulated. The building was connected with the Powder Line. The cartridges were dealt with in the laboratory buildings.

From the end of May 1889, dummy 6-pounder and 3-pounder cartridges were issued for training purposes. Instructional handbooks for the 4.7-inch QF were eventually issued in February 1890, the

guns being first mounted on the torpedo gunboat *Sharpshooter* (which had been completed in August 1889) and the remainder of its class, the battleship *Trafalgar* (completed in March 1890) and the *Barracouta* class of Third-Class cruisers (all completed during 1890). By April 1891 it was expected that the new building at Priddy's Hard would have the capability to fill 1,000 shells per week, with Woolwich and Bull Point filling 3,000 and 2,000 respectively. In the event the supply of cartridge cases was, by June 1891, insufficient for them to be sent to the outports for filling, though shells and fuzes had been sent to Priddy's Hard and Bull Point. By the next month filling was well under way at Woolwich and Priddy's Hard, although slow at Bull Point. This vast amount of QF ammunition coming into service required additional storage, as it was forbidden to lodge it

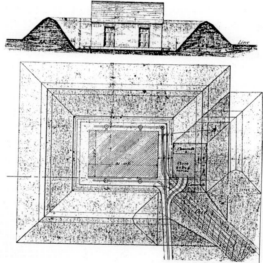

6.9 The QF filling room at Priddy's Hard. Above: plan and section of February 1887, showing the protected storeroom and skewed entrance, which were not built in the form shown. The flat roof was applied in the Second World War. *(Adapted from PTM/2958)* Below: the building today. *(Stephen Dent)*

with any other ammunition or explosive. In the summer of 1888 a QF shell store at Priddy's Hard was designed and placed in the programme of works for 1888–9.[7]

As well as Priddy's Hard, the other depots required updating. At Bull Point the principal need, apart from accommodation for QF ammunition (a store for which was authorised for 1888–9) was for improved wharfage. At low tide the shell camber was quite dry, and the powder pier had only two to three feet of water alongside it. There were only five lighters, one or more being generally away, and the cranes were old and hand-worked. A lighter could not be cleared in less than 24 hours. As elsewhere, more floating magazines were required and *Newcastle* was provided; it was at first thought that three more would be needed, *Valorous* for powder and *Kent* and *Bellerophon* for QF ammunition. Additional lighters and two extra piers were needed, one 350-foot long for powder, and another 100-foot long for shells. Little had happened at Upnor save the acquisition of a third shell store in 1882–3, and, around the same time, an alarming demonstration of geological instability at Chattenden, where remedial work took place. Chattenden's accommodation had soon proved to be insufficient, and in 1885 the War Office decided, without consulting the Admiralty, to again use Upnor as a Magazine Depot, restricting the storage to gun ammunition in metal cases (i.e. excluding loose powder in barrels or cases). At the same time it was decided to forbid laboratory operations there. Shell storage was reasonably well catered for at Upnor, but the provision of a modern laboratory was now absolutely necessary. However, although a laboratory was planned for, it was never built. The problem of ordnance facilities on the Medway was to prove one of the most intractable of all, and no part of this laboratory project was to be realised during the next decade. And when it did finally materialise it was on another site altogether (see pages 171–181).[8]

Another key new requirement was the provision of heating for cartridge filling and examination rooms. This was required by the latest pattern of gunpowder to enter service with the navy. Of the 420,000 lbs held at Priddy's Hard, 120,000 were large prisms (see Glossary), unsuitable for 6-inch breech loaders (BL). New chemical explosives were in the pipeline, but experimental firing at the old ironclad *Resistance* in 1889 had shown that powder was still the most effective form of explosive for attacking armour plate. Dry rooms for filling cartridges existed only at Woolwich, Priddy's Hard, Bermuda, Trincomalee and Simons Town, as at the time these were ordered they were not considered, for climatic and other reasons, to be required at other places. However, all cartridges were now to be issued to the navy pre-filled by Ordnance Store Departments at the several stations, and as it was essential that they be made up in a dry atmosphere, a more general provision of these rooms was necessary. The Director of Naval Ordnance held that the provision of proper dry rooms for filling cartridges with the new E.X.E. powder (see Glossary) was absolutely essential for its introduction. This new powder was to have a short service life, but future explosives were to require a much more extensive system of environmental control; the heating at Priddy's Hard was originally provided by the boiler housed in the old Small Arms Cartridge Factory (see plan in Appendix A).[9]

While Priddy's Hard was being so tortuously developed, the Admiralty was making equally convoluted progress toward taking control of its own ordnance stores. It was not only the Admiralty who were dissatisfied with the conduct of the Ordnance Department. In 1886 Lieutenant General Sir Garnet Wolseley complained bitterly of the Department's treatment of inventors (see the discussion on Boxer, Chapter 5, page 86), and about defective ammunition and other stores, which had led to unnecessary casualties in recent colonial wars. Colonel Hope V.C., a man without Wolseley's gravitas, aired the matter in the press:

'The jobbery, the ignorance and prejudice, the insolence and obstruction, and the unpatriotic conduct generally of the high officials of the Ordnance Department for the last quarter of a century are almost incredible to any honest tax-paying outsider... . I have been at war with the department for the long period of 29 years... . These men "alike unknown in the field of science and the fields of battle"... [were responsible for Colonel Palliser's early death through worry] ... Last year were done to death, through the faulty ammunition supplied by the Ordnance Department ... Herbert Stewart and Fred Burnaby [in the Sudanese campaign], besides many humbler but good men and true...'.

The complaints about warlike stores were officially collated in response to these pressures. This was a formidable list, covering everything from defective bayonets to horse harness, the principal shortcoming of naval equipment being the fuzes used at the bombardment of Alexandria. Pettman General Service fuzes seemed the worst: glancing blows rendered them ineffectual. Wooden time fuzes burnt irregularly and were unreliable; they were to be withdrawn at the beginning of 1890.

The future Admiral of the Fleet, Sir John Fisher, had his own views on the matter. In his memoirs he claimed that he bent his efforts whilst Director of Naval Ordnance to wresting control of naval ordnance from the War Office, but the facts were not exactly in accordance with his memory. In April 1887 Fisher was all in favour of the current position, stating in a discussion of the matter: 'The clear and very great gain to the Navy of the present system (with all its faults) lies in the fact that the Admiralty invariably get the latest and best guns and stores for the Navy, and the Army use up the obsolete Naval Ordnance (which is quite good enough for the purpose) for land service. In these days of such rapid and enormous changes in all war matériel, this is a very important advantage.' This was reworded more tactfully in the final version seen by War Office representatives. However, the disadvantages of the situation were very obvious, and with the rapidly growing differences between land and sea service weaponry, Fisher's point was not going to be true for much longer. As it was, the Admiralty could not give direct orders to the gunwharves as to particular fitments for particular ships. All their directions had go through the Ordnance Department. The Admiralty wanted an independent Ordnance Department, common to both services, and on 27 June 1888 an agreement was made with the War Office, the Admiralty agreeing to pay for its own ordnance and the War Office to provide storage and staff. This was to prove a short-lived arrangement.[10]

The Naval Defence Act and its aftermath

Much had been accomplished in the modernisation of the three great issuing and manipulating depots of Priddy's Hard, Upnor and Bull Point, but all three underwent even greater development during the 1890s. There were three main reasons for this: the great increase in the size of the fleet

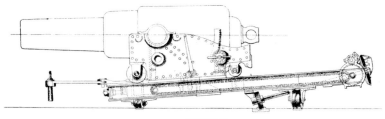

SIDE ELEVATION.

following the Naval Defence Act of 1889; the introduction of cordite as the new propellant; and the Admiralty gaining effective control over the storage of its ordnance. The Naval Defence Act was effectively the catalyst for all else. During the 1880s the French Navy underwent a period of growth, in particular leading the way in equipping its battleships with BL guns, while the Royal Navy appeared to stagnate. In September 1884 a celebrated article by the campaigning journalist W. T. Stead ('What is the Truth about the navy', in the *Pall Mall Gazette*) brought the matter into prominence. Fisher, characteristically operating behind the scenes, had furnished much of the information to Stead. In response, Northbrook, the First Lord, announced a programme of construction worth £3,100,000 in addition to that proposed in the Estimates. A further naval scare followed in 1888, largely over the realisation that the navy was too small to contest an alliance between two other naval powers, and the consequence was the Act of March 1889, which initiated a new building programme costing £21,500,000. This injection of cash brought difficulties in its wake. The Armaments portion of the Naval Defence Act was to be £2,500,000, and the Commissary General of Ordnance stated that there was insufficient

6.10 A 9-inch naval RML converted with a mounting for army use. *(From Treatise on Military Carriages, 6th ed., 1902)*

6.11 The working party of the floating magazine *Carnatic*, photographed on the upper deck, shortly before 1891. Back row: A. Pink; C. Johns; unknown; J. Hines; unknown; T. Champion; unknown. Middle row: Mr Pink; unknown; Mr Osborne, Foreman (wearing necktie); Mr Treby, Storekeeper (wearing peaked cap); unknown; V. Osborne; unknown. Front row: G. Butt; unknown; P. West; E. Primmer; Mr Duke; H. Osborne, unknown. The majority seem to be wearing a form of magazine clothing, i.e. woollen trousers and Guernsey-type sweaters and leather-soled shoes. Note that none of the shoes are hobnailed, which would be usual with labourers in other trades. The different hats worn denote, both officially and unofficially, the various ranks. *Carnatic*, a Third Rate dating from 1823, served as a hulk until being sold in 1914. *(Priddy's Hard Archive 1998.3.135)*

6.12 *Newcastle* was
a typical floating
magazine of the
late 19th century.
A former frigate,
she served as a
hulk at Plymouth
until sold in 1929.
(*From TNA ADM
1/7549/B*)

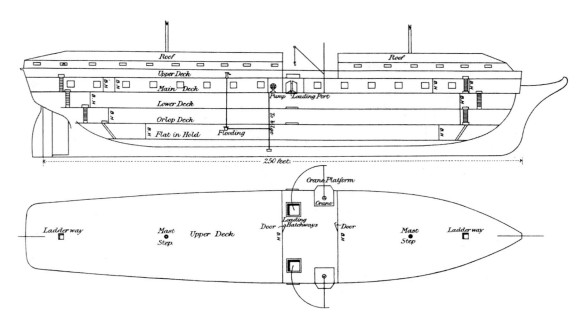

magazine accommodation and stores to keep all this material. Fisher concurred, noting that the War Office had recently made demands on the Admiralty to the tune of about £150,000 for providing additional accommodation for the existing naval ordnance stores, without any reference to those which would be called for by the new shipbuilding programme.[11]

During 1890, the dispute between the War Office and the Admiralty was largely settled through the deliberations of a committee chaired by Arthur Forwood, the Financial Secretary to the Admiralty. The committee's remit was to enquire into the purchase, custody and accounts of naval Warlike Stores. The matter had recently been stirred up again by the Treasury ruling that some £50,000 should be paid out of Admiralty funds for new storehouses and two floating magazines. The committee established the current position as regards ordnance stores and the accommodation available for them; incredibly, no accurate knowledge was readily accessible. Neither the War Office nor the Admiralty knew to within £3,000,000 how they stood, and many demands were grossly inflated as a consequence.

The continuing requests for floating magazines provided an obvious focus for these concerns, the basic question being: were floating magazines a good form of storage? Fisher, still Director of Naval Ordnance, was positive that because they deteriorated continuously they were extremely expensive to keep up. In addition, he knew from experience that Bull Point and Tipner could be extended. The Director of Artillery, Major-General Alderson, combated Fisher's view with a string of plausible arguments. He estimated the cost of storage of a barrel in a hulk as 5 shillings, while the expense of building a land magazine raised it to £2. A floating magazine could be converted in eight months at the outside, while it took two to

three years to build a magazine, and twenty men on the ship would do the work of one hundred men ashore. He countered the point about deterioration by the fact that the expensive and relatively recently completed depot at Chattenden was already under repair, not mentioning the (so far) unique geology of the site. Alderson's position was undermined by the discovery that the majority of the ships were not actually required. The Treasury commented approvingly on the findings of Forwood's first report:

'the magnitude of the Land and Sea Store business, when united, has hitherto prevented the present Store Staff from mastering such essential statistics as the proportion borne by the total working capacity of each Magazine to current requirements, and by the aggregate of available store accommodation to the aggregate of stores to be housed. In the spring of 1890, the War Department demanded the supply of four hulks for the storage of Navy powder and quick-firing ammunition, at a cost of £18,500 for fittings alone, in addition to two other hulks which had been supplied in 1889, and were being fitted at a cost of £15,000. This demand far exceeded the provision in Navy Estimates; but the only reply of the War Department to the representations of the Treasury and Admiralty was that the expenditure was *necessary* and *urgently required*. As shewn in the Report, the Committee have proved that no further hulks are required. This incident emphasizes in a striking manner the expediency of placing upon each Department, the direct responsibility for demands involving expenditure in respect of its own requirements.'

As a result of the committee's investigations, the list of ships to be converted was reduced to *Thalia* and *Newcastle*. With Treasury backing, any recommendations made by the committee were likely to be implemented.[12]

The matter of the floating magazines settled, the committee proceeded with a second report, which analysed the current use being made of the depots and recommended their division between the services. In the Portsmouth area, four-fifths of the business at Priddy's Hard and Marchwood was for the navy, while the army required one third more than the navy at Tipner. It was a natural consequence to allot Marchwood and Priddy's Hard to the navy and Tipner to the army. Stores transferred to Tipner from Priddy's Hard and Marchwood were to be kept in *Thalia*, which was to be moored off Tipner. Marchwood had recently stored 50,000 barrels, acting as a depot for powder from Purfleet. There was spare space for 26,000 barrels and this could be used to take QF ammunition under order for Priddy's Hard but for which there was insufficient room. *Carnatic*, *Grampus* and *Melampus* were allotted to Priddy's Hard. The Portsmouth Gunwharf was to be divided, the army retaining the Old Gunwharf. On 31 March 1890, Bull Point held 2,940 barrels for land service and 21,457 for sea service, and it was consequently proposed that the majority of the depot should be transferred to Admiralty control. The gunwharf and part of Bull Point (No.4 Magazine, the basin area and the buildings associated with it) were to go to the army, the rest of Bull Point and the floating magazines *Newcastle*, *Eclipse* and *Conquestador* to the navy. Gunwharf business was to be transferred to a portion of the Royal William Yard at Plymouth, which was to be separated by a wall from the Victualling Department. On the Medway, Chattenden was to be retained by the army. At the great deposit magazines, Purfleet was equally divided in accordance with the anticipated receipts for 1890–91 (51,000 barrels for land service and 58,518 for sea service), while Weedon,

acting as a relief depot to Purfleet and Woolwich holding naval powder and land service filled shells, went entirely to the army. The arrangements at Plumstead remained undisturbed. At the beginning of February 1891 the committee's recommendations were generally accepted, with division of the depots to take place on 1 October 1891. The new Naval Ordnance Store Department was placed under Colonel Thales Pease, a man who had worked his way up through all the organisational changes from clerk at Woolwich in 1855, and was appointed the first (and in fact the only) Storekeeper General of Naval Ordnance. As Senior Ordnance Store Officer of the Southern District he had overseen the conversion of the floating magazines, and he was to be instrumental in unravelling the confusion of accounts he inherited. [13]

In December 1891, the Commander in Chief (C-in-C) Portsmouth, Admiral the Earl of Clanwilliam, suggested that all works proposed for the gunwharf and Priddy's Hard were in need of justification. He also suggested to the Admiralty that they hand Marchwood over to the War Office, and that the Marines be removed from Marchwood; they had replaced the military guard on 11 April 1891, when the depot was transferred to the Admiralty, but were a very expensive mode of providing labour in an unwholesome situation. As Clanwilliam said:

'Marchwood is in a most insanitary condition, and how it has escaped an epidemic is a wonder. There is no water supply for latrines or w.c's; there is not an adequate supply of fresh water – there are several holes, on the average 8 to 9 feet deep, full of water, but only one of them gives drinking water, and that, as one of the men said, "is the best we have." That one is 10 feet from a pigstye in full use, with a gravelly soil, and when the water gets

6.13 The shell store at Priddy's Hard. Left: before its extension after 1892. Note the pale powder line and darker shell line, showing it also functioned as a manipulating room. *(Illustration by David Evans and Stephen Dent, derived from PTM/3105)* Right: The building today. *(Patrick Brown)*

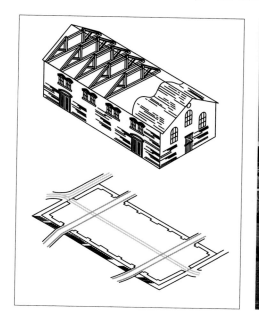

low in dry weather becomes thick and bad. The drainage may be said not to exist; it is so much the reverse of what it ought to be…I do not recommend any expenditure on the place. It would be much better to build on available space at Priddy's Hard, and let the military take Marchwood back again. As I hear the War Department are thinking of building a powder magazine at Tipnor, it might be considered advisable to have a Naval powder depôt at Tipnor, instead of putting up additional buildings at Priddy's Hard.'

Fisher's successor as Director of Naval Ordnance, Captain Kane, disagreed about the Marines, and was also decidedly opposed to abandoning Marchwood: 'I can hardly think it would be seriously entertained that enormous magazines containing 6,000,000 lbs. of powder, which have hitherto been purposely placed in isolated positions, should be transferred to the middle of Portsmouth harbour.' Clanwilliam had a point about the unhealthy environment of Marchwood, but it is hard to see the new works at Priddy's Hard as extravagances. These included: enlarging tinsmiths' shop (£50); new painters' shop (£400); enlarging shell store (£500); enlarging rocket store (£400); improving laboratory (£430); improving water supply (£365); dredging camber (£100). The shell store was duly enlarged, assuming the proportions it retains to this day, and the rocket store (in the building that used to house the cottages) was extended to the rear, again giving it its present form. An extension to the gunwharf smithery (the old factory) was proposed, but the Admiralty contemplated selling the site to Portsmouth Corporation for development as commercial docks and moving the gunwharf facilities to the north-east corner of the dockyard. That plan, however, was abandoned in January 1894, though as will be seen, projects for such a move remained in the air. The Smithery extension was finally carried out in 1897.

The establishment of telephonic communications between the gunwharf and Priddy's Hard was now vital, as all the filled shells were stored at the gunwharf, while the filling was done at Priddy's Hard. Various types of telephone system were in use on board ship, but it is more likely that a civilian type of communication system was used, as in 1890 the Postmaster General was authorised to place *Grampus* in telephonic communication with Priddy's Hard through the laying of a direct wire. At its greatest extent the filled shell storage at the gunwharf comprised: A Magazine (720 square feet); BI (720 square feet); BII (1,200 square feet); C (1,036 square feet); D (518 square feet); Shell Store (2,400 square feet); Balaclava Shed (3,300 square feet). Of the space in the Balaclava Shed 1,000 square feet were reserved for painting filled shells, so as to facilitate work at Priddy's Hard. This separation of filling and storing facilities for shells was soon to be removed after the next transformation of Priddy's Hard. There had never been such a separation at Bull Point, but the shell filling facilities had not been modernised, and for the first time since its construction the depot now seemed outdated. It would have been easy to strengthen the floors of the empty barrel and case store to take filled shells, and in 1892 a concrete shell base was designed for open-air storage, but the pressing need was for modern shell filling rooms to increase the output of heavy shells. A set of buildings virtually duplicating those at Priddy's Hard were duly designed in August 1893 and a workshop for cleaning cartridges, a fuze proving room and a boiler house to provide the necessary heating followed in 1894–5.[14]

Overseas depots

The warships ordered under the 1889 Naval Defence Act were now coming into service, and it was plain that the size of the fleet would continue to increase. But Lord George Hamilton, the First Lord, viewed the implications for ordnance storage in an extraordinarily perverse way when he announced the new developments to a committee of the House of Commons in March of that year. He forecast that in two or three years the ordnance votes would be considerably diminished, and proposed to decrease the reserves of ammunition. He justified this with the words:

'The proportion of reserves was fixed many years ago, when production was limited and slow. Now that production has rapidly increased, I do not think it advisable to keep large stocks of perishable material. I hope I shall be able to make emergency contracts with the great firms who manufacture these articles, and, if so, we shall be able to accomplish a substantial reduction in our ordnance vote. Therefore … I think I may say our scheme carries with it, as it progresses, a reduction rather than an increase of expenditure.' ('Hear, hear,' and a laugh.)

6.14 The 1890 shell store at Portsmouth Gunwharf was a more ornate design and, unlike the Priddy's Hard shell store, only intended for storage. (From PTM/1818)

The laugh was the more appropriate response. Such limited developments as had taken place at the major naval Ordnance Depots were, in varying degrees, inadequate to meet the situation.

The problem of ammunition storage and supply was at its most critical in the Mediterranean, the theatre where the Royal Navy was most visibly present. This was a problem that predated the Naval Defence Act. In the summer of 1889 Vice-Admiral Sir Anthony Hoskins, C-in-C Mediterranean, tested the efficiency of the Gibraltar magazines for supplying ammunition. There were three magazines, Sandpits between the dockyard and Alameda for powder only, Dutch Magazine between New Mole and Rosia Bay for QF and MG (Machine Gun) ammunition, and Sands Magazine in Alameda Gardens for tubes and fuzes. Supplying any ammunition at all to the fleet only occurred with much difficulty and delay. The laboratory was only an 'utterly inefficient' hut, and no reserve of filled shell and made-up powder cases was held. It was recommended that extensions and additions be made, to include at least six laboratory buildings. In 1892, Hoskins' successor, Vice-Admiral Tryon, reported that storage was urgently required for sixty per cent of the reserve cartridges, and for fifty per cent of the filled shells. A third of the reserves for the Mediterranean Fleet were kept at Gibraltar, the balance at Malta. All the reserves for the Channel Fleet were kept at Gibraltar. Tryon thought that the effectiveness of the Mediterranean Fleet – the most powerful in the world – was seriously compromised by the lack of magazine accommodation, both at Gibraltar and Malta:

'It is quite clear that with the exception of the very limited amount of ammunition that is kept ready for issue, that England, and not Malta, is now perforce the base of the Fleet for the supply of ammunition. A very serious matter to contemplate and one that might even seriously cripple the Fleet ... It would appear as though for some years we have gone on building new Ships, improving and changing their gun power, and have not hand in hand provided for all the consequences entailed, and at this time there are two Naval bases, Malta and Gibraltar, unprovided with what is required, and a Fleet without an adequate reserve of ammunition, such as was up to recent years always kept up on this Station and at the absolute disposal of the Commander in Chief.'

Mending matters would not be cheap; the Governor of Gibraltar thought that no less than £100,000 would be required at the Rock.

The needs of the navy at Gibraltar seemed far more urgent than those of the army, and so in 1893 the Admiralty suggested that the land service magazine in the North Gorge be transferred to them; this was not large enough, but could be extended to give the required space for 12,000 barrels, and be connected to Rosia Bay by a tunnel. In return, a new magazine would be excavated at Genista Cave for the use of the army. But this was only a beginning – and as it turned out, an unfortunate one. Additional works were required: magazines for 24,000 barrels, shell stores and a laboratory were suggested. Colonel Pease thought half the new magazine should be for cordite cartridges, and as all cartridges and shell were sent out filled a new laboratory was not needed, just a room for examining purposes. The War Office proposed to meet the requirements by building two magazines for 12,000 barrels each rather than one of 24,000, in conformity with the Magazine Instructions, which limited the contents of a magazine to 8,000 barrels. By April 1896 this was revised to three magazines of 12,000, 6,000 and 6,000 barrels. Tryon's successor, Vice-Admiral Sir Michael Culme-Seymour, found the situation no better than his predecessors had done; it would be quite impossible to supply a fleet with ammunition in a short time. By April 1897 the new magazines had still not been authorised and the estimate has risen to £80,000; the original was £46,000. By June, Pease noted that the War Office were still vacillating over the design, and had reverted to the idea of two magazines. He suggested that one of these might be the cheaper option of an explosive store for QF cartridges and that the new ammunition gave the opportunity for further savings; together with the North Gorge extension, an explosive store for 52,800 cubic feet

6.15 Excavation of Corradino magazine, Malta. This 1904 photograph is of the main tunnel looking back towards the entrance, with magazine chambers to each side. (TNA ADM 195/68)

(equivalent to 16,000 barrels) would now be adequate, giving a saving of some £20,000. In January 1900 a conference was held to deal with what was by now a seemingly intractable problem. The new C-in-C, Vice-Admiral Sir Harry Rawson, reverted the plan back to square one by suggesting that the new magazines should be excavated in the rock at the back of Ragged Staff. This site would be practically on a level and comparatively close to the place of shipment, while the transit from North Gorge would be very slow and difficult, with a steep gradient. The naval stores and ammunition were sprinkled over a space of more than 2 miles, a great part over roads with long and very steep gradients. The cost of cartage was about £2,000 a year. Furthermore, the cost of North Gorge magazine was still escalating, and was currently estimated at £51,856 against the original £21,800. In addition, two magazines for QF ammunition were required.

In all, no less than £47,000 was needed to put the magazine accommodation on a proper footing. The Senior Naval Officer at Gibraltar proposed a drastic solution. The North Gorge would, '… never be satisfactory. It will always be damp, very difficult to work, and any breakdown of machinery or accident in the tunnel may completely block our supply when most needed,

and I consider it would be best to write off the £33,859 [spent] as lost entirely and build new magazines, than to go on wasting money finishing it.' This was agreed to, and, happily, all the money spent on North Gorge was not lost, for (in a possibly unique re-use of a magazine) it was turned into a cold meat store for both the services, so reducing the loss to a mere £3,000. It was agreed that all the magazine accommodation for cartridges and QF be placed at the back of Ragged Staff, and that the War Office would not carry out the construction (since the expense and slowness of their operations were such a sore point with the sister service). The work would instead be undertaken by the Admiralty Loan Works Department, which had a large staff and already had work in hand at the Rock. The new magazines were to be cut in the rock behind Trafalgar cemetery, with a capacity of 118,000 cubic feet, and would cost some £138,000.

No fiasco comparable to that of North Gorge happened at the other great Mediterranean base of Malta. A joint Naval and Military Committee reported in January 1891 and recommended new magazines at Corradino for £20,000, the extension of the laboratory (located at the head of French Creek) and shell stores for £3,000, and a railway between the laboratory and the Corradino

magazines for £6,000. In October 1893 the Admiralty agreed to plans for the new naval magazine for 24,000 barrels on Corradino Hill, and here the first great underground ordnance stores were excavated. It was decided to concentrate the whole of the naval ordnance on the Grand Harbour front of Corradino, with a view to ultimately freeing the south end of French Creek from laboratory operations. As at Gibraltar, Pease thought a laboratory unnecessary, but in the end Malta was to see undoubtedly the most splendid ever created by the army or navy, a fitting addition to an island filled with magnificent stonework. Following the separation of the army and navy Ordnance Establishments at Malta in 1902, the work pressed ahead, a total sum of £100,000 being appropriated under the Naval Works Act of 1895 (see pages 122 and 145–6). The final sum was a relatively modest £81,500, and by the end of 1908 the work was complete.[15]

Fleet requirements

Back in England, by far the worst problems were on the Medway, where, having lost the facilities of Chattenden, Upnor now had to try to meet the needs of ships based at Chatham and Sheerness. The alarming proximity of dangerous explosives to the dockyard (and the civilian population) was highlighted when, on 1 March 1894, the forepart of the floating magazine *Leonidas*, holding guncotton and mines, was discovered to be in flames. Sailors of the Steam Reserve put them out, but the cause was never discovered. Colonel Thales Pease set out the position in May 1894. The apportionment of Chattenden to the War Office and Upnor to the Admiralty had been reasonable in 1891 because of the relative use by the two services at that time, but since then, 'the Naval Defence Act Ships having gradually been brought forward, the Gun Ammunition, that should be kept at Upnor, has assumed proportions to an extent which prevents the complete storage thereof at that Station…'. The largest gun charge in 1870 had been 110 lbs; it was now a massive 900 lbs.

Furthermore, the 4.7-inch and 6-inch QF cartridges occupied four times the space of cartridges for BL of equal calibre. Accommodation was required for: big gun cartridges and powder, dry guncotton, wet guncotton (including mines and warheads), QF ammunition, small arms and machine gun ammunition, detonators, fuzes, tubes, and filled shells. The first two required new magazines to be built, although storehouses with proper precautions would do for the others. Following the fire, *Leonidas* had been condemned as a Magazine

6.16 An annotated photograph from 1904 showing the Corradino laboratory buildings and their concrete traverses. The strategic importance of Malta had been heightened by the Crimean War in the 1850s. The Corradino Lines were built in the 1870s but were short lived. *(TNA ADM-195/68)*

Colonial magazines

Britain also had many overseas stations throughout its naval history, necessitating ammunition stores in key locations around the globe. By the end of the 19th century the navy had acquired a worldwide system of Ordnance Depots as well as coaling stations, the two often being combined. Many of these small establishments were to be abandoned in 1907 as part of Fisher's concentration of the fleet in European waters, and others were taken over by navies of the Dominions, but in their time they were an important part of the worldwide Imperial presence, where of necessity relations between the two services were much closer than at home. However, their planning could be completely dysfunctional. In response to a War Office question in May 1877, as to whether Barbados or Antigua was preferable as a coaling station, the Admiralty replied that Port Castries, St Lucia, was preferable to either. It might have been thought that an ordnance store would be established there as a consequence; a Royal Commission of 1881 recommended that the entire Imperial troops in the West Indies should be concentrated at Jamaica and St Lucia. However, in 1888, a naval Ordnance Store was established at Barbados, to hold 2,000 barrels (600 for the army, 1,400 for the navy). In a rapid response the War Office in November 1889 requested that this store be moved to St Lucia. The magazine and QF store at St Lucia was completed in 1894, but proved to be a further instance of the services failing to keep step. The Barbados magazine had just about sufficed in size, but

the St Lucia magazine's capacity was only 1,200 barrels (600 for the army and 600 for the navy). According to the Ordnance Stores Department's calculations, the navy actually required 750 barrels without allowing anything whatever for loss in storage or emergencies, or the fact that visiting ships would need to lodge their powder there too. In short, the navy needed the whole magazine. Moreover there was no provision for a filled shell store. The depot was, not surprisingly, one of those selected by Fisher for closure. An outbreak of rioting on the island in April 1907 gave those sections of the press who saw Fisher's ruthless pruning of ships and bases as a betrayal both of the navy and the empire, scope for headlines such as 'The Rioting in St Lucia:- the Indefatigable 1,500 miles away' and 'The Unready Navy: no help for British Colonies in time of emergency: St Lucia's Peril.'[1]

Similar complaints (though not made more acute by rioting islanders) followed the closure of Esquimalt, on Vancouver Island, the base of the Pacific Squadron. That removed a considerable future financial liability. In September 1901 the Commander-in-Chief of the Station and his Superintending Civil Engineer for Esquimalt reported that the ordnance stores should be removed from Cole Island, where the existing buildings were of a very temporary nature, almost beyond repair, and so crowded together that magazine regulations could not be complied with, to a new site on Paterson's Point. The new scheme was estimated at nearly £90,000, and included a local innovation; a high wall was

proposed to surround the magazine buildings, rather than an unclimbable fence as at the home depots. This was because of the danger of bush fires. In December 1903 it was decided that only one-third of the reserve for the Pacific Squadron was to be kept at Esquimalt, and as a consequence there was sufficient accommodation in the inadequate magazine. The scheme was scrapped and negotiations for the purchase of Paterson Point abandoned. In 1908 Kipling visited the former base, stripped of most of its resources; this induced one of his downbeat moods and he described it as 'A marine junk store which had once been Esquimalt, a station of the British Navy.' In April 1909 the site was handed over to the Canadian Government.[2]

Not all the colonial ordnance yards were as ramshackle as Esquimalt. The magazines at Simonstown, by the Cape of Good Hope, were to be used in both world wars and the base is still in use. By the summer of 1898 the three existing magazines at the Kloof, holding about 25,000 cubic feet, were quite inadequate to the requirements of the station; they were crowded, making the proper arrangement of the contents impossible. Furthermore, part of the QF ammunition was stored in an unsuitable and exposed locality. The Commander-in-Chief, Vice-Admiral Rawson, asked for new cordite magazines of 30,000 cubic feet, to be built close to the existing magazines. He was supplied with the latest explanatory notes drawn up for guidance on construction, together with a print of a typical cordite store type (see Ordnance and Armament, page 125). However, the Boer War delayed the construction of these magazines.[3]

The greatest of all the colonial Ordnance Depots, was, of course, Singapore, though this was destined to be the worst investment of all. The committee which reported in March 1922 on the establishment of a naval base there thought there was a suitable site for underground magazines about half a mile to the west of the proposed dockyard. One outfit of ammunition per ship of the proposed Eastern Fleet was to be kept at Singapore. The Ordnance Depot was estimated at:

Mining depot with jetty = £129,483
Fixed ammunition depot with jetty = £100,750
Propellant depot = £55,267
Total estimate, including reclamation,

6.17 RNAD Singapore, main gates with guards, circa 1945–55. Note the signs; that to the right details the Magazine Regulations, written in English and Malay. *(Priddy's Hard Archive 2002.249.1)*

levelling, trolley ways, railways and roads, and accommodation = £608,700

By September 1937 the sixteen magazines were well on their way to completion. One hundred per cent of the reserves were to be kept on the China Station, seventy-five per cent at Singapore and twenty-five at Hong Kong. All were scheduled for completion by 1939.[4]

[1] ADM 116/843; H. F. Wyatt & L.G.H. Horton-Smith, *The Passing of the Great Fleet*, London, 1909, p.49

[2] ADM 116/675, ADM 116/993, Wyatt & Horton-Smith, p.384

[3] ADM 116/670

[4] ADM 116/3149, ADM 1/8653/262, ADM 1/27765

6.18 RNAD Bermuda; the Keep Yard, photographed in 1946–7. Around the keep pond (detail, inset), from which lighters could serve the fleet via a tunnel through the rampart, were two sets of bombproof powder magazines, a shell store, filling room, shifting room, receiving room and cooperage, as well as other stores. (*Priddy's Hard Archive 2002.226.5*)

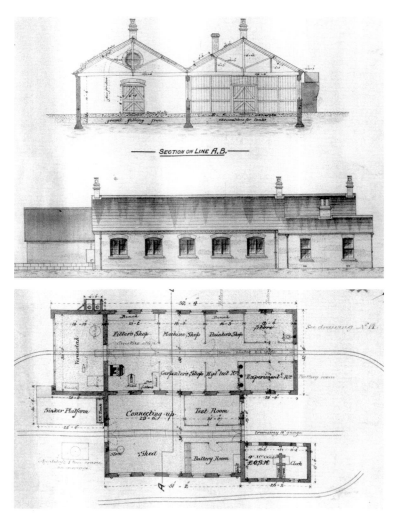

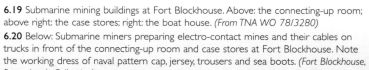

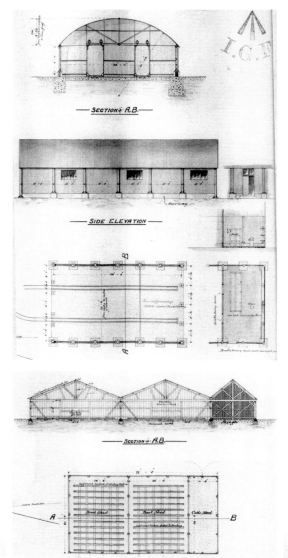

6.19 Submarine mining buildings at Fort Blockhouse. Above: the connecting-up room; above right: the case stores; right: the boat house. *(From TNA WO 78/3280)*

6.20 Below: Submarine miners preparing electro-contact mines and their cables on trucks in front of the connecting-up room and case stores at Fort Blockhouse. Note the working dress of naval pattern cap, jersey, trousers and sea boots. *(Fort Blockhouse, Barraclough Collection)*

Depot. Its mines were sent to Sheerness where they were stored in the cellar of an army building, the first floor of which was heated by open fires. Only a portion of the mines allotted to the Nore could be kept there, the remainder being stored at Woolwich and, even more inconveniently, Priddy's Hard. This was not all. Wet guncotton and torpedo warheads were kept at Horsted Fort in Chatham, so that every receipt or issue had to be carted through the town's streets, and the Fort was now full. Dry guncotton, detonators, fuzes and tubes were stored in the Castle at Upnor. Not understating the case, Pease thought: 'the above arrangements are, on the score of danger, manifestly unsatisfactory in the highest degree.'

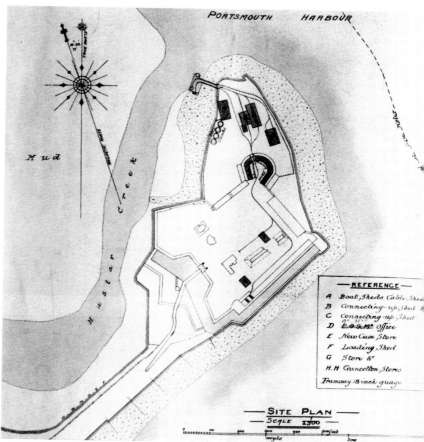

6.21 Right: Fort Blockhouse in 1886, showing the internal 18-inch gauge railway system introduced after the establishment of the Submarine Mining Establishment and its buildings (highlighted) in 1873. Clearly visible is the horseshoe-shaped round bastion, which was built in 1848. In 1885–90, the Royal Engineers inserted through the bastion the railway that supplied equipment to the Mine Yaws via the Jetty to the north. *(TNA WO 78/3280)*

6.22 Below: Fort Blockhouse from the air, looking south-west. The site was fortified by the 15th century, remodelled as a bastioned fort between the 1770s and 1815, and further remodelled from the 1840s. The barracks buildings date from the 1870s and in particular from after 1904, when until 1999 it served as HMS *Dolphin*, the base for the Royal Navy's Submarine Service. *(Fort Blockhouse)*

6.23 Above: Electro-contact mines with their cables, slinging chains and sinkers, on the jetty at Fort Blockhouse, ready for loading. In the background is the old First-Rate HMS *St. Vincent*, which in 1862 became a naval training ship for boys. Below: loading the mines onto one of the engineers' purpose-built mining vessels. Mines were seldom laid permanently, due to salt-water corrosion, and buoys were usually substituted. *(Fort Blockhouse, Barraclough Collection)*

The magazines at Upnor were out of date and built on long-discarded principles, being two large blocks of magazines, instead of separate magazines, divided by traverses.

Something had to be done; would a floating magazine do, either as an interim measure or long term solution, or would new land magazines be provided? Captain Kane, Director of Naval Ordnance, confirmed that the situation was about as bad as could be. The guncotton from *Superb* and *Immortalité* had to be kept in barges at Upnor pier. Chattenden was full, or nearly so, but in any case the War Office could not be expected to give it up. There was no land available for building near Upnor, and so a hulk appeared to be the only solution. *Euryalus* was selected. The Director of Works suggested that the War Office be approached to see if they would take all the powder at Chattenden; if that were possible, the Upnor magazines could then be used for guncotton and QF ammunition. The army was more responsive than Kane had expected, but could only offer room for 2,000 cases (including some that were already there). Colonel Pease thought the situation would only get worse. Already the outfit of ammunition for one Chatham battleship was kept in hired barges at Woolwich.

All this was the consequence of a failure to plan ahead. As Pease said: 'The present congested state of the storehouses at every depot (Plymouth excepted) is attributable to the fact that when the equipments for the Naval Defence Act Ships were purchased, no provision was made for housing them, and as a consequence, accommodation that was ample for the equipment of the navy as it existed 10 years since, is altogether inadequate now.' It was concluded that the use of a hulk was essential, but that the Director of Works should arrange to buy land at Chattenden if possible, and prepare plans for a proper magazine. In January 1895 a mishap, which no amount of forward planning could have prevented, took place: the War Department sailing barge *Petrel* blew up after going aground at Hope Point near Purfleet, and the master was drowned. It was suggested that he had fired the vessel in a state of insanity. An opportunity to save the situation unexpectedly appeared in February, when the War Office offered a deal to exchange Chattenden for the Admiralty portion of Purfleet, retaining only space for 10,000 barrels for proof. Pease thought that as powder was on the way out the Admiralty would only need space for 5,000 barrels at Purfleet, enabling a straight exchange to be done. The Admiralty had another carrot to offer the War Office: a wet guncotton store for Upnor had been placed in the 1895–6 Estimates and in proposing a straight swap they additionally offered to store army guncotton. This arrangement would have saved the situation. However, the two Services did not work together

on the Medway. The laboratory proposed at Upnor (see page 106) had not materialised, probably because of the failure to procure land from the War Office for the connecting railway to Upnor. At the division of the depots, the shell pier had been retained for army use, and in October the Admiralty asked for it to be transferred, but this was refused as it was needed to serve Chattenden. It would be retained [ominous words] until, and if, those magazines were transferred. On 1 November, the War Office pulled out of the deal and everything was back to square one. The Admiralty were now desperate for better landing facilities, with the proximity of the dockyard to Upnor and the constant coming and going of steamers making the mooring and unloading of powder barges dangerous. Following a suggestion by the War Office, they now proposed to build a new pier downstream at the relatively isolated spot of Teapot Hall, to be connected by rail with the depot. The fate of this scheme will be seen later on (see pages 149–50). [16]

However, not all sites presented Colonel Pease with such intractable difficulties. The abolition of floating magazines was an ultimate aim. At Portsmouth, if *Carnatic* were to be abolished, it would reduce the available accommodation by

6.24 Fitted with powerful winches, and derricks on the masts and at the bow, the vessels could carry up to thirty-two mines. Submarine mining was demanding work, requiring both physical strength and mental ability to deal with all the bulky, heavy but highly technical equipment. *(Fort Blockhouse, Barraclough Collection)*

6.25 The Crutch system of storing mines, adopted by the Royal Engineers. *(From Manual of Submarine Mining, Vol. 1, 1901 ed., plates)*

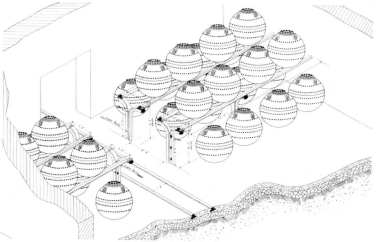

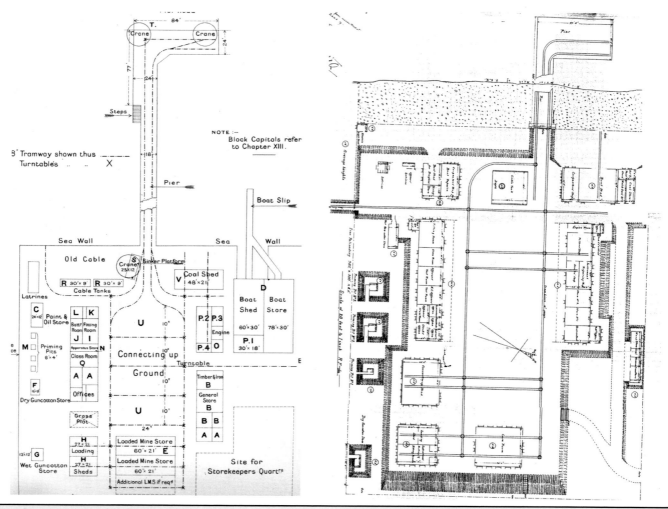

Submarine Mining Depots

The manning arrangements for Submarine Mining Depots were complicated and subject to constant change. Three classes of men staffed the depots: Regular Royal Engineers, Militia and Volunteers. Regulars occupied the three main centres – Chatham, Portsmouth and Plymouth – as well as Pembroke Dock, because of its remote location. Many were stationed abroad at the colonial depots.

The Submarine Mining Militia was first raised in 1878 to serve the mine defences of the principal ports. The men, mainly required for water work, were enlisted from local boatmen. Their annual training was fifty-five days, the maximum permissible for Militia. The first company of Volunteers was formed in 1883. As with the Rifle Volunteers, their social standing was a cut above the Militia, most strikingly exemplified by the Corps of Electrical Engineers Volunteers, which was composed of members of the Institution of Electrical Engineers, whose Honorary Colonel Commandant was no less an electrician

than Lord Kelvin, and had occasionally drilled in Westminster Hall. Based in Regency Street, London, they sent detachments for electrical work to several out-stations. The Volunteers were shepherded by sections of the Coast Battalion, whose officers had been promoted from warrant and NCO rank in the Royal Engineers and whose NCOs and other ranks were Regulars.

Chatham

The first accommodation for submarine miners, in 1873, was split between the hulk *Hood* and Brompton Barracks, with the building of a Submarine Mining School commencing in Gillingham in 1880. *Hood* was abandoned in 1883, and officers and men moved into St Mary's Barracks in Chatham Lines. This was also the headquarters of the Thames Militia Division until 1892.

Gosport

Mining began at Gosport in 1873, using Fort Gilkicker. However, Fort Blockhouse

became the principal mining establishment, while Fort Monckton housed the Portsmouth Companies of the Southern Submarine Mining Militia. In 1892 it was decided to open an additional school, which occupied premises at Stokes Bay already erected for training purposes. In order to house the Regulars closer to the school the Militia moved to Blockhouse and the Engineers went to Monckton.

Plymouth

The first mining establishment was set up at Fisher's Nose, on the south-east corner of the citadel, in 1882. The headquarters of the Militia Division was at Elphinstone Barracks from 1888, which was also the headquarters of the Western Militia Division from 1893 to 1904, when it transferred to Mount Wise Barracks. As at Gosport, it was decided to open a further Submarine Mining School there in 1892, and this was transferred to new and far less cramped premises between North and South Yards at Devonport, adjacent to the Torpoint ferry.

90,000 cubic feet, and thus further accommodation on shore would be required. This could be provided easily if Marchwood was utilised to its full extent. Pease thought that both from a store and a financial point of view the future utilisation of Marchwood should be fully considered and determined. Unlike Admiral the Earl of Clanwilliam, he rated those magazines highly, considering them to be the largest and finest in the world and assets that the navy ought not to abandon lightly. The previous restrictions on their use had been made when powder was almost entirely manipulated loose in barrels, which was attended by the dangers of leakage in transit. Now this was no longer the case: loose powder was kept in waterproof bags inside powder barrels or in metal-lined cases, or was made up into ammunition packed in metal cases, making the old danger a thing of the past. Furthermore, powder was quickly being replaced by the comparatively harmless cordite (see pages 128–9). However, it was perhaps over optimistic for Pease to state:

'It is my belief that whatever sentiment did exist with Southampton Corporation twenty years ago, it does not exist now. Indeed, this Station is, at the present time rather regarded as an advantage to the Town, it being seen that these fine magazines and their undoubted facilities for lodgment [sic] of explosives might, in some degree, expand the commerce of Southampton by the shipment of explosives from there to Foreign Depôts.'

Be that as it may, the situation was advantageous, and this would especially be the case in time of war, the railway facilities from Southampton to London and the North being even more efficient than from Portsmouth. In addition, it would be a great boon to be able to utilize Southampton at a time when Portsmouth would be congested with the fitting out of ships of the Fleet Reserve. Pease's view was accepted and in March 1898 Marchwood became a much more important element in the ordnance store complex around Portsmouth, with the decision to use its capacity to the full. [To run ahead of the story a little, in February 1901 it held 70,000 barrels and cases and had never been so full.] [17]

Tipner now lay outside Pease's domain. The War Office wished, in opposition to the recommendations of the Forwood Committee, to have its own laboratory there to make up for the loss of the Priddy's Hard facilities and one was immediately added, together with a QF store. In 1899, two well-traversed buildings, a shell filling room and cartridge filling room replaced the laboratory buildings. At Bull Point the laboratory was used for both land and sea service ammunition, but that was an integrated site. Tipner was by far the largest ordnance storage site used by the army in the Portsmouth area, though not the most interesting.

6.26 Opposite, left: The general plan of a Submarine Mining Establishment. *(From Manual of Submarine Mining, vol. 1, plates [1901 edition])*

6.27 Opposite, right: The Stokes Bay Establishment. *(TNA WO 78/4755)*

Pembroke Dock
Headquarters of the Milford Haven Division from 1888. Also headquarters of the Western Militia Division from 1888 to 1893.

Fort Victoria
Headquarters of the Needles Militia Division after 1893.

Sheerness
Garrison Point Fort was the headquarters of the Medway Militia Division after 1892.

Gravesend
Shornemead Fort was the headquarters of Thames Militia Division after 1892.

Harwich
Landguard Fort was the headquarters of the Harwich Militia Division from 1888.

Falmouth
Headquarters of the Falmouth Volunteer Division, converted into Militia in 1892. Also Coast Battalion Section.

Paull-on-Humber
Paull Fort was the headquarters of the Humber Volunteer Division, who converted into Militia in 1891. Also Coast Battalion Section.

Weymouth
Section of Coast Battalion, became 6th Company of Coast Battalion in 1905.

Newcastle-on-Tyne
Cliffords Fort, North Shields, was the headquarters of the Tyne Volunteer Division, which regularly sent detachments to Portland for mining, and to the Humber and Portsmouth for electric light work. Also Coast Battalion Section.

Middlesbrough
Headquarters of the Tees Volunteer Division. Also Coast Battalion Section.

Liverpool
Headquarters of the Mersey Volunteer Division, housed in the hulks *Danae* and *Annetin*. Also Coast Battalion Section.

Cardiff
Headquarters of the Severn Volunteer Division, who also provided men to serve the electric lights at Pembroke Dock. Also Coast Battalion Section.

Dundee
Headquarters of the Tay Volunteer Division. Also Coast Battalion Section.

Leith
Headquarters of the Forth Volunteer Division, housed initially in the hulk *Dido*, later moving to a permanent establishment at North Queensferry. Also Coast Battalion Section.

Greenock
Fort Matilda was the headquarters of the Clyde Volunteer Division. Also Coast Battalion Section.

Derived from Lieut. Col. W. Baker Brown, *History of Submarine Mining in the British Army*, Chatham, 1910

6.28 Landguard Fort originated in the 1530s and was rebuilt as a bastioned fort in 1744. During remodelling in the 1870s, as part of Palmerston's coastal defence scheme, the curved battery facing the river and the inner keep of the curved barrack and offices were built. The controlled minefield dates from 1877, when the V-shaped Ravelin Block (to the left of the fort) was built in order to provide additional defence. This was served by a pier, the remains of which can be seen in the foreground. (*English Heritage, NMR 23161/13*)

The increasing activities of the Submarine Miners (a body of men which at its peak numbered 243 officers and 4,206 other ranks – including Militia and Volunteers) not only resulted in the further development of Fort Blockhouse but also the design of a purpose-built establishment at Stokes Bay. This was a model of its kind, setting the general layout that was laid down in the official textbook (the *Manual of Submarine Mining*). The Royal Engineers favoured more complicated electrical systems to operate and detonate their minefields, the navy preferring something simpler and easier to handle on board ship. As a consequence they did not require the range of specialist building to be found at Stokes Bay. Their mines were prepared as a laboratory operation and kept in hulks, *Grampus* and *Melampus* being moored together with enlarged entry ports to facilitate the transfer of 500 lb mines from one to the other. The storage systems developed by the army were more sophisticated and were used by the navy when a shore-based Mine Store was created at the Royal William Yard, Plymouth. The most striking mine store to survive from this time is the Ravelin Block at Landguard Fort, which protected the approaches to Harwich.[18]

The problems of ordnance storage that were now so apparent and having such dire consequences at the Medway were shortly to be addressed in the only effective way: a massive injection of money. The consequences of the 1889 Naval Defence Act (see page 107) bore heavily on the dockyards, and few engineering enterprises could compete with dockyard enlargement for cost. The normal means of financing Admiralty expenditure would be quite inadequate to meet the massive programme of works required, it was necessary to resort to special measures. On 6 July 1895, the Naval Works Act came into force, which initially provided for a loan of £8½ million, to be repaid by terminable annuities over a period not exceeding thirty years. In September the Treasury accepted the principle of separating Loan Works from the works and buildings covered by Vote 10 (the normal way of financing them) of the annual Estimates. At first new magazine buildings did not figure in the programme of Loan Works, but that oversight was soon put right by two new players in the game.[19] That story will be told in Chapter 7.

Developments in Ordnance and Armament

As has been seen, ordnance developed continually since the 18th century, with all advances in design requiring changes to working practices, storage facilities and equipment. Changes in any one area of ordnance practice – be it a new gun, propellant or technique – initiated changes to all other areas, in a continual process to meet the needs of an ever-changing world. Major components can, and did, occasionally get out of step with each other, but the development of ordnance and armament itself goes hand in hand with the development of the sites that were built to create, store and examine them.

Guns

The ammunition and cartridges for smoothbore (SB) artillery, together with the necessary accoutrements for loading, aiming and firing, were very simple and made little demands on the magazines and gunwharves apart from storage and labour.

Smoothbore loading

The 18th-century practice described here may be taken as representative of the way this weapons system was served during its entire life. After firing, any debris remaining in the barrel was cleared out with a worm, a corkscrew-shaped piece of metal on the end of a pole. The barrel was then cooled down with a similarly mounted sponge soaked in seawater, while the vent (the narrow hole filled with powder by which the gun was fired) was cleared of combustion products by a gimlet. A cartridge (after the late 18th century usually of flannel, earlier of paper or parchment) filled with gunpowder was then pushed by a rammer down the barrel to the breech, and held in place by a wad. While this happened the gunner 'served the vent' by closing it with his thumb, to prevent air being forced through, which might re-ignite any remaining fragments. The cannon ball was then rolled down the barrel and another wad rammed down to retain it. The vent was then filled with fine-grained powder and the gun was ready to fire, in earlier periods by applying a lighted match to the vent, after the late 18th century by a flintlock mechanism fitted to the vent. Often a flexible sponge and rammer, which were at opposite ends of a stout rope, replaced the separate rammer and

sponge (with long handles that could prove awkward between decks).

In close quarter engagements it was not uncommon for guns to be loaded with two cannon balls, usually with an increase in the amount of gunpowder. Double-shotting did nothing to increase the accuracy of an inherently inaccurate weapon, and many officers disliked the practice. Sometimes attempts were made to cut the rigging of the opposing ship; special expanding shot were employed for this, but probably just as effective was langridge, a term which covered any assortment of scrap metal rammed home and fired. Grape-shot was an anti-personnel weapon used against men exposed on an upper deck; the effect was like a giant shotgun. Red-hot shot was an extremely effective weapon against a ship; if it lodged in the woodwork a serious fire could ensue. For obvious reasons this was far more suited to being used in coastal fortifications where specialised furnaces were provided for heating the projectiles, though inserting them in the muzzle of the gun can never have been a popular job.

Rifled breech loading

Between the years 1850 and 1890 the construction and design of guns went through several changes, and corresponding processes of evolution took place in projectiles and gunpowder. During the 1850s, the engineers Sir William Armstrong and Sir Joseph Whitworth developed two alternative systems of rifling. Armstrong offered a combination of rifling with breech loading which appeared very attractive, showing exceptional accuracy on trial, and his guns (known by the abbreviation RBL) were ordered for the services. Portsmouth

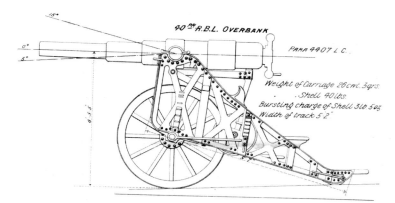

OA.1 This 40-pounder Armstrong gun was still in the army's inventory in 1890. (From Major JW Savage, 'Diagrams of Service Ordnance etc' in Professional Papers of the Corps of Royal Engineers, vol. XVI, 1890)

Gunwharf was informed in October 1860 that the intended armament for *Warrior*, the Royal Navy's first ironclad, was to include four 40-pounder Armstrongs (see Glossary and figure OA.1). The first ironclad to be built in a Royal Dockyard, *Achilles*, was intended to mount forty-eight 100-pounder Armstrongs, the work again to be done by Portsmouth Gunwharf. The projectiles and cartridges, and indeed the weapons themselves, did not comprise an enormous number of new components, but when added to the existing armoury, the workload, on the gunwharves in particular, was notably increased. The gun proved a relative failure in service, notably at the bombardment of Kagoshima in 1863, when twenty-one guns, in firing 365 rounds, sustained twenty-eight accidents. Subsequent writers have made this appear a complete fiasco, though it did not appear so at the time, the Admiral in command being well satisfied by their accuracy and destructive power at 4,000 yards. Most of the troubles were caused by vent pieces in the breech splitting or jamming, the weapons gaining the unflattering nickname of 'two-muzzled guns'. In 1864 the largest calibre, the 110-pounder, was withdrawn from service, though the smaller ones lingered on, performing well at the bombardment of Cape Haytien in 1866, avenging an insult to the British flag that occurred during a Haitian civil war. The considered judgment of a gunner officer working at Woolwich was: 'their performance on the whole was excellent and fully justified their adoption … [no] system of rifled artillery could, like the mythic Minerva, be brought complete and perfect into existence by one blow of a blacksmith's hammer.' With altered breech arrangements, the Armstrongs lingered into the 1890s.

Any ordnance system replacing the smoothbore clearly needed to employ rifling of some sort, and with a satisfactory system of breech loading not having been evolved by British designers, muzzle loading was reverted to. A useful and long-lasting

OA.2 The simplification of the construction of the RML effected by Fraser is evident. (Adapted from Captain FS Stoney, 'The Construction of our Heavy Guns' in Minutes of Proceedings of the Royal Artillery Institution, vol. VI, 1870)

stop gap was devised by Captain Palliser (see Palliser shells, page 129). He bored out a smoothbore cannon, inserted a rifled liner, and fired the gun with a heavy charge. This expanded the liner to a tight fit and created a perfectly usable new weapon. Armstrong rapidly put his rifled muzzle-loaders (RML) into production, which were built up by shrinking multiple jackets of wrought iron over a barrel forged from coiled iron, but in 1867 his design was replaced by a simpler form of construction over a steel barrel, devised by Mr Fraser, the Deputy Assistant Superintendent of the Royal Gun Factory at Woolwich. This reduced the cost of a barrel by thirty per cent. The squat appearance of the guns, quite different from anything seen in Europe before, was due to the rapid-burning pebble powder (see Glossary) used as the propellant. The very large charges of it required for large-calibre guns produced enormous pressures in the breech, which necessitated massive constructions to prevent the guns from bursting.

The combination of rifling and breech loading was not finally settled in the British services until the 1880s. Slower burning prism powders (see Glossary), where the powder was compressed into hexagonal nuts, were developed on the continent during the 1870s. This enabled the gun's construction to be much less massive and allowed the barrel to be lengthened, so increasing its accuracy. Length was also required to allow the slower burning powder to develop its full force. Satisfactory breech-closing mechanisms had also been developed on the Continent, the firm of Krupps leading the way, and by 1880 the armament of the Royal Navy looked decidedly antiquated.

The new and revolutionary method of mounting heavy naval guns in turrets or barbettes in order to provide a far greater field of fire than was possible in a broadside or end-on mounting also told against the retention of the RML in two ways. Loading the gun within the turret was far more awkward than with a breech-loader, and as the gun had to recoil within the turret in order to load, the dimensions of the turret dictated the length of the barrel of the gun, so that the advantages of greater barrel length offered by the prism powders could not be taken. These objections also applied to guns mounted in fortresses. There was also the possibility of double-shotting a muzzle loader, as happened with disastrous results on *Thunderer* in 1879. On 2 January of that year both 38-ton guns in the fore turret were fired, and the left-hand gun misfired. The turret crew did not notice this and reloaded both guns. When fired again the double-loaded gun burst, killing eleven men and injuring many more. Such a mistake could not be made with a breech-loader. Breech-loading (BL) guns were therefore reintroduced in the navy, and the small battleship *Conqueror*, laid

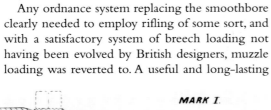

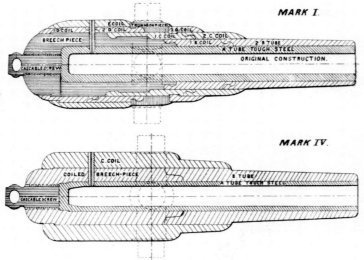

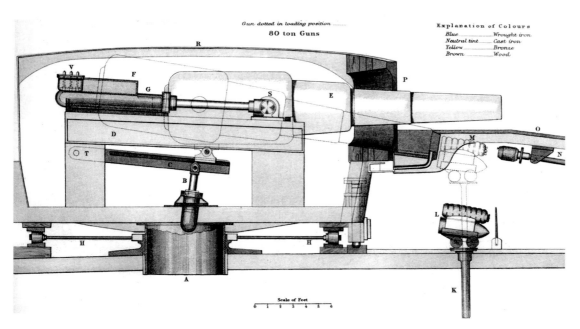

Gun dotted in loading position
80 ton Guns

Explanation of Colours
Blue — Wrought iron.
Neutral tint — Cast iron.
Yellow — Bronze.
Brown — Wood.

Scale of Feet

OA.3 The turret of HMS *Inflexible*, showing the arrangements for muzzle loading. *(From Encyclopaedia Britannica, 9th ed., article 'Gunnery'. Engraving by W & AK Johnston.)*

down in the year of *Thunderer's* accident, was designed for 12-inch BL guns.

The first Woolwich BL guns were constructed in a similar manner to the RMLs; later they were made entirely of steel, a material that English gunmakers felt was available in sufficient quality and quantity for them to use. By 1882 preparations were in train at Waltham Abbey to manufacture prismatic powder (see Glossary), and in the meantime large quantities were imported from Germany. Prismatic powder was improved by replacing black powder with so-called cocoa powder (also developed in Germany), in which rye grass was used as the source for charcoal, and its manufacture at Waltham Abbey began in 1885. The new guns were much more powerful than their predecessors; the 12·5-inch RML had a

muzzle energy of 13·554 feet per ton, while the 12-inch BL gave 23·569 feet per ton.

The intimate connection between gun and propellant at this time was shown by the fact that only three 9·2-inch had been delivered to the navy by that time, for experimental purposes, the delivery of the remaining fifteen of the batch being delayed pending a decision on the type of powder to be used with them. The inability of Woolwich Arsenal alone to provide the necessary supply led to Armstrongs, which had been sustaining a thriving trade in arms for export, re-entering the scene; its most striking (and unsuccessful) contribution to the story of the early BLs being the 110-ton gun, whose unfortunate propensity to droop was never cured. The eventual adoption of breech-loading, with complex mechanisms for operating the

OA.4 HMS *Inflexible*, pictured late in her career at Portsmouth where she served as guardship between 1895 and 1897. Her four 16-inch, 80-ton guns were the heaviest muzzle-loading weapons ever fitted in a Royal Navy ship, and the 24-inch armour of her central 'citadel' was the thickest ever sent to sea by any navy. She originally carried a full sailing rig, but this proved a failure and was replaced by the 'military' rig shown here. Clearly visible amidships is one of the twin turrets for her 16-inch main armament. *(Conway Maritime Press)*

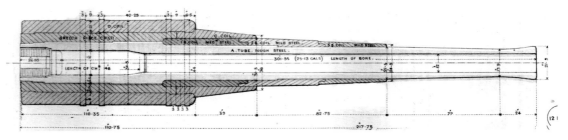

breech and controlling the recoil, was a qualitative leap for the gunwharves; less so for the Magazine Depots, where there was a continuity in the make-up of cartridges, though the multiplication of types of powder to be stored meant a relentless increase in the paperwork.[1]

Examination and storage

As long as gunpowder remained the principal propellant and explosive, the examination and storage requirements at magazines were very simple. From the very first it was essential to check that the powder entering a magazine was in serviceable condition, particularly if it was being returned from a ship, and to see that the barrel was not damaged. Allowing for enormous changes in both the explosive and the packaging, the same processes have always been necessary. As a consequence, the first ancillary buildings to the

magazine proper were the examining house (whose earlier title was the shifting house) and the cooperage, for the skills of the cooper were needed to rapidly unhead and head the barrels, which were all made by hand until 1866, when machine-made barrels began to be introduced. The powder was examined for the presence of dust, foreign bodies or damp. Flannel cartridges filled with powder were examined for wear, moth-holes or discoloration. As shown elsewhere, damaged powder could be downgraded to non-operational uses, restored or, if too far gone, have the valuable saltpetre extracted. The powder magazines needed to be kept well aired, and ventilation passages were built into them as a matter of course. In addition, when the humidity conditions were favourable, the doors were to be opened as often and as long as possible, preferably in cold, dry weather, in the early morning in summer and at midday in winter. The advent of wet guncotton as the explosive filling for mines and torpedo warheads did not introduce any great complications; the naval mines, and also those of the Royal Engineer Submarine Miners, in use in the latter part of the 19th century, were weighed when received into store, and re-weighed at subsequent inspections to determine whether loss had occurred through evaporation or weight gained through leakage into the case. The advent of cordite, the first of a new range of chemical explosives, brought about the necessity for chemical testing of explosives and the beginnings of the need for a controlled environment for storage (see page 129).

Shell emptying and filling

The simplest version of the shell, as used from the 15th century, was a hollowed-out round filled with powder and ignited by a fuze. The manufacture of shells was, in its day, a reasonably sophisticated piece of metallurgy, particularly in contrast to that of shot and its variants. In contrast, their filling and emptying were very simple operations, which enabled the Ordnance Depots to function without numbers of formally educated staff. In May 1849 the following instructions for examining shells returned from and for re-issue to naval vessels were in force:

'1st. The Shells when returned from a Vessel should be
    arranged in a proper place (constructed of Wood is

preferable) when the Fuzes and bursting powder should be taken out of the latter by rolling the Shell in a shell horse with the vessel underneath and the bursting powder be considered and returned as 'unserviceable for extraction.' The Shells and Fuze holes are then to be carefully cleaned out, the former with copper scrapers, the latter with oily tow: and if there is any suspicion of powder remaining under the fuze hole, the shell is to be taken aside, and specially pointed out to the Superintending Foreman, who after most carefully examining each shell by itself in order to be certain that it only contains a few grains of Powder, will take that Shell, apart from the others, and then with an Iron Hook heated at the end, any grains or particles which are sometimes found clogged there are to be ignited, – but should more powder than a few grains still remain attached to the Shell – the heated iron is not to be used, but the Shell should be immersed for some time in boiling water and afterwards carefully cleaned out and dried inside and out.

2nd. Then the Shells are to be classed Serviceable or Repairable according to their shaping, woulding [sic], or Wood bottoms; and the Fuzes are to be examined and classed accordingly, after being well cleaned of grease & verdegris and repaired if necessary.

3rd. In the re-issue of Naval Shells after putting the bursting powder in, fresh grease is to be applied to the Fuzes, and great care taken before screwing them in, that the Screw hole in the Shell, is free from grit or powder.' [2]

These shells were little different from their predecessors in being hollow iron spheres. They were attached to wooden bases, which served to align the shell in the barrel so as to keep the fuze in the correct position (see figure OA.8). The proportions of the different calibres in use can be seen by those which had been examined at Priddy's Hard Laboratory between November 1852 and January 1853: 3,620 in all, comprising 506 x 10-inch, 1,433 x 8-inch, 1,479 x 6-inch, and 200 x 56-pounder shells. The filling of these projectiles was an operation of the simplest description, a measured amount of powder being poured in through a funnel made from copper.

By 1860 Armstrong's breech-loading artillery system had been introduced, ten 12-pounder guns with 1,000 rounds each having been ordered to be sent to Portsmouth in November 1859. These shells were of the pointed shape familiar today, and were iron castings rebated to take a lead coating, which engaged with the grooves of the rifling. The need to protect the gunpowder filling from dangerous abrasion on any roughness in the casting was met by coating the interior of the shell with a mix of twenty-four parts asphalt, twelve parts pitch, six parts resin, and four parts tallow.

OA.7 Lead-coated 20-pounder solid shot for an Armstrong rifled breech-loading gun, from the mid-19th century. In the collection at Explosion! Museum of Naval Firepower. (Stephen Dent)

The other ingredients were added to the melted asphalt and poured into the shell, which was at once reversed. Armstrong shells were all nose-fuzed, and filling was consequently done through the fuze-hole.

As has been seen, the Armstrong guns and their ammunition were soon withdrawn and replaced by rifled muzzle-loading guns. These, with the exception of Palliser shells, which had noses specially tempered for armour-piercing, were filled in the same way. After March 1869 all common rifled shell, from 64-pounders up, were fitted with unloading holes closed with a metal screw plug and papier mâché wad. Palliser shells were an exception, as they did not have fuzes; the bursting charge was placed in a serge bag inserted through a filling hole in the base of the shell and subsequently filled. The bag performed the same function as the tallow mix in Armstrong shells. On firing, the acceleration of the shell compressed the powder into a hard mass at the rear of the powder chamber; the impact propelled this forward with sufficient violence to cause detonation.

By 1876, although the insides of shells had changed, the procedure remained essentially the

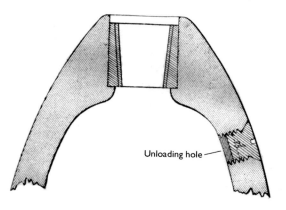

Unloading hole

OA.8 The unloading hole in the nose of a rifled common shell. (From A Manual of Gunnery for Her Majesty's Fleet [London, 1873])

OA.9 A Palliser shell. *(From A Manual of Gunnery for Her Majesty's Fleet, London, 1873)*

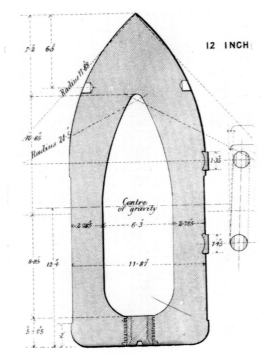

12 INCH

same. The only difference was that instead of being poured through a funnel, a brass filling rod – either 3 or 5 feet long with a knot at the end for tamping the powder – was inserted through the fuze hole into the cartridge bag, with care so that it did not slip into the shell case. After the funnel was inserted into the neck of the bag, the powder was tamped down using the filling rod to enable the filling. The neck of the bag was then singly tied with twine. The procedure was different for Palliser shells. In order to unscrew its bottom plug, the shell was to be placed upon its point, inserted in a block of wood hollowed for the purpose. Filled shells, Palliser and common, were examined according to these directions.

'Remove plug & shalloon primer. Draw out the neck of the serge bag by copper hook & untie twine round neck. If powder is caked empty the shell; up-end the shell as required; insert the filling rod or any suitable sized piece of brass wire, so as to facilitate the exit of the powder, and to prevent the bag from doubling up, &c, until the whole of the powder is extracted. Take out the bag and if it is in a serviceable condition, replace it, if not insert new bag & refill. If means are available, a wooden box placed over the open mouth of an empty powder-barrel should be used when emptying shells by up-ending them; and a piece of metal tubing, or a piece of sheet copper rolled up into a tube as large in diameter as can be inserted, will greatly facilitate the extraction.' [3]

The Queen's Regulations of 1868 – the Handbook for 9-inch RML 12-ton guns – laid down the procedure to be adopted for shell emptying, a procedure that was little changed by the end of the century. The unscrewing of fuzes was only to be undertaken by trained men, whose experience enabled them to judge the amount of force that could be used with safety. Shells fitted with Hotchkiss fuzes required a special tool, as that fuze was regarded as extremely dangerous. First, the fuze was unscrewed. Shells requiring more than usual force were to be sent to Woolwich or thrown into deep water. In the Naval Ordnance Store Department this work was only to be done under supervision. The operation was considered dangerous, even in a properly constituted laboratory, so there was no question of it being performed afloat. Only one shell was opened at a time, and the powder then poured into a bucket half filled with water. If the powder was at all caked (not at all an unusual circumstance), hot water was poured into the shell; this directive was issued after the accident of 1889 at Priddy's Hard. When the powder was thoroughly saturated the lumps were broken up with a copper scraper. After emptying the shell was filled with boiling water or steamed. When a fuze proved stubborn and could not be extracted in the approved way, if not provided with an unloading hole, the shell was to be placed under water and bored to admit water, the powder to be thoroughly saturated before any further steps were taken. When this could not be done, drastic measures were taken and the shell thrown into the sea. If an unloading hole was present, the plug was to be unscrewed and water poured in. Fuze removal was to be done in a building dedicated to that purpose, only one shell being worked on at a time. When the fuze had been removed, the fuze hole plug was screwed in to secure the powder, and the shell then taken to another building to be emptied, while resting on a cradle. Empty shells were to be marked on the head by the letter E, white at Woolwich and red at other stations. Some shell filling was done at sea, with unsatisfactory results. [4]

The introduction of cordite and lyddite

Shell filling was a hazardous operation, the worst accidents occuring at Priddy's Hard in May 1883 (see page 99) and on 5 December 1889, when there was another explosion, this time in one of the new shell filling rooms. A 'careful man' with seven years experience of laboratory work was emptying a 12-inch shell, from which the fuze had been correctly extracted. The man was killed and the room destroyed, although no report was made of any damage to the other buildings in the complex, showing that the system of traverses had performed very satisfactorily. The room was rebuilt in 1891. In the circumstances the cause of the accident was a matter for conjecture, but it was supposed that again excessive force had been used in employing a copper rod to break up caked powder. In consequence the regulations for shell emptying were changed. To the simple tools required for the job (a key, a copper scraper and a bucket), hot water was added in order to make safe the caked powder. At that time, gunpowder was still the propellant and the shell filling, but this would shortly change when a smokeless propellant, long desired, became available. Cordite (see Glossary), patented in 1889, was not only smokeless but, having a slower rate of combustion, enabled a much greater volume of gas to be generated without excessive pressure in the barrel, which in turn enabled higher velocities (and therefore greater ranges) to be obtained. The first issue of the explosive (made entirely at Waltham Abbey) was on August 17 1891, but it was not until August 1893 that a Fleet Circular announced that cordite charges were to be issued for 6-inch and 4.7-inch QF, and 6-pounder and 3-pounder QF. Later in the year it was decided to adopt the propellant for the 9.2-inch and 12-inch BL, and the 4-inch and 12-pdr QF.

At the end of that year the Director of Naval Ordnance proposed to reduce the stock of reserve ammunition to avoid the wholesale waste that was liable to occur on any change of pattern in powder or projectiles, the disposal of the old creating unproductive work for the laboratories. When the supply of cordite was available all QF ammunition would need to be emptied and reloaded with the new propellant, and the larger the stock the greater the expense. In April 1894, 642 6-inch QF were supplied to three of the *Royal Sovereign* class of battleships to be test stored in the hottest 6-inch magazines and used as practice ammunition. An explosion at Waltham Abbey on 7 May delayed the QF gun changeover of propellant, making the rate of production of cordite uncertain, and none was expected from the trade for at least a year. The explosion also resulted in the formation of the Danger Buildings Committee (see pages 151–3), which was set up in January 1894 under the chairmanship of Lord Sandhurst, the Parliamentary Under Secretary of State for War, to enquire into the accident.

The workload of the laboratories continued to increase and by the beginning of 1895 the only shells fuzed at Woolwich were the 4.7-inch and the 12.5-inch, all the rest being fuzed at Priddy's Hard, Bull Point and Upnor. It was decided that a proportion of filled shell on Reserve ships should be examined every three years, and also of ships paying off into Reserve if the ammunition had not been examined within the previous three years, and of those commissioned from the Reserve whose ammunition had not been examined for two years. Three additional men were taken on at each of the depots of Upnor, Priddy's Hard and Bull Point for this work. One of the reasons for

these measures was the discovery that cracks in the mouths of 3- and 6-pounder QF cartridge cases were liable to extend with even a slight jar, and all cartridges with cracks were to be returned. Despite the fact that manufacturing difficulties were being experienced with cordite (nearly 100 tons of cordite had been rejected in the first four months of 1895), the Admiralty decided in April to adopt the newly developed explosive lyddite (see Glossary) as a filling for 6-inch and 4.7-inch shells (see Chapter 10). Thus the importance of gunpowder was further diminished. The problems of storing and handling these new explosives were now to figure largely in a massive rethinking of the whole question of naval Ordnance Depots.[5]

The replacement of gunpowder by lyddite as a shell filling changed the nature of the operation. It was decided in March 1896 to commence with the 4.7-inch and 6-inch steel common shell, replacing ten per cent by an equal number of lyddite shells. The explosive entered the shell not as a dry powder but as a hot liquid. The nose plug of the shell was removed and a canvas jacket placed round the shell. A metal tray was secured to the fuze hole; together with the jacket this protected the shell from splashes and overflows of lyddite. A metal funnel resting on asbestos washers was secured in the hole. The picric acid, which had

Palliser shells and metallurgical weaknesses

The advent of the ironclad warship meant that, for the first time, shells specifically designed for piercing armour plate had to be provided. Nor was this a specifically naval problem, for iron armour began to be incorporated in land fortifications as well, though in England its use was confined to arming the embrasures of coast defence fortifications against naval gunfire. In 1863 Major Palliser (see page 124) designed an armour-piercing shell so successful that it was to remain in service for nearly fifty years as the navy's principal weapon for attacking armour. The metal of the shell was made exceptionally hard (so hard that it could not be worked with a tool) by casting the projectile in a metal mould to chill it. Both shot and shell were produced by the Palliser process, the shot giving better penetration on oblique impact. The shot were originally cast solid, but because of weaknesses in the internal structure of the metal, caused by the difficulty of casting such a mass of iron, it was found that some projectiles were cracking while in store, and breaking up on hitting the target. In 1890 it was decided to do away with Palliser shells, but because of the close similarity between the shot and shell it was possible to convert the shell to shot. The process began in February when it was ordered that all 6-inch Mk.I filled Palliser shells be returned to ordnance stores to have their bursting charges removed. They were made up to the equivalent weight by filling with sand. Previously the projectiles had only been made for the larger calibres, but now they were made for 5-inch and 4-inch guns as well. By the end of 1897 all Palliser shells still on hand were to be filled with salt, plugged, and used as practice ammunition. Though the shot were still in service, the advent of compound armour plating, which had by this time replaced the wrought-iron armour that the Palliser had coped with so well, meant that its days were numbered. They broke up on impact with these plates, which needed forged and tempered steel shot to penetrate them.[6]

been heated for about five hours until it was sufficiently melted, was brought to the filling house in cans containing about 30 lbs, and poured into the shell until about 2 inches short of the fuze hole. The filling funnel was then withdrawn and replaced by a long tube known as a 'former', which was also fitted with a funnel. As the acid cooled and solidified, shrinking as it did so, the formers were rotated by hand to prevent them sticking, and when the process was complete the filling was topped up through the funnel of the former. When this supplementary pouring was over the former was again rotated until solidification, when it was withdrawn, together with the lyddite, which had solidified within it; this was sometimes not an easy operation and the shell had to be heated to loosen the former. The lyddite was subsequently melted out of the formers and they were then boiled out with soda before being used again. The purpose of the former was to leave a space within the shell for the insertion of the exploder, a long cylinder of picric powder in a shalloon bag (see Glossary).

In June 1903 an explosion occurred in a filling room at Woolwich Arsenal, killing several men; the cause could not be positively traced but it was thought the forcible removal of a sticking former might have been a reason. Possibly because of this, a change was made in the technique of forming the exploder cavity. An asbestos paper tube, closed at the bottom, was inserted into the lyddite before it set. This prevented any friction between the former and the lyddite, and the former was no longer used to top up the contents, a space being

left beneath the fuze-hole. In November 1904 solid filling was introduced for shells of 6-inch calibre and above. Formers were no longer needed, and the space above the lyddite was filled with seven dram exploders of picric powder in small seamless bags. In 1909 this method was extended to BL and QF ammunition from 12-pounder to 4.7-inch. A process that had not changed was the need to provide a protective coat on the inside of the shell, though the requirement was not now to stop friction between powder and a rough casting, but to prevent chemical reactions occurring between the shell and the filling. Lyddite, in contact with certain metals, was apt to form dangerous substances known as picrates, and the interiors of the shells were lacquered accordingly; the exteriors were coated with a leadless yellow paint and the fuze-hole bush and plug made from leadless alloy.

The introduction of trotyl (see Glossary) as a filling to supplement and replace lyddite meant that solid filling had to be abandoned, owing to the initiation train needed to detonate it. A cavity had to be formed within the shell filling to accommodate a Gaine. This was a device adopted for initiating detonation of high explosive (HE) shells (see Glossary) when such shells are used in conjunction with a powder-filled fuze. They were necessary because HE fillings could be detonated by gunpowder, and were much more complicated animals than the picric powder exploders. No.2 Gaine was a steel cylinder containing a fairly large quantity of CE (see Glossary). Above this was placed a large fulminate detonator, and above that

OA.10 Left to right: a shell being filled with lyddite, with the funnel placed on the former, which is shown in place for inserting the exploder of picric powder *(From TNA SUPP 5/148)*; a filled lyddite shell, with exploder in place and nose fuze fitted *(From TNA ADM 151/68)*; the later type of filling for lyddite shell, dispensing with the use of the former. *(From Treatise on Ammunition, 10th ed., London, 1915)*

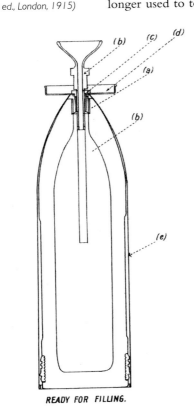

READY FOR FILLING.

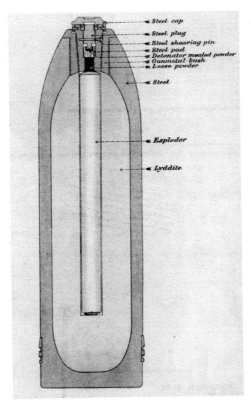

Steel cap
Steel plug
Steel shearing pin
Steel pad
Detonator mealed powder
Gunmetal bush
Loose powder

Steel

Exploder

Lyddite

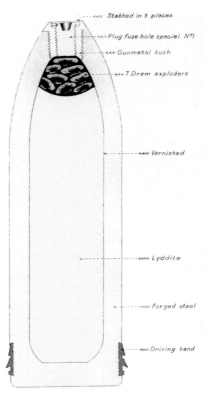

Stabbed in 3 places
Plug fuze hole special Nº1
Gunmetal bush
7 Dram exploders
Varnished
Lyddite
Forged steel
Driving band

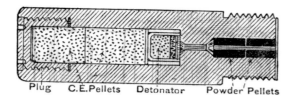

OA.11 The Gaine used to detonate a high explosive shell. *(From 'Ammunition' in Encyclopaedia Britannica, 12th ed., 1922)*

again a small quantity of gunpowder. The gunpowder was ignited by the fuze, and in its turn caused the fulminate detonator to disrupt and initiate detonation of the CE pellets, which communicated the detonation to the shell filling. When amatol (see Glossary) was used as a filling, this could be cast in blocks ready for insertion into the shell. Trotyl could also be cast, and this was the technique preferred in Germany.[7]

Cartridge filling

As with shell filling, the processes and tools involved were very basic. Smoothbore cartridges were flannel bags containing a weighed amount of gunpowder.[8] The cartridges for Armstrong guns were not dissimilar, but the need to prevent fouling of the rifling led to the attachment of lubricators to the tops of the cartridge bags. These thin metal cases contained tallow and linseed oil, which was squeezed out on discharge, and the felt wad attached to them wiped the bore. The introduction of the rifled muzzle loader and the development of slower-burning powders of moulded form completely changed the technique of making up cartridges for the large guns. By 1873 it had been found that the corners of the grains of pebble powder cut the material of the

OA.12 Actual size of prism powder used for 12.5-inch, 16-inch and 17.72-inch RML guns, and 10.4-inch and 12-inch BL guns. *(From Lynal Thomas, 'The Action of Fired Gunpowder in Guns' in The Illustrated Naval and Military Magazine, vol. 1, 1884)*

bag, and the heavier cartridges had a tendency to split from the weight of the powder. Silk cloth was recommended as a replacement. In 1876 52½ lb cartridges for the 38-ton 12.5-inch RML were made up with prisms of powder arranged in layers on a block of wood of the same outline as a section of the finished cartridge, and on which the silk cartridge bag had been laid. Two layers of eighteen prisms were arranged in the form of a hexagon, with central prisms removed. On top of the second layer was placed a perforated disc of wood ³⁄₁₀ inch thick, and saturated with paraffin. Three further layers were then arranged on this and the cartridge bag drawn over the powder and secured. Four of these cartridges formed the full charge. In September 1883 at Priddy's Hard these were being made up with the following staff:

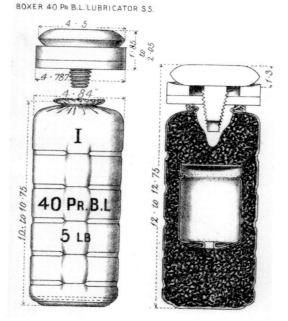

OA.13 The cartridge for a 40-pounder Armstrong gun, with its lubricator. *(From Majendie and Boxer; this plate 1869)*

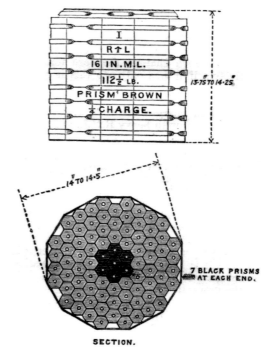

OA.14 The cartridge for the 16-inch RML, built up from prism powder. *(From Treatise on Ammunition, 4th ed., London, 1887)*

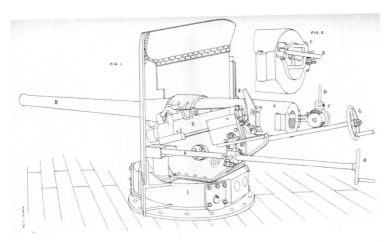

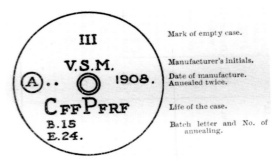

OA.16 Markings on the base of a QF case. This example, made in 1908, has been annealed twice, as shown by the two dots. It has been filled twice with cordite and three times with powder, once with a reduced charge. *(From Treatise on Ammunition, 10th ed., London, 1915)*

OA.15 The 4.7-inch QF gun in its original form. *(From Brassey's Naval Annual for 1887, Portsmouth, 1888)*

Six men sewing six quarter charges working with 315 lbs of powder
Two men building up cartridges, say two powder boxes open with 225 lbs
Two cylinders in the packing room adjoining the making up room containing 210 lbs
Total powder being manipulated at any one time, 750 lbs

This technique remained in use until powder ceased to be used as a propellant, though the type and arrangements of the prisms varied. The 112½ lb cartridge for the 16-inch RML, for example, was filled with brown prism powder, but the central prisms of the top and bottom layers were of the faster-burning black powder, which acted as a primer and prevented hang fires. These cartridges, and those for the 17.72-inch gun, were

made up within a zinc envelope of the dimensions of the fitted cartridge, with a detachable wooden bottom. Cartridges for large guns not built up out of prisms were often fitted with internal sticks to prevent compression when rammed home. These were filled using a simple apparatus to keep the stick in position during the operation; the neck of the cartridge bag was secured around the copper ring, while the stick was held vertical by the central cylinder. In 1892, cartridges for the 13.5-inch BL were assembled in similar fashion to the RML of 1876.[9]

The original Armstrong 4.7-inch (in actuality 4.724-inch, or, much more neatly, 12-cm) QF gun fired a shell of 30 lbs with a cartridge containing 12 lbs of SP [selected for high quality] powder. It was clearly expected that it would become the standard light cruiser armament and secondary

OA.17 Rectifying cartridge cases during the late 1940s at Crombie Naval Ordnance Depot. Crombie was opened in 1915, in order to supply the new naval base at Rosyth on the Firth of Forth (see pages 190–91). *(From HRO 109M91, PH/34)*

armament of battleships, but the 6-inch QF, first tried out by Armstrongs in October 1890, supplemented it rapidly. Unlike the smaller calibres of QF ammunition, the shell and cartridge were loaded separately, though when supplied to foreign navies fixed ammunition could be provided. The shell was base-fuzed. In the case of muzzle-loading and conventional breech-loading guns, the flannel or silk cartridges were consumed in firing; with QF guns the brass cases remained, were ejected, and could be re-used after immersion and washing. The rapid expansion of gases within the case on firing expanded the case, which needed to be cleaned and reformed, an operation known as rectifying. The tools employed were again very simple. They comprised a steel spring clip, a chamber gauge, a copper hammer, an iron holder, a wooden mallet, a steel mandril, a screw press and a tap wrench. All these operations weakened the case, and consequently a limit was placed on the number of times the operation could be performed safely: eleven times when fired with gunpowder and six when fired with cordite (see above). The number of firings and types of filling were stamped on the base of the case. New buildings had to be added to the depots for rectifying purposes. As with many other warlike stores, difficulties were found at first, partly caused by the fact that many were carried on small, wet ships.

When fixed QF ammunition had to be dismantled for inspection or other purposes, a special piece of equipment was required; this was, in the contorted syntax of official nomenclature the Machine, Extracting Shell, QF. This extracted the projectile from the cartridge case; the reverse operation was performed by the Machine, Coning or Indenting, QF, which forced the shell into the case and indented the metal to make a solid fit. The introduction of the QF gun on a large scale coincided with the great increase in the size of the fleet under the Naval Defence Act of 1889; Lord George Hamilton, when he announced that the 4.7-inch QF would replace the smaller calibres of BL guns, was probably unaware of the enormous increase in magazine accommodation that would entail. The gun was not to play any significant part in the coming First World War, but its ammunition would help to change the scale of operations of the Ordnance Depots just as much as that of the big guns.[10]

By 1894 cordite was beginning to replace powder as the propellant, and new procedures were laid down placing a limit on the amount of cordite to be handled in each building and providing instructions on how handfuls of cordite could be loaded in to the cartridge cases.[11] The internal layout of the resulting cartridges was completely different. The QF cartridges were all issued in brass cases; the BL cartridges were contained in silk or shalloon bags, and built up in the following

OA.18 Top: A QF shell placed in the extracting machine in order to remove the projectile from the cartridge case.
Below: The indenting or coning machine performed the opposite function, securing the projectile to the cartridge case.
(From Treatise on Ammunition, 10th ed., London, 1915)

manner. The cordite sticks were cut to the required length by a simple guillotine (a slightly more elaborate device was needed for cordite later than Mark I) and weighed. A small bundle of sticks was tied with silk sewing, and this formed a core. A few more sticks were placed around this core and held

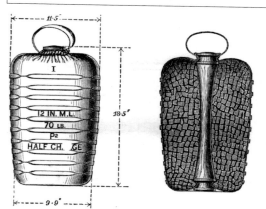

OA.19 Cartridge for 12-inch RML, filled with pebble powder and showing the Mark II Stick cartridge. To the right is the copper collar used to keep the stick centrally placed in the cartridge while filling. *(From Treatise on Ammunition, 4th ed., London, 1887)*

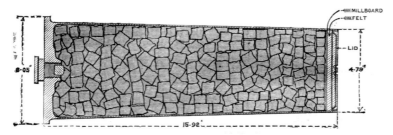

OA.20 The 4.7-inch QF gun cartridge was made of solid drawn brass, with the inside varnished. The charge, 12 lbs of powder, was placed loose in the cartridge, with a millboard disc and a thin felt wad over it, and the mouth closed by a cap containing a mixture of equal parts of beeswax and tallow, to act as a lubricant. *(From Treatise on Ammunition, 5th ed., London, 1892)*

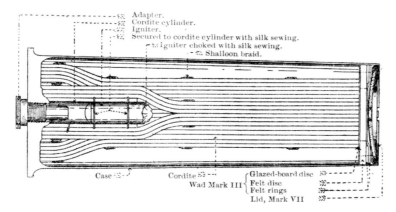

OA.21 Cartridge for the 4.7-inch QF, filled with 5 lbs 7 oz of cordite. *(From Treatise on Ammunition, 10th ed., London, 1915)*

by an elastic band while being shaped; they were then tied with silk sewing, and the process repeated till the whole charge was built. It was then securely tied with silk braid. The two outer rows of sticks were slightly longer than the remainder, in order to form a recess for the igniter (as cordite needed a gunpowder initiator) to settle down into. When the whole charge had been built it was placed in its bag, which had all the particulars marked on it, and the exact weight was made up by pushing in small

pieces of cordite. The igniter was then sewn on. A millboard 'tear-off' disc, covered with silk cloth and marked with a red cross, was placed over the end of the cartridge to protect the igniter, and secured to the cartridge bag by sewing in four places. This was torn off before firing.[12]

Fuzes

A fuze is required to ensure that a shell bursts where the firer intends. It may be an air-burst weapon, such as shrapnel, in which case a time fuze is required; it may be required to explode on impact or after penetrating its target, or on a graze. It was to be many years before really consistently performing fuzes were made available, though it was sometimes difficult to see if the missile had failed to explode properly because of the fuze, the shell filling or the structure of the shell itself. All fuzes contained a small amount of combustible material, which was intended to set off the main explosive. Filling them with these compounds was, for many years, carried on entirely at Woolwich.

Simplest of all were the wooden time fuzes. As designed by Colonel Boxer they stayed in service until 1890, having most recently been found unreliable at the bombardment of Alexandria in 1886, burning irregularly, though not the worst-performing fuzes at that engagement. The original design was very simple. A wooden cone was filled with inflammable composition; a paper label on the fuze indicated the distance this would burn in short intervals. Before firing, the fuze was drilled by means of a special auger at the required spot, the fuze inserted into the shell and the protective cap torn off. On firing, the rush of flame ignited the composition, which flashed through the fuze case

OA.22 Above: Cordite cartridge for a 12-inch BL gun. *(From Treatise on Ammunition, 10th ed., London, 1915)* Right: A replica quarter cordite charge, at Explosion! Museum of Naval Firepower, one of four needed to propel the shell from a 15-inch BL gun the full range of 17 miles (27 kilometres). The full charge weighed 432 lbs. Broken down into four parts it was easy to manhandle. There were also occasions on which a full charge was not required, for example, practice firings and close range actions. *(Stephen Dent)*

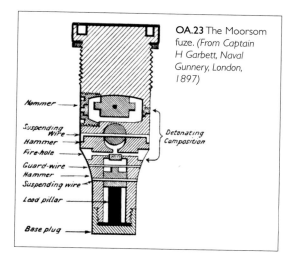

OA.23 The Moorsom fuze. (From Captain H Garbett, Naval Gunnery, London, 1897)

Hammer

Suspending Wire
Hammer
Fire-hole
Guard-wire
Hammer
Suspending wire
Lead pillar

Base plug

Detonating Composition

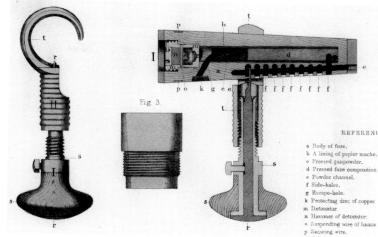

OA.24 The Boxer time fuze for rifled ordnance. Left: the special auger; right: the fuze being prepared by means of the auger. (From Majendie and Boxer, Descriptive Plates to Ammunition, London, various dates, this plate 1867)

where it had been drilled and detonated the shell filling. Far more complex was the contemporary fuze designed by Captain William Moorsom, R.N (see Glossary). This was a percussion fuze and although withdrawn from service in 1865, being designed for spherical shells, it demonstrated the principle of using the force of discharge of the projectile to set the fuze. Unfired, the fuzed shell was theoretically perfectly safe and ordnance officers acted on that assumption. Three gun-metal hammers were suspended by wires; the shock of the detonation severed these, allowing the hammers to strike patches of detonating composition on impact, which exploded the shell. The three hammers were arranged so that the composition would be struck by one of them no matter what side of the shell struck (except if the shell happened to strike base first). The construction of this fuze was kept as secret as possible, only Moorsom and his workman making the final assembly. The fuze was introduced cautiously; in 1852 half of 8-inch and 10-inch shells supplied to all ships were fitted with them, but in May 1853, on Captain Chads' (the commander of the gunnery training ship HMS Excellent) recommendation, the proportion was to be extended to half the establishment (7,000 shells). The same number of fuzes were to be prepared for 6-inch shells. These fuzes were a significant item in the budget of the Board of Ordnance, costing more than the shell itself. An 8-inch naval shell cost 5/4½d, a Moorsom fuze about 6/-. By 1858 the Admiralty considered the secret of Moorsom's fuzes to be generally known, and thought it unnecessary to continue the practice of sealing the boxes containing them, though a writer in that year, giving a very generalised account of their operation, thought that 'the telling of it might be considered an act of bad citizenship'.

Armstrong designed special fuzes as part of his weapons system, and described his fuze to a meeting of the Institution of Civil Engineers. He explained his openness (so unlike Moorsom's conduct) by the impossibility of maintaining secrecy in England, and the fact that specimens

had been stolen from his Elswick factory. His sea-service fuze was designed not to be too sensitive to allow the projectile to ricochet from the water without exploding until the target was struck. It contained a central pillar with hole through it, filled with powder, and tipped at the upper extremity with detonating composition. This extremity projected into a cavity in the cover, a clearance of about 5/100 inch being left around the detonator. Were the pillar to move forward or to one side the detonator would be exploded by contact with either the top or the side of the cavity. A leaden hoop, called the guard, rested on the pillar by a flange and prevented any movement of the pillar. When fired, the acceleration caused the flange to strip off and the guard to be set back at the bottom of the fuze, removing its support from the pillar. The pillar was then maintained in position by a little leaden cup called the regulator; the thickness of this cup determined that the pillar be held in place when grazing the water, but was crushed on impact with a ship, allowing the detonator to impact against the inside of the fuze. Armstrong claimed that the action of the fuze was so rapid that in firing a 100 lb shell against a butt 18 inches thick the shells burst in the act of passing through the timber. Unfortunately these fuzes soon acquired an unfortunate reputation. For example, in June 1860, when a 12-pounder Armstrong was fitted for trials on Bacchante it was supplied by Priddy's Hard with 200 rounds of various types of ordnance. It was ordered that the fuzes for the Armstrong shells be kept separate from powder and live shells and not be deposited in a magazine. The Commanding Officer was warned that there was some doubt as to their liability to spontaneous combustion.

The custodianship of fuzes was the subject of one of the turf wars between the Ordnance Yard and the gunwharf. In 1865 Boxer wooden fuzes for rifled ordnance had previously been a gunwharf store, but were being supplied from Priddy's Hard, and the Storekeeper wanted the charge of them again. However, in July 1869 it was

Fig. 3.

REFEREN(
a Body of fuze.
b A lining of papier mache.
c Pressed gunpowder.
d Pressed fuze composition
e Powder channel.
f Side-holes.
g Escape-hole.
k Protecting disc of copper
m Detonator
n Hammer of detonator.
o Suspending wire of hamm
p Securing wire.

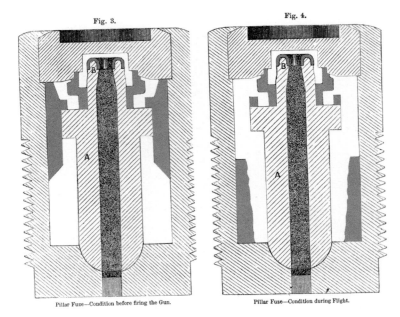

Fig. 3.   Fig. 4.

Pillar Fuze—Condition before firing the Gun.   Pillar Fuze—Condition during Flight.

OA.25 Above: on the left can be seen the Armstrong fuze before firing. The central column, containing gunpowder and tipped with detonating composition, is held in place by two lead hoops, the guard and the regulator (both shaded grey). The force of firing strips the guard off, leaving the column during flight supported solely by the regulator. On impact, this is crushed and the composition strikes the inside of the fuze. *(Adapted from Armstrong's contribution to 'The National Defences' in Proceedings of the Institution of Civil Engineers, vol. 20, 1861)*

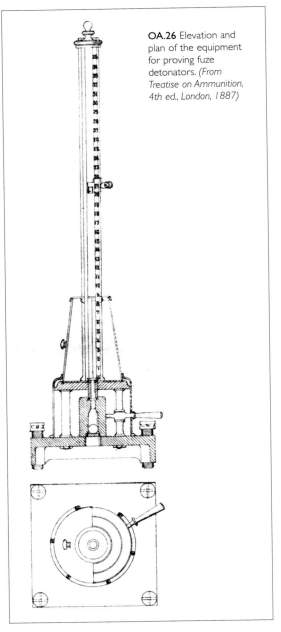

OA.26 Elevation and plan of the equipment for proving fuze detonators. *(From Treatise on Ammunition, 4th ed., London, 1887)*

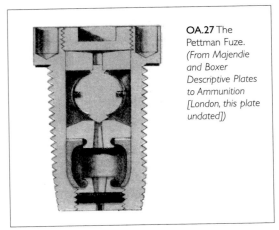

OA.27 The Pettman Fuze. *(From Majendie and Boxer Descriptive Plates to Ammunition [London, this plate undated])*

ordered that all tubes, fuzes, lights and signal rockets were to be transferred to Priddy's Hard. The gunwharf officers may well have felt glad by this time to be relieved of the responsibility for fuzes, for not only were the several kinds of Armstrong's time and field service fuzes undergoing rapid deterioration, but Colonel Boxer was gravely concerned about the Pettman fuzes, which had succeeded Moorsom's in naval service in 1862:

'The condition of these fuzes shews that far from overestimating the liability to disarrange the internal parts of the Fuze accidentally I rather underestimated it in recommending that the operation [of examining the fuzes] should be performed at Portsmouth & Devonport [Laboratories].... The state of things is now [so] serious [that] there are in store fuzes liable to explode at a blow, such as might be caused by a fall ... and such fuzes if fixed in filled shells may cause serious accident ... and cannot fail to explode prematurely in the bore...'.

He recommended the immediate prohibition of protection of the fuzes from damp at the outstations, and that all those prepared to resist moisture be returned to Woolwich at once. The Pettman fuze was a more complicated device than the Armstrong or Moorsom, having two alternative means of being made live, according to whether it was used with breech-loading or muzzle-loading guns, and it was probably for this versatility that it had such a long life, staying in service to be the worst fuze employed during the bombardment of Alexandria in 1883, and still kept in store in 1897. It was not only the safety of the fuze that was in question in 1870, when at a discussion at the Royal Artillery Institution it was stated that: 'We have no reliable percussion fuze'. The device was improved over the years, but the 1887 *Treatise on Ammunition* noted that some dangerous Mark I fuzes were still around, and, disconcertingly, that '...percussion fuzes are liable to give prematures from causes which at present are somewhat

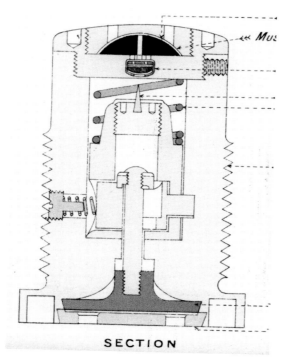

SECTION

OA.28 Left: The Fuze, Percussion, base, Large, No.11, Mark V(C). *(From Treatise on Ammunition, 10th ed., London, 1915)*

OA.29 Above: Two nose time fuzes photographed at Explosion! Museum of Naval Firepower, the fuze on the left is sectioned for instructional purposes. *(Stephen Dent)*

obscure. A fuze that will act admirably in one gun will cause a premature in another or even in the same gun when fired in a differently designed projectile.'

Many types of fuze had been issued by the end of the century; after 1870 they were issued to the depots in tin cylinders each containing five fuzes, the cylinders being issued in wooden cases. When examined, three per cent were to be tested when the batch to be examined numbered a thousand or more, and no fuzes were to be condemned on a trial of less than twenty. They were to be condemned if eight per cent of the sample failed. Equipment was provided by Woolwich to conduct proof of the fuze detonators. This consisted of a cast-iron base-plate on which three wrought-iron pillars carried a brass plate, on which three steel guide bars formed a rigid framework within which a weight could be dropped 35 inches onto a detonator placed on an anvil. The operator was protected from the explosion that followed a successful proof by a movable brass screen. Separate weights and anvils were provided for each description of fuze. To prove the Pettman GS detonating balls an 18 ounce steel weight fell on them from a height of 25 inches. The dismantling and testing of the fuzes was a proof house activity, though other buildings were adapted to this function. Buildings still survive at Priddy's Hard and Lodge Hill (see Appendix A) where shoots have been inserted in the wall for the hasty disposal of any composition that showed signs of ignition when a device was being taken apart for proof purposes.

With the advent of BL and QF guns a host of new fuzes, both for land and sea service, were devised. The way in which the development of all aspects of ordnance had a knock-on effect led to a

fundamental redesign of those fuzes whose action depended on the acceleration of the projectile severing a wire which released the mechanism; the slow burning powders and longer barrels now employed meant that the momentum of the shell was now only such as to shear a wire of one-tenth of the strength formerly employed. Rather than relying on such delicate wires to retain the fuze in an inert condition, the impact of the shell on hitting (or missing) the target was consequently relied on to initiate the action of the fuze. The enormous demands of the First World War led to sets of fuze rooms being added to the laboratories, though most of the actual fuze manufacture was undertaken at Royal Ordnance Factories. The men who worked there were some of the few people in the Ordnance Depots who required a high level of technical skill; as the illustration of the Fuze, Percussion, Base, Large, No.11, Mark V(C) – to give its full title – shows (see figure OA.28), working with these was of a different order from cartridge filling or shell scraping. None of these fuze rooms have survived at Priddy's Hard, Lodge Hill or Bull Point.[13]

Packaging for sea

In its first report, the Magazine Committee of 1865 (see Chapter 5), noted the changes that had taken place during the century to the packaging of gunpowder. The barrel, for years the traditional container, was rapidly being supplanted. It had the advantage of being the cheapest and lightest case, but had many disadvantages. Opening and closing were primitive operations, and the powder was very liable to be split in the process, if not performed by an expert. Adepts, however, could do

OA.30 The
improved type of
powder barrel.
(From Treatise on
Ammunition, 4th ed.,
London, 1887)

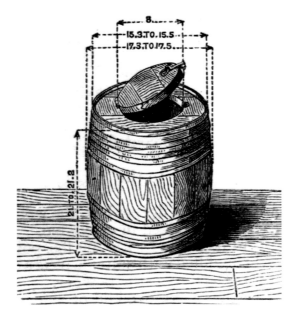

this with speed and safety; four coopers at Purfleet could open and close 800 barrels in the space of nine hours; and during the Napoleonic War 50,000 barrels were delivered there every year, each one being unheaded twice and headed three times without a single accident. However, such levels of skill could not be expected everywhere. Furthermore, the method of construction led to an occasional leakage of the powder from the shrinking of the staves in hot climates, and when being moved, a cooper needed to be in attendance to tighten the staves. Barrels also occupied a great

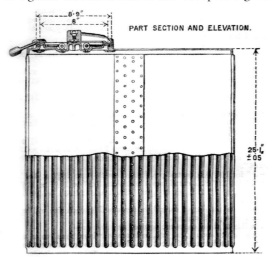

PART SECTION AND ELEVATION.

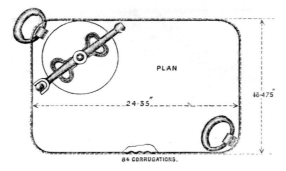

PLAN

OA.31 The
corrugated metal
powder case, for
sea service only.
(From Treatise on
Ammunition, 4th ed.,
London, 1887)

space in stowage, and when placed in piles needed strong lateral support. Some changes in packing and handling had taken place; by 1847, as a consequence of improved manufacture, the gunpowder was of a greater density, allowing the barrel to be filled with 100 lbs of powder, instead of 90 lbs. Outside magazines, the barrels had always been moved in tumbrils or barrows; at the same time, the practice of rolling them in magazines was discontinued. Proposals had often been made to improve upon the system of packing gunpowder loose in barrels, by enclosing it in bags of flannel, linen or waterproof cloth within the barrel. Colonel Boxer brought this system into practical use during the Russian war, when all the powder sent from England for the use of the Siege Train was enclosed in waterproof bags of linen and caoutchouc (see Glossary). This method of packing was found to answer all expectations in preventing grains of powder from filtering through the staves of the casks, and in preserving the powder in good condition when lodged in damp. The barrel had been recently improved by the application of a large well-secured opening at one end for access.

In the navy, cases had long been exclusively used instead of barrels for additional security as well as to save space – an object of the greatest importance. These comprised rectangular metal-lined cases, made to contain about the same quantity of powder made up into cartridges as the barrel, or if filled with spare powder, the same amount in flannel bags of 15 lbs each. From September 1848 the cases were made in the Royal Carriage Department at Portsmouth Gunwharf, and probably at the other gunwharves also. A further improvement on the metal lined case had been effected by the employment of cases made entirely of metal; these were more secure and more durable, but far more heavy and costly, the barrel weighing 29 lbs, and costing 12s 6d, while a metal lined case weighed 48 lbs and cost 40s, and a brass case turned the scale at 61 lbs, and cost £3 10s 2d. Dell's pentagonal metal cases (see Glossary) provided a most efficient means of filling the awkward spaces encountered below decks, and weighed 63 lbs. They were used for 7-inch cartridges and smaller. In 1858, seventy-six bays of A Magazine at Priddy's Hard were fitted up to take them. The shells fired by smooth-bore (SB) guns were each packed in a wooden box, from which they were taken only when being prepared for firing. This practice ceased with the introduction of the Armstrong gun, and it was decided at the end of 1861 that its projectiles were to be stored piled in the same way as SB shot, boxes only being employed when they were in transit. By 1875 the advent of the rifled muzzle loader (RML) had further increased the size of the cases. The corrugated rectangular powder case for 38- and 35-ton 12-inch RML, which held two 110 lb or three 85 lb charges, weighed 72 lbs. There were thirteen sizes of these cases, which were only issued for sea service, made of corrugated sheet brass with gunmetal tops and fittings.

An indication of the number of packages needed to contain the outfit of powder is given by those supplied by Priddy's Hard in 1878 to the small ironclad *Repulse* (incidentally the last timber-hulled capital ship to be built for the Royal Navy). For the ship's armament, comprising twelve 8-inch RML, 380 corrugated rectangular brass powder cases were required. The two 20-pounder saluting guns were provided for by a single whole (they were supplied in whole, half and quarter sizes) metal-lined wooden case, made of deal with oak corners and lined with tinned copper. But this was only part of the armament, as the men of the Victorian Navy were far more likely to see action ashore or in small boats than firing the great guns. The boats' ammunition was carried in twenty-eight wooden half-cases, and six metal-lined quarter cases. Small arms ammunition occupied 170 Mk. V boxes, 11 tin lined boxes for Adams revolvers, 20 wooden half cases and 16 metal lined quarter cases. The costly metal cases proved very liable to damage, and many edicts were issued on the necessity for careful handling, but to little effect. This indeed partly explains the legendary lack of enthusiasm for target practice shown by Victorian naval officers. New packaging systems were introduced with the new armaments. Zinc cylinders were used in land service to transport, store and bring the cartridges to the guns; in the navy they were employed for the temporary storage of reserve ammunition until its issue to vessels. Then cylindrical brass cartridge cases were used for 12-inch breech-loading (BL) and above; the charges were brought from the magazines to

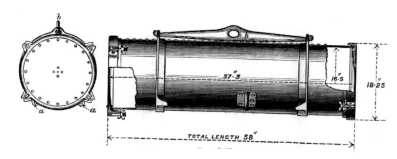

the guns in these. The 4.7-inch quick-fire (QF) cartridges were issued either in corrugated brass cases or wooden boxes, teak being used for sea service and deal for land service. Each held six cartridges. All other ammunition was kept in wooden metal-lined cases or ammunition boxes; the latter were soldered closed and only used for machine gun and small arms ammunition. By 1900 ammunition boxes were wooden, and cylindrical cases were used for 10-inch BL and above. The advent of cordite brought about little change in the appearance of the packaging.

Related to packaging was the use of colour coding, which became increasingly important with the passage of time. Experience in the Crimea had shown the necessity of being able to lay hands on the right things when required, and in April 1857 the stores for the China expedition were colour coded at Portsmouth Gunwharf. The colour coding of ammunition grew in complexity in parallel with the increasing variety being supplied, and by 1900 painting had become a major trade within the depots and substantial shell painting rooms were added to Priddy's Hard and Bull Point. The paint had to be removed when shells were reclassified; scraping was the normal method, and shell scraping rooms were partnered with shell painting rooms.[14] (See back cover.)

OA.32 The cylindrical cartridge cases for large-calibre naval BL guns. (*From Treatise on Ammunition, 4th ed., London, 1887*)

OA.34 Shell scraping by hand at Crombie Naval Ordnance Depot in the late 1940s. (*From Hampshire Record Office, HRO 109M91, PH/34*)

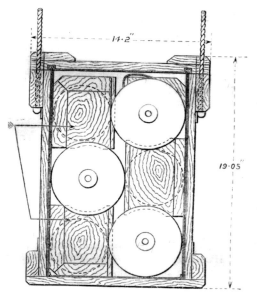

OA.33 The teak box in which naval 4.7-inch QF cartridges were packed. (*From Treatise on Ammunition, 5th ed., London, 1892*)

OA.35 The shell painting room at Crombie in the late 1940s. *(From HRO 109M91, PH/34)*

Testing powder and cordite

During the 18th century a specialised building type was developed for estimating the quality of gunpowder. Samples of all batches of powder were proved at Waltham Abbey before issue, but stored powder needed to be tested before its re-issue, and it had to be determined if powder returned from ships or army units was still usable, and if so, what type of service it was fit for.

A trained man could tell a lot by eye and touch alone, but other methods were also needed. A process called 'flashing' tested the degree of incorporation of the various ingredients as a homogeneous mixture. Eight drachms of powder was placed in a small copper cylinder, which was then inverted on a plate of glass, porcelain or copper. Upon removal of the cylinder the powder would fall into a reasonably consistent pattern, which

Proof ranges

The force exerted by the powder when fired was determined during the 18th century both by firing a mortar and measuring the fall of the shot, and by a variety of devices called éprouvettes. The vertical éprouvette, a small strong barrel, used the gases released by the explosion to raise a weight; the accepted standard was for two drachms of powder to raise 24 lbs to a height of 3½ inches. The mortar method was shown by Congreve to be more accurate, and an 8-inch mortar was taken as the standard, firing a 68-pound shot with a charge of 2 oz powder. This had the merit of simplicity and the range could be set up at any depot. A far more accurate method of

firing proof followed from Wheatstone's invention of the chronograph in 1840, and this method was adopted at Waltham Abbey in 1862. Several varieties of this machine for measuring the velocity of a projectile were developed, that of Navez being originally used at Waltham Abbey, replaced by that of Le Boulengé in 1870; this apparatus continued in use into the 20th century. Much more room was needed for the firing range, the muzzle of the gun being 180 feet from the face of the butt. At that time RLG powder (see Glossary) was proved using a 12-pounder rifled Whitworth cannon, firing that weight of shot with a charge of 1 lb, or a 9-pounder shot with a 1½ lb charge.

OA.36 Diagram of the proof range at Waltham Abbey. The projectile severs a wire stretched across two metal screens, so breaking an electric current. The chronograph enables the time between breaking of the two wires to be determined. *(From Captain F Smith 'The Examination and Proof of Gunpowder as carried on at the Royal Gunpowder Factory, Waltham Abbey' in Minutes of Proceedings of the Royal Artillery Institution, vol. VII, 1871, p.56)*

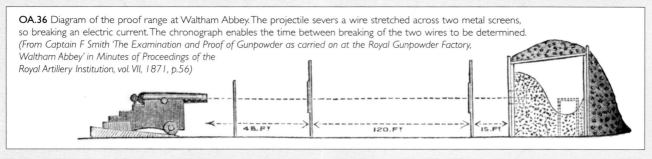

OA.37 A disc of guncotton supplied to Upnor in a dangerous state. (*From Captain Victor Majendie, Report on the Explosion of Gun-Cotton at Stowmarket, London, 1872*)

OA.38 Purfleet Proof House. This substantial construction was to be abandoned in later proof houses. (See also figure 1.12.) (NMR BB94-8149)

OA.39 Interior of the proof house at Crombie. (*From HRO 109M91, PH/34*)

enabled accurate comparison of different powders to be made. The powder was then ignited with a hot iron, and, if the incorporation were good, only a few smoke marks would be left on the plate. Otherwise, residues of sulphur and saltpetre would leave a dirty residue behind; with experience and constant practice the degree of incorporation could be estimated. Powder that had been damaged by damp always left a very bad residue, no matter how well it had been made in the first place. In order to prevent the building becoming choked by fumes and smoke, high ceilings with some form of ventilation were a feature of these early proof houses.

The density of the powder was originally measured by weighing a box containing exactly one cubic foot (for cannon powder this would have been 55 to 56 lbs) but this rough test was unable to detect slight variations in the density, and by 1870 this had been replaced at Waltham Abbey by a much more elaborate piece of equipment, the densimeter. It is not known if this was issued to the Ordnance Depots. Proving the density and quality of the powder through firing was not performed at the depots, and the proof houses there only performed simple inspection and 'flashing' tasks (see Proof ranges text box).

However, the advent of a whole range of new explosives after 1870 ensured that the proof house remained a vital component of the Ordnance Depot. Guncotton, the first to come into service, showed plainly visible signs when in a dangerous condition, but the instability of cordite was harder to detect.

The possibility of an accident occurring when explosives were being inspected ensured that the new generation of proof houses were not substantial constructions such as at Purfleet. Like the pioneering cartridge filling rooms at Priddy's Hard, they were frangible buildings, usually supplied with internal walls acting as traverses so that several people could work in safety. Accidents could happen; in 1921 four men were killed when moving a batch of condemned detonators from the Priddy's Hard Proof House, and the building was effectively demolished. Following the rash of explosions in 1906 (see page 181), the reliability of cordite, once thought so safe, was investigated. Suspect cordite was sent to the depots, where it was to be tested frequently. The cordite was examined visually first; deteriorated cordite was more brittle and usually darker than the new, and had a sour smell, caused by the release of nitrogen peroxide.

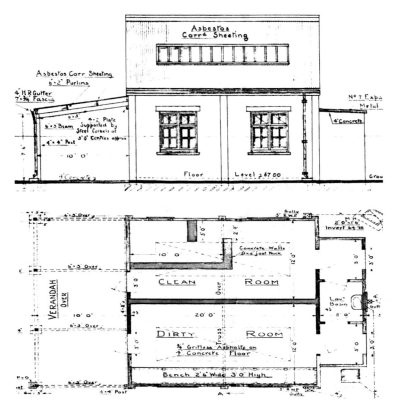

OA.42 The equipment for Abel's silver flask test. *(From Text Book on Explosives used in the Service, London, 1938)*

OA.40 The new proof house of 1934 at Bull Point. Note the internal blast walls. *(From DML fiche 038255)*

The heat test was applied to all forms of cordite. This had been devised by Professor Abel (see page 89), and consisted of heating a crushed sample in a test-tube placed in a water bath maintained at around 80°C. A partially wetted test paper was suspended over the sample, and a cover placed over the tube to prevent light affecting the experiment. The release of nitrogen peroxide caused a change in colour at the junction of the wet and dry portions of the test paper, which would gradually match the sample test paper.[15] Such a simple test could be performed on board ship. A more elaborate test, requiring not only more complicated equipment, but also much more time in order to simulate adverse storage conditions, was devised at Waltham Abbey following spontaneous combustions in

OA.41 Priddy's Hard Proof House after the explosion in 1921. *(From HRO 109M91, PH/50)*

OA.43 The interior of the proof house in the laboratory at Priddy's Hard, in about 1950. The building was divided into a 'clean' and a 'dirty' area – the barrier between these can be seen across the floor – with separate ways in to each. Items such as fuzes were prepared for proofing in the 'clean' area and then actually proved in the 'dirty' area. Note the heating pipes on the wall, and the equipment for proving fuze detonators on the work bench. (Priddy's Hard Archive 1998-4-194)

magazines in India (see page 181). A weighed amount of ground cordite was placed in a vacuum flask whose outer skin was silvered, and was provided with a side tube so that any fumes could be easily observed, with the bulb of a thermometer placed in the cordite. The apparatus was maintained by a water bath at 80°C until the cordite began to decompose, when red fumes were visible in the side tube, and the thermometer rose by 2°. It would take 500 or 600 hours for a good cordite to reach this point. By noting the time the probable safe life of

the cordite could be estimated. The rate of deterioration increased approximately 1·8 times with every 10°F rise in temperature, so that a cordite which had a safe life of 30 years at 70°F would have a life of 9·2 years at 90°F.

This had clear implications for the design of magazines and stores intended to store cordite. The cool interiors of great structures like E Magazine at Priddy's Hard were advantageous, giving them a new lease of life, but it was also important to keep the temperatures above 40°F, below which decomposition also occurred.

The first major warship to be lost during the First World War was the pre-dreadnought battleship *Bulwark*, destroyed by the explosion of her

OA.44 The equipment for Abel's heat test. (From Text Book on Explosives used in the Service, London, 1938)

OA.45 The cordite testing room at Crombie, during the 1940s. (From HRO 109M91, PH/34)

OA.46 One of the shell examining rooms at Priddy's Hard, in about 1950, showing a 15-inch shell with a lifting ring attached. 6-inch and smaller shells could be handled manually; the crane was used for all larger calibres. The pit and supports were so that shells could be inverted during examination. After examination shells would be sent to the shell scraping room and subsequently the paint shop, or returned to store if in good condition. (Priddy's Hard Archive 1998-4-186)

cordite magazine on 26 November 1914. The subsequent enquiry produced a collection of statistics, which show how the depots operated just before the outbreak of war. Cordite from the ship had been tested at the various home stations in the following quantities between 1909 and 1914: Woolwich 3; Upnor 4; Lodge Hill 66; Priddy's Hard 76; Bedenham 1; Bull Point 43.

The last supplies of ammunition to *Bulwark* from Lodge Hill were listed (see table). Two of the samples supplied to the *Bulwark* were under the 10-minute limit, and those asterisked were then subjected to the silvered vessel test. All gave a result of over 500 hours. As the tests were satisfactory, it was thought that the 1902 6-inch cartridges had been ignited through resting on a hot bulkhead.

The introduction of new explosives during the First World War meant that suitable tests had to be devised for them. High explosives generally proved to be very stable, with the exception of tetryl, for which the vacuum test was devised. This, together with the Will test for guncotton, required much more elaborate apparatus and correspondingly greater laboratory space. The so-called solventless cordites, which were developed during the war for naval propellants, had a longer life and gave a superior ballistic performance, could be assessed by means of a colour test. Simplest of all was a surveillance test applied to cordites containing mineral jelly as a stabiliser (and lubricant, to reduce wear in the barrel of the gun). All previous tests were, of necessity, only conducted on random samples, and could not guard against the possibility of a poorly manufactured batch amongst the rest. The mass production of cordite during the war meant that the quality was variable, with some manufactured under less than ideal conditions, and the 100 per cent surveillance test was introduced. Packages of bulk cordite or cartridges were provided with a glass window through which a test paper could be seen. Originally blue, exposure to the gases from decaying cordite turned the paper through a range of colours to a purplish red; these were matched against a colour chart, and the condition of the explosive assessed. The resulting workload could be considerable; when the average temperature of a magazine ranged between 70° and 80°F, all packages had to be checked twice weekly; when 70°F or below, every week. These operations were not performed in the conditions thought suitable for a laboratory today. However, in active service explosives were often stored under less than ideal conditions and the checks made were proportionate.[16]

Ordnance supplied to HMS *Bulwark* from Lodge Hill (1914)

Date of supply	Cordite cartridges	Quantity	Date of manufacture	Heat test result, in minutes and seconds	
7 May 1914	6-inch 10 lbs	112	March 1902	9.27	*
3 July 1914	12-inch 52½ lbs	112	November 1901	18.00	*
	6-inch 11½ lbs	336	November 1910	Over 30	
	12-pdr 11⁵⁄₁₆ lbs	400	February 1902	12.24	*
	12-pdr 2 lbs	330	April 1908	Over 30	
	6-pdr sub-calibre	88	July 1901	30.00	*
	3-pdr sub-calibre	32	February 1900	8.50	*
		62	January 1901	13.00	
		30		12.50	*
		34	July 1901	13.14	
	3-pdr steel shell	112	August 1900	20.10	
8 July 1914	Lyddite 6-inch shells	13	N/A		
	Lyddite 12- & 14-pdr shells	1000			

Chapter 7 The Great Expansion

On 30 June 1895 the Prime Minister, Lord Salisbury, wrote to Austen Chamberlain, offering him the post of Civil Lord of the Admiralty: 'The office is interesting in many ways, but specially in the fact that it has on many occasions been the first step in the ladder to many who have, afterwards, achieved for themselves a considerable name.' Here was an offer an ambitious young politician could not refuse.

Repercussions of the Naval Works Act of 1895

The Civil Lord's responsibilities included building works. The First Naval Lord, Admiral Sir Frederick Richards, was determined to push for the maximum resources available to the navy as a consequence of the Naval Works Act (see page 122). The only moneys allotted for magazine construction when Chamberlain took office were on Vote 10, and were £30,000 for Gibraltar and £5,000 for Malta; £1,000 and £5,000 respectively had been taken in the financial year 1894–5. In February 1896 Chamberlain drew up a memorandum in which he drew attention to the fact that the great growth that had taken place in the navy during the past ten years had been accompanied by no equivalent growth in the Works Department, although every increase in any Naval Vote naturally brought with it increased demands on the Works Vote. In ten years the Navy Estimates had increased fifty per cent, from £12,000,000 to £18,000,000; the tonnage of ships afloat, building, or completed for service, had nearly doubled; and whilst the number of men had gone up from 58,000 to 88,850, the Works Vote had remained practically stationary. 'In 1885 it was £517,700; in succeeding years it was £468,000, £403,000, £376,000, £451,000, £417,000, £380,000 and so on. In 1894–5 it leaped up to £650,000; in last year, 1895–6, it was £547,000 … I venture to urge that the Works Department cannot be allowed thus to lag behind other branches of the Admiralty without serious inconvenience, at least, in time of peace, and serious danger to the country in war.' The options were either to greatly increase the sum for Vote 10 Works at once, and permanently, or to place on the Naval Works Loan some of the large works that could no longer be postponed. George Goschen, the First Lord, had already

decided that the floating magazines would have to be replaced by land magazines; not only were their hulls time-expired, but the fire on *Leonidas* had demonstrated their vulnerability. It was proposed to replace the hulks for about £105,000. A further £285,000 was required for additional ammunition accommodation due to the introduction of QF weapons and the increase of the fleet under the Naval Defence Act and the Spencer programme within the following three years, together with the £70,000 for Gibraltar and Malta. The total cost was £460,000, which was to be met by the Loan.[1]

The enormous amount of work to be executed as Loan Works would throw a burden on the Works Department that could not be supported by the current system of administration. In July 1895, Major Pilkington, the Director of Works, urged that special arrangements be made for their superintendence. It would be impossible for him to complete all the details, arrange for the necessary inspection and control the expenditure of some £1½ million a year on the Loan Works, while at the same time carrying out the current duties of the office of the Director of Works. This job was complicated by the fact that his staff in London was now distributed between two offices, one in Craven Street, The Strand, and one in Parliament Street, Westminster, with a third separate office shortly to be provided. To counter objections that no new arrangements had been made for the War Office Barrack Loan of about £4 million, he pointed out that the types of construction involved were quite different. In the case of barracks, one building was very much like another, and once the design was fixed the progress of the buildings took a well trodden path, but in the case of Naval Works, each item was a study in itself, and standardisation virtually impossible. He submitted therefore that the best arrangement would be that he should be appointed Engineer-in-Chief for the Loan Works only, with a separate office and staff, and that a new Director of Works be appointed to take up the ordinary duties under Vote 10. As Engineer-in-Chief he should report directly to the Board, independently of the Director of Works. Pilkington proposed Major Raban, Superintending Engineer at Portsmouth Dockyard, as Director of Works, and W. E. Riley, Superintending Civil Engineer at Devonport, as Assistant Director of Works. On 14 October 1895,

7.1 Britain's naval mastery of the late 19th century is usually represented by views of lines of battleships at fleet reviews, but this panorama (a montage of six photographs) of Portsmouth Harbour in 1881 gives a much truer idea of British sea power at the time, as well as the form and function of the dockyard and naval base in its heyday. At far left, beyond the Isle of Wight paddle steamer, is Fort Blockhouse, with the old 100-gun ship HMS *St Vincent*, formerly Portsmouth flagship, moored nearby. To her right is the training brig *Martin*. Moored off Gosport is another 100-gun ship, HMS *Victory*, at that time serving as tender to the port flagship HMS *Duke of Wellington* (120 guns, formerly HMS *Windsor Castle*), seen to the right of *Victory*. (It would be another 40 years before *Victory* was taken into dock in Portsmouth Dockyard for preservation.) The large vessel in the centre foreground is the troopship *Serapis* which was designed to carry a full battalion of infantry, including their families: a total of 1,200 people. Beyond the

these appointments were approved. Pilkington was to be paid £2,000 a year as Engineer-in-Chief, which included his pension of £250. Major Exham replaced Raban at Portsmouth. By March 1896, £3,407,000 had been added to a new schedule of additional Loan Works; this included the £460,000 for the magazines. For work on the magazines alone three Assistant Civil Engineers, six draughtsmen, three accountant clerks and six foremen of works were taken on as temporary staff, at a total cost of £3,503 a year. The same month Chamberlain set up a committee to consider the reorganisation of the Works Department, which reported in August. As a consequence, the department was strengthened by providing an assistant to the Director of Works; placing the engineering branch under the Superintending Civil Engineer instead of the Assistant Director; improving pay; moving staff around to gain experience of conditions at the outports; and creating a lands department. A Superintending Engineer was now required for Devonport. Pilkington wanted a man who, apart from dockyard work, '… can also build the Dartmouth College[2] & the New Magazines & who is up in sanitary work &c &c.' Major Kenyon was thought to have the all-round skills required and in October was appointed for the next four years. His title had been changed from Superintending Engineer of Devonport Dockyard to Superintending Engineer of Devonport District, reflecting more accurately the geographical scope of his responsibilities. Chamberlain proposed that similar changes should be made to the job title at Portsmouth and Chatham.[3]

The Portsmouth Committee

While the Civil Lord assembled the administrative machine, the Naval Lord determined to ensure that the new magazine and ordnance storage arrangements were established on an adequate scale and met the demands of each location. The three main Ordnance Depots had, as has been seen, evolved in completely different ways on very different sites, and Richards clearly felt that each case had to be treated individually. Accordingly, in

July 1895, Committees on Magazine Accommodation were set up for the Portsmouth, Devonport and Medway areas, each presided over by the local Commander-in-Chief. The Portsmouth Committee comprised Admiral Sir Nowell Salmon, Captain Kane (the Director of Naval Ordnance), Colonel Sir Thales Pease and Major Raban. The DNO had prepared a paper (in which the capacity of magazines was no longer expressed in terms of barrelage) showing the magazine reserves necessary for: two-thirds of reserves for the Channel Squadron; full reserves for training and coastguard squadrons; outfits and half reserves for fleet and dockyard reserve; outfits of tenders to gunnery ships, merchant cruisers, ships building, etc; supplies for gunnery ships, marines, harbour ships, etc; and the land magazine. Provision of 237,000 cubic feet was required for cartridges, QF, small arms and guncotton, together with 21,700 square feet for shells. (The provision of covered accommodation was not critical for shells.) In limiting the amount at Marchwood to 168,000 cubic feet the majority of the committee felt they should adhere to the agreement between the War Office and the Southampton Corporation not to stow more than 40,000 barrels. Furthermore, they wished a large proportion of the storage to be within the Portsmouth defences.

Major-General Nicholson CRA and Colonel Fraser CRE of Southern District attended and suggested Horsea as the best place for cannon cartridges and all the guncotton, with extra accommodation to be provided at Priddy's Hard for 6- and 3-pounder QF and filled shell, on the understanding that there would be no large increase in the laboratory at Priddy's Hard. The next best site was Foxbury Point. Frater was thought to be too close to Fort Elson. Wicor Marsh actually offered most advantages for a site in Fareham Creek, but being near the house and estate of Cams Hall the committee could not recommend it. *Carnatic*, filled with gunpowder and cordite, and *Melampus*, holding mines and wet guncotton, were inspected. They were sound and considered to be good for some years. *Grampus*, holding dry and wet guncotton in boxes and wet guncotton in mines, was very rotten and a serious

source of danger; she needed to be removed as soon as possible. The dry guncotton could be placed in the two small guncotton magazines built at Frater Point for naval use, but never used and handed over to the army. The military had no need of them. The wet guncotton could be placed in *Emerald*. She was being fitted out to replace *Leonidas* at Upnor, but could be diverted to Portsmouth, with *Melampus* being sent to Chatham instead.

However, land magazines would be far superior, and the committee recommended an early adoption of a permanent scheme, to be completed soon because the dredging of the harbour currently being carried out would provide cruisers' berths in close and dangerous proximity to the floating magazines. The greater cost of building permanent land magazines had to be accepted. Major Raban prepared an estimate on the supposition that Horsea would be used. The new works were estimated to cost £60,000, plus an additional £25,000 for piers, tramways and ancillary buildings. In addition, the dockyard reported that it would cost £564 to prepare *Melampus* for towing to Chatham.

Colonel Pease dissented from this, presenting what was virtually a minority report, and his view ultimately prevailed. He considered that the new accommodation to be provided should not be as powder magazines but as cordite magazines, and a far preferable site to Horsea was shortly to become available. The committee on Naval Warlike Stores had recently recommended that a very large piece of land belonging to the War Department at Priddy's Hard should be transferred to the Admiralty, and it was there, on the north side of Priddy's Hard, that cordite magazines should be built. He concurred with the rest of the committee on the question of the floating magazines. Raban thought that the land in question should be kept clear for security. The village of Hardway was growing and it did not seem wise to him to build new magazines closer to it. It was objectionable to build magazines within a quarter of a mile of an army laboratory, let alone a naval one. Priddy's Hard Laboratory might have to be extended one day, and magazines should not be at a laboratory at

all if it could be avoided. The Admiralty approved of the immediate abolition of *Grampus* and the substitution of *Emerald* for *Melampus*. Boom defences were to be fitted ahead and astern of the floating magazines. These were the only immediate consequences of the first report of the Portsmouth Committee; events were to show that it was the Storekeeper General of Naval Ordnance, Colonel Pease, who had the best grasp of the situation.[4]

The Reports of the Devonport Committee

The Devonport Committee devoted its first report to the question of floating magazines. In view of the decision to ultimately substitute land magazines for those now afloat, they had no intention of incurring any large expenditure on them, restricting themselves to making proposals that would render them reasonably safe until the magazines on shore could be constructed. Until recently floating magazines had been moored opposite to Bull Point, in a locality free from traffic and facing the magazine station, so they were always under supervision and within reach of immediate assistance. However, in order to make room to berth the Fleet Reserve ships, it had become necessary to remove the magazines to a position above Saltash Bridge, where traffic was heavier and from which they were not visible from Bull Point. Special precautions were now necessary. Although the roofs of the hulks were covered with canvas and the roofs and sides coated with six layers of red lead, which made them hard to ignite, it was considered that as a further precaution *Newcastle* should be covered with non-flammable paint on her roof and exterior and should be fitted with a bow and stern boom defence. She needed more comprehensive treatment than the others, as she carried powder and filled cartridges. *Eclipse*, holding guncotton and mines, was in sufficiently good condition to last until the magazines on shore were built, and only needed a coat of non-flammable paint. *Conquestador* was in an exceedingly rotten and worn-out condition, not only unsafe as a magazine but a positive danger to the

Serapis are the buildings of Royal Clarence Yard (victualling yard) and Rat Island (also known as Burrow Island, formerly the site of Fort James, part of the earlier defences of the dockyard) at the entrance of Weevil Creek. The creek later acquired a naval fuel depot on its southern bank. To the right of the creek are the long piers of Priddy's Hard, projecting out into the harbour, just beyond the coaling hulks and the hulk of the 80-gun ship HMS *York*. Further to the right is the newly commissioned battleship HMS *Inflexible*, alongside another hulk, HMS *Hannibal*, formerly a 100-gun screw driven sailing ship. Behind *Inflexible* is the Royal Yacht *Victoria and Albert II*. In front of these is the small troopship *Assistance* and to her left another Royal Yacht, the *Royal George*. The small low lying warship just to the left of the flag and flagstaff is HMS *Cyclops*, an armoured coastal defence monitor. On the far right, being launched, is HMS *Canada*, a screw corvette of the *Comus* class. (Portsmouth Museums and Records Service)

others, but could not be disposed of until a small dry guncotton store and a store for empty powder cases had been erected on shore. Alarmingly, her condition and contents were exactly the same as those of *Leonidas* at Chatham. In regard to the *Leonidas*, exceptional measures had been taken to erect a dry guncotton store on shore, so as to dispense with her. The committee agreed that immediate steps should be taken to erect buildings at Bull Point for these stores, without waiting for the Estimates of 1896–7.

A second report in October 1895 dealt with the proposed new buildings. Contract particulars were being prepared with a view to obtaining tenders for the buildings proposed in the previous report. The committee turned to the question of the accommodation on shore that would be required when *Newcastle* and *Eclipse* were abolished. There was ample space available at Bull Point, but even so the question of taking over the Army Ordnance Store Depot had been raised. However, the existing buildings there were not best adapted to store the new explosives being obtained for the navy. It would be more advantageous for any future outlay of money to be spent on the latest design of buildings for holding cordite, for which solidly constructed magazines were not needed. The new requirements were for buildings with bullet-proof walls, roofed as lightly as possible. This increased accommodation of 149,000 cubic feet for cannon cartridges should be provided in the form of cordite magazines. Beyond the construction of the cordite magazine and quick-firing ammunition store, a 14-foot wall would be required to enclose the cordite magazine. *Eclipse* needed to be replaced by a filled shell store of 10,700 square feet (which could be provided by roofing over the present shell base), a store for mines and countermines of 11,400 cubic feet and a store for wet guncotton of 9,500 cubic feet. The arrangements for transport and shipping were inadequate for the working of the establishment in ordinary times, and in time of mobilisation or emergency they would be totally inadequate. It was imperative that the arrangements should be considerably strengthened and improved. The present pier and jetty were very old and rotten, and required immediate renewal. The railway was also worn out, and its wide gauge made it cumbersome and inconvenient to work. Moreover, the small draught of water at the end of the pier made rapid mobilisation impracticable. The essential and absolutely necessary measures were the construction of a new jetty into deep water, and the conversion of the railway into narrow gauge (18 inches). These improvements would also be sufficient to deal with the Mercantile Auxiliaries (the use of armed merchant ships to supplement the navy was much in the air at the time) and therefore the committee did not recommend the connection of Bull Point with the local railways at St Budeaux, the expense of which was estimated at £22,000. The whole works were estimated at just over £74,000. They should be phased, with the cordite magazines, QF magazine, offices, jetty and tramway to be completed in 1896–7, the remainder in 1897–8. [5]

Problems for the Chatham Committee

Bull Point had plenty of space for new facilities, while Portsmouth presented an embarrassingly large number of potential sites. The problem for the Chatham Committee was to find a site at all. An obvious partial solution would have been the acquisition of Chattenden, and despite the failure of the recent negotiations with the War Office it still figured in the calculations. Accommodation of 210,000 cubic feet was required, a figure that could be reduced to 140,000 if the Chattenden Magazines could be procured. The committee recommended that the accommodation should take the form of cordite magazines. Dry guncotton was currently stored in the castle at Upnor, a very undesirable and dangerous arrangement. The total accommodation required was 950 square feet, and a guncotton store was being erected, but its capacity was only 400 square feet. An additional 550 square feet was required, which could be provided at Chattenden. Wet guncotton had been formerly stored in *Leonidas*, but after the fire (see page 113) her contents were transferred to Fort Horsted and a dumb barge moored alongside the pier at Upnor. The fort was dangerous and the guncotton stored there tended to deteriorate. *Melampus* had been transferred from Portsmouth to Chatham, and the wet guncotton had been removed from these unsatisfactory locations and placed in her.

However, this was merely a temporary expedient, since the decision had been taken to abandon the use of floating magazines altogether, as soon as accommodation on shore was available. The accommodation required for wet guncotton was 6,000 square feet. This could be met by appropriating No. 3 Store (now used as a shell store), which would take 2,800 square feet, and the new wet guncotton store under construction, which would take the remainder. Filled mines had until recently been kept temporarily at the Army Gunwharf at Sheerness, and at Woolwich. As a provisional arrangement they were to be removed to *Melampus*, but this would soon have to be replaced by 1,200 square feet of accommodation on shore. In order to render the receipt and issue of heavy mines efficient and practicable, it was essential that they be stored at Upnor. It was also desirable to store filled shells at Upnor. The space required for filled shells was 24,000 square feet, and the only way to store the mines and shells would be to acquire the premises adjoining Upnor magazines, at present private property that was occupied and used as a wharf and barge-repairing yard. The committee recommended that the Admiralty purchase this property for two reasons: firstly, because the space and locality were well adapted and required for the storage of filled mines and shell; and secondly, because an element of danger to the Upnor magazines as a whole would be eliminated if these private premises were secured as property of the Crown. At present there were two filled shell storehouses, containing areas of 3,050 and 2,800 square feet respectively. The latter was to be appropriated as a wet guncotton store, and the former as a layout store, holding stores for individual ships, a vital necessity.

The committee was convinced that it was necessary to transfer the whole premises at Chattenden to the Admiralty, namely, the magazines, storehouses, barracks, depot staff quarters (including workmen's), police quarters, and other ancillary buildings. The marines could undertake the bulk of the explosive handling, as at Marchwood. The costliest part by far of all these works was the provision of a rail-connected pier at Teapot Hall, where the bulk of the loading and unloading would take place. The whole scheme would cost £174,100. A copy of the report went to the Commander-in-Chief at the Nore, who thought the cost exorbitant. He proposed it be reduced to £82,900 by halving the cost of the shell store and additional cordite magazines proposed at Chattenden, and drastically reducing expenditure on railways and properties to be bought. He was particularly annoyed by the allocation of £20,400 for storing War Department requirements (presumably put in as a sweetener to the War Office), writing 'Bosh!' against the offending article. Colonel Pease thought the purchase of the properties at Upnor ought to go ahead at once, as this did not depend on any favours from the War Office, which would mean that construction could begin on the mine store and shell store. He rejected various aspects of the Commander-in-Chief's critique. He had envisaged that all the additional storage could be crammed into the existing site. Pease explained that such a concentration was no longer acceptable:

'No doubt, so far as mere area of land is concerned, and if all regulations established by the proper authorities were ignored, buildings could be erected which could be made to contain the requisite quantity of explosives, but no sooner would the buildings be erected than they would have to be taken down or we should not be allowed to use them. If the stores to be housed were ordinary non-explosive stores additional ground would be unnecessary, but where dangerous explosives have to be housed there, according to the Home Office Regulations certain

safety conditions have to be observed, and we are compelled to abide by these, or to accept responsibility for rejecting them. It will be apparent to any one who has followed the recent reports of the Danger Buildings Committee, that the tendency of the War Office and Home Office authorities is to insist upon the explosives being stored upon a much more extended area of ground than heretofore. The Committee made their recommendations on the regulations then in force, but it is feared, for the reasons given above, that the storage of the Warlike Matériél will have to be extended beyond the area originally contemplated. It may therefore be taken for certain that what the Commander-in-Chief says cannot possibly be adopted. Moreover, clearance rights are necessary to prevent buildings and dwellings being erected in the immediate vicinity of the Magazines.'

The Commander-in-Chief had pointed out that the present magazines at Chattenden were of very inferior construction, built on a space excavated from a hillside of very treacherous soil. Here the passage of time has shown he was quite right. The committee had enquired into this as they feared the magazines would be damp, but the representative of the Director of Works on the committee considered that in view of the arrangements made for drainage no apprehension on this score need be entertained. Pease added that these buildings were designed and constructed by the Royal Engineers staff of the War Department, 'who have considerable experience and are regarded as experts in the construction of magazines.' The committee was not prepared to criticize them in the face of the expert opinions expressed. They had an even stronger reason; as the Admiralty had asked the War Office for the whole of Chattenden to be handed over and the War Office appeared to be inclined to concede, it would not have been prudent for the committee to have reported disparagingly on buildings and land it was seeking to have presented to the Admiralty. The project was expensive, but costly schemes had been approved at Portsmouth and Devonport. It was no good thinking ordnance storage could be done on the cheap any more; as Pease insisted, '… of this, I am certain, that in view of what is taking place in regard to Danger Buildings and the regulations that are insisted on by the Home Office, the total cost when the work is done will not be less than the amount included in the Naval Works Loan. Whether it will be more, time alone can show.' On 5 November 1896, an appropriate day to discuss the storage of explosives, a conference was held in Austen Chamberlain's office. It seemed probable that the War Office was going to back off again over Chattenden and in any case negotiations would be prolonged. The committee was reappointed to report on the best alternative. Chamberlain commented: 'The great object in getting Chattenden was to avoid delay, which it now appears is in any case unavoidable. I believe that the Navy can do as well for itself by a new scheme.'

The committee presented its second report in March 1897. Questions of design were left to the conclusions of the Danger Buildings Committee (see below), but it was decided to acquire land at Lodge Hill that was currently leased by the War Office, the Admiralty to subsequently purchase the freehold. On 30 July 1897, Chamberlain was told that the War Office would not relinquish Chattenden but were prepared to transfer the Lodge Hill land. Chamberlain had interviewed the chairman of the Danger Buildings Committee, whose members had no objection to large magazines on the site. Bearing out Pease's expectation that standards would become ever more stringent, the Danger Buildings Committee had condemned Purfleet, reviving the recommendations of 1875 (see page 92) by saying two out the five magazines there had to be turned into traverses for the protection of the rest. The Chatham Committee estimated the cost of the proposed buildings at Lodge Hill as £22,500 for two cordite magazines and £500 for a dry guncotton magazine. At Upnor the property to be purchased would cost £27,000, on which would be built a mine store for £1,100 and shell stores for £19,900. The total expense, including railways, pier, cranes, vessels, etc, would come to £174,100, £51,000 being for the Teapot Hard line and pier on the site of Teapot Hall. It appears that the dealings with the War Office followed their usual course, for a third report was made in November 1897, which recommended a completely new site at Sharnal Street; this was not in War Office hands and would leave the Admiralty free of interference. Admiral Sir Frederick Richards minuted this: 'It is…clear that nothing further is to be gained by association with the War Office and its Committee & if strangulation is to be avoided the Admiralty must act independently.' Chamberlain agreed. The urgency of the situation was further stressed by the sinking at Woolwich of a barge loaded with filled shells. This, together with six others, was being used to store ammunition for which there was no room at Woolwich or Upnor. At last some positive action was taken; the land at Upnor for the mine and shell stores was compulsorily purchased. In April 1898 the committee presented its fourth report. It now appeared that nearly 500 acres of the War Office site at Lodge Hill could be obtained for less than £15,000, much cheaper than the Sharnal Street site, which was going to cost something in the order of £80,000. Purchase was recommended. The War Office, still blowing hot and cold, now wished to get rid of their railway line. The

committee therefore suggested that the Admiralty take over the guarding of the Admiralty and Army Magazines, the Admiralty to have the use of the railway on a repayment basis, offering free accommodation of army shell at Upnor equivalent to the army shell store at Chattenden. On 3 August 1898, the committee presented its fifth (and final) report. The Lodge Hill land was to be purchased for £16,000. Plans of the magazine enclosure were drawn up, comprising two cordite magazines of 40,000 cubic feet, three explosive stores of 44,000 cubic feet, one dry guncotton store, two examining rooms and one deposit magazine. The Admiralty approved all this and ordered the earthworks to be proceeded with. Steps were to be taken to acquire land for the Teapot Hall railway and pier, and negotiations were to begin with the South Eastern and Chatham Railway about a junction at Sharnal Street. The Teapot Hall line was intended to replace the Upnor line.[6]

The reader may well think that the tale of the acquisition of land at the Medway for ordnance purposes is now over, but that is not so. It will be seen that another five years were to pass before the tortuous dealings between the War Office and the Admiralty were to be finally wound up.

The question of cordite

The Committees on Naval Magazine Accommodation had very different problems to tackle, but the need to provide buildings of a new type for the new propellant, cordite (see Ordnance and Armament, page 128), was common to them all. However, the models were not to be found in the Portsmouth, Plymouth or Medway districts. While the development of the three Ordnance Depots that principally served the navy had been non-existent or inadequate during the late 1880s and early 1890s, significant changes that experimented with the future shape of magazine design had occurred on the Thames estuary. The first developments were in the vicinity of the great 1859 magazine at Plumstead, which was built for storing gunpowder for the army. The 1865 Magazine Committee (see pages 81–4) thought its only fault was its proximity to the river, and recommended it be used solely for small arms ammunition. Its location close to Woolwich Arsenal made it suitable to store the ammunition for both services that had been made or filled there. In 1886 this complex of buildings was joined by a store for Hotchkiss machine gun ammunition. This building conformed to an established magazine style, with a brick vault supporting a concrete roof. Presumably because of concerns about the ground, a vaulted foundation (not repeated again nearby) was provided, and the walls were substantially thicker than those of the stores that followed. In 1888 a store for 6-pounder QF ammunition was added.

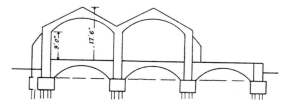

7.2 Section through the store for Hotchkiss machine gun ammunition at Plumstead. *(From TNA SUPP 5/1031)*

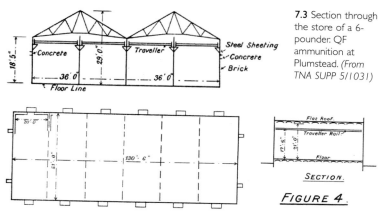

7.3 Section through the store of a 6-pounder QF ammunition at Plumstead. *(From TNA SUPP 5/1031)*

FIGURE 4.

7.4 Plan and section of No.1 Magazine at Plumstead. *(From TNA SUPP 5/1031)*

7.5 No. 1 group of buildings at Plumstead as completed by 1905. The magazine of 1859 is top left, highlighted. *(From TNA SUPP 5/1031)*

This was of very different construction from the contemporary QF store at Priddy's Hard, the walls being two-thirds height in 18-inch brickwork, the remainder concrete with steel sheeting on iron stanchions above. The roof was of wood and iron trusses covered with slates on boarding, and the floor of tar pavement over brick rubbish. Both these buildings were charged to army funds; No.1 Magazine, which followed in 1889, charged to the navy, was adjacent to the 1859 magazine and of different construction again. It was a brick building of six bays, not unlike an Upnor magazine in plan, but there all resemblance stopped: the main and division walls were 18 inches thick and the floor was of concrete arches supported by girders; the flat roof, covered in asphalt, was of brick and concrete jack arches supported by girders.[7]

Slightly downriver, at Crossness, a further complex evolved on a site purchased from Messrs. Hall, the gunpowder makers, and used for holding combustible stores but not powder. The first new building on the site was a rocket store erected in 1884. In 1893 the first magazine designed for the storage of cordite was built there to take the first service issues of the new explosive for the army. Colonel Sale, the Superintendent of Building Works at Ordnance Factories, stated that the restrictions essential for a gunpowder magazine need not apply to cordite, the only conditions considered necessary for its storage being the use of properly ventilated magazines with a temperature kept below 100°F. With this one exception, cordite was to be treated as gunpowder. The resulting building was approximately 40 feet by 100 feet, comprising a dwarf brick wall, with wood on both sides and one end up to the light slate roof. There was a brick wall round the magazine and a moat, but no traverses. The magazine held 200 tons of cordite. In June 1895, the Ordnance Committee (another new committee), reversing Colonel Sale's judgment, decided that magazine regulations for powder should apply equally to cordite, with the exception that the buildings in which cordite was stored could be of light construction, and, in a notable change, that iron might be used in the walls and roof. The cordite magazine built at Crossness did not come up to magazine regulations, and the design was never used again.

Mention has been made of the Danger Buildings Committee (see page 129), which enquired into the serious accident at Waltham

Abbey in December 1893. The proceedings of this committee were to have a great influence on the future design of Ordnance Depots (see page 153). Colonel Sale proposed that very radical changes of design should be made with cordite magazines, with the aim of extreme lightness of structure. Experiments had shown that if not closely confined, the substance did not explode but burnt fiercely, which meant that buildings could be built side by side as long as walls (as traverses) were used to separate them to prevent flames spreading. Asphalt was the best floor covering. Very light materials should be used, with iron frames, the spaces between the standards being filled with thin

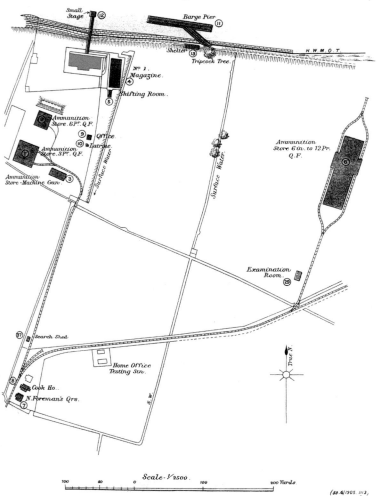

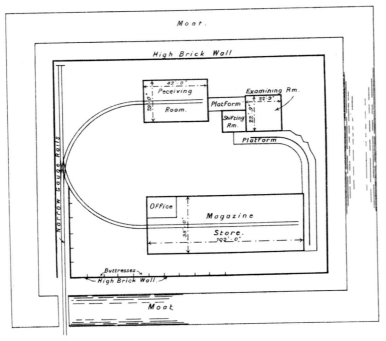

7.6 Crossness: the first magazine to be built for cordite. The moated and walled enclosure also contained a receiving room, examining room and shifting room. The design was never repeated. (See figure 7.9.) (TNA SUPP 5/1031)

brickwork to guard against fire from outside. Roofs should preferably be iron trussed, with slated wooden roofs; any lighter form would give too much variation in temperature. The use of copper should be discarded except for lightning conductors.

The Admiralty were sending their Superintending Engineers to Woolwich to consult on how their own cordite magazines were to be built, and it was important to decide on an approved method of construction. The

Superintendent of Building Works stressed that the usual conditions for a powder magazine need not be followed, and Sir Frederick Abel (who had developed the explosive in collaboration with Sir James Dewar) could see no reason why the rigorous precautions observed in powder magazines should apply to cordite magazines, but proper shifting rooms should be provided. A design for five closely grouped cordite magazines was produced according to the Superintendent's principles, to be built at Crossness, but was condemned by the November 1895 Interim Report of the Danger Buildings Committee. The members thought that the buildings were too close together, their capacity of 200 tons each excessive, and that the proposed traverses would not be effective. The Chief Inspector of Explosives, Colonel Sir Victor Majendie (see Bibliography), commented that it was too early to say that an explosion of ignited cordite was impossible, and thought that where the risk mainly arose from within the building, the construction should be kept as light as possible. Where material was stored and scarcely handled at all, the building should be of a substantial character. He was anxious that safety standards in Government establishments should be no less rigorous than those enforced on the private trade. As has been seen, Purfleet was severely criticised in the same report (see page 150), which also revealed that for want of any other location, naval cordite had been kept there, though as a precaution the powder and cordite were not kept in the same compartments of store magazines. Colonel Hildebrand, Assistant Commissary General of Ordnance at Woolwich, testified: 'I never liked cordite from a storage point of view, and I fought hard against its being received into the magazines at Purfleet, because I think we do not know enough about cordite to store it with gunpowder, but my objections were overruled – as the Naval Ordnance pressed in the matter...'. In the same report, the Danger Buildings Committee also condemned the 1859 Plumstead magazine.[8]

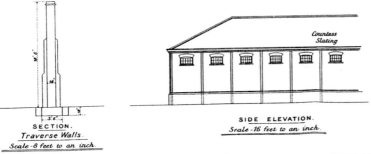

SECTION.
Traverse Walls
Scale -8 feet to an inch.

SIDE ELEVATION.
Scale -16 feet to an inch.

7.7 The rejected plan for cordite magazines at Woolwich, and the design for the buildings and the inadequate traverses. (From TNA WO 33/56)

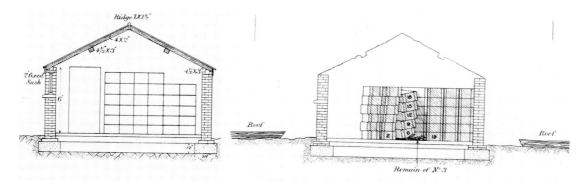

7.8 The Lydd experiment of igniting cordite in a magazine, before and after. *(Adapted from TNA WO 32/7129)*

In August 1896 discussions took place between the War Office and the Admiralty concerning a site for new cordite magazines close to Woolwich. Unless the navy wished to bring the findings of the Danger Buildings Committee into question it was clear that the Crossness project had to be abandoned. Still undecided about the preferred method of construction, the committee recommended, as an experiment, exploding 3 tons of cordite in a magazine of light construction and one of strong construction. It was clearly expected that this would replicate the findings of similar tests that had taken place in 1872 (igniting guncotton in simulated magazines), which showed that little damage took place at the light structure. Experiments were duly carried out at Lydd in September 1897. On igniting cordite stored in a magazine of light construction, the effect of firing one 100 lb box at the bottom of a stack was a very bright flame, but no explosion. Nearly the whole of the box burnt out and the exposed surfaces of all the boxes were scorched, but the cordite in the adjacent boxes was uninjured. A shutter simulating a window was blown out about 12 feet, the roof was lifted off and part slipped down each side, but very few of the slates were broken. The wall with the door bulged out about 4 inches at the top.

While all this uncertainty about cordite storage was going on, the Portsmouth Committee on Magazine Accommodation presented a second report on progress, which highlighted the importance of replacing the old laboratory. The Director of Works, Major Raban, had been uneasy about it during the whole time he was Superintending Engineer at Portsmouth, and did not think a private firm would have been allowed to carry out work in such an establishment. The report maintained that no decisions should be made about the sites of any new buildings at Priddy's Hard until the new laboratory was approved, when a general site plan showing the proposed utilisation of the land at Priddy's Hard should be prepared, to encroach on the safety limit as little as possible. Captain Kane commented on the new proposals:

'It is quite correct that the proposal for a new Laboratory is a fresh departure, and was not put forward in the first report of the Portsmouth Committee. The reasons for the change are to be found in the report of the War Office Danger Buildings Committee, which has appeared since our first report was sent in. In view of the very stringent conditions therein laid down … our Committee considered they would not be justified in perpetuating the present Laboratory, which the Danger Buildings Committee would undoubtedly consider unsafe.'

The final recommendations of that committee were not published until June 1898, but Kane would certainly have known what their proposals might be (see below). [9]

The Admiralty's needs, in the autumn of 1896, were now pressing; 2,000 tons of cordite were on order and apart from the small amount held unsatisfactorily at Purfleet, there was still nowhere to store it. The decision to discontinue floating magazines meant that no relief could be expected from that area. Something needed to be done soon, and it seemed unlikely that any site at Woolwich or

Recommendations of the Danger Committee in 1898

- Gunpowder and cordite should not be kept together in the same compartment of a storage magazine.
- Home Office rules and regulations regarding construction and the distances of such buildings from one another should be adhered to in all new magazines.
- Wood should enter as little as possible into the construction. Asphalt free from grit was well adapted for floors, and a rendering of neat cement for linings. Removable wooden dados might be provided to prevent the cement becoming detached by packages knocking against the walls.
- Cordite magazines should be of light construction (provided that they are still secure against unlawful entry), not be of inflammable material, and so constructed and arranged that the internal temperature should not fall below 45 degrees or rise above 120 degrees Fahrenheit.
- Magazines in Fortresses and defensive works, including expense magazines, must be of sufficiently strong construction to keep out projectiles and traversed as far as possible.
- Laboratories and examining rooms should be under full danger precautions. Gunpowder and cordite should never be present together in any building of this description.

WO 32/7129

Plumstead would be considered fit for the naval cordite reserve store. The Admiralty imagined that there was very little chance of being allowed to build stores of the magnitude required on the space available. However, as will be seen, the definitive designs for cordite magazines were about to be worked out on that very spot. No great process of gestation was necessary to design the new laboratory for Priddy's Hard. In November 1896 the Admiralty ordered the Commander-in-Chief Portsmouth to see to the preparation of a general site plan showing the location. As Raban had wanted, the scheme was to be a comprehensive one for 'a really complete Establishment'. A new shell store was to be built on the southern side of the existing laboratory, while the replacement buildings were to be placed in the ditch outside the ramparts, which formed a ready-made traverse to screen the laboratory from the rest of the depot. The existing earthworks were to be augmented and adjusted to provide comprehensive protection. Drawings for the earthworks and buildings were produced in the summer of 1897. The old Small Arms Cartridge Factory was to undergo its final transformation; its proximity to the new buildings meant that it could no longer be used as accommodation and it was converted into non-danger buildings, including a proof house, to work in conjunction with the laboratory. By this time, the additional QF store was in hand and due to be completed three months later. A portion of the

new shell store was to be completed in the same period, the remainder being deferred until the removal of the laboratory. Drawings of the extension to the shell pier – to facilitate the rapid movement on and off site of empty and filled cartridges – had been sent to the Admiralty. There was a great deal of magazine accommodation before the site was transformed. The whole of the available space was required for ammunition from *Trafalgar*, *Crescent* and *Inflexible* then being discharged. All shell buildings at Priddy's Hard were only workshops and not available for storage purposes.[10]

The troubles over cordite storage were now nearly at an end. In November 1897, Fisher's successor as Controller of the Navy, Admiral Sir A. K. Wilson, was informed about the new type of cordite magazine that had been developed by the War Office for the Plumstead area. Five of these magazines were due to begin construction at the Crossness site to hold the naval reserve stores of the propellant, replacing the design that had been rejected by the Danger Buildings Committee. These were wholly different in concept to the 1893 magazine on the site, in use by the army and still the only one of its kind. The buildings were nearly square and very low, only ten feet high, and of the recommended light construction. What set them apart from all previous magazines was the traversing; a nearly circular earth traverse surrounded each one, the entry being covered by another traverse. It was submitted to Wilson that

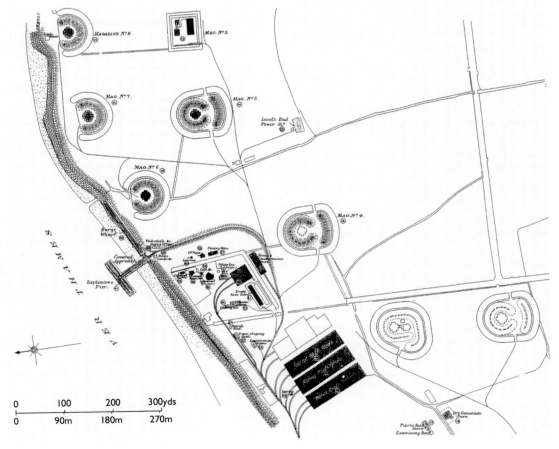

7.9 The Crossness magazine complex in 1905. The original cordite magazine is at the top, and the subsequent ones follow a quite different design. The three black buildings at the bottom are filled shell stores. *(From TNA SUPP 5/1031)*

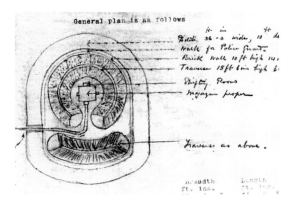

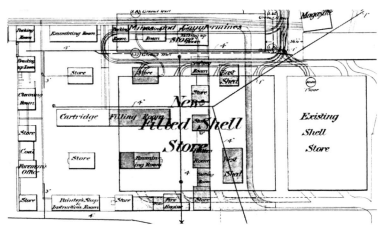

7.10 Sketch of a cordite magazine sent from the War Office to the Admiralty in 1897. *(From TNA ADM 116/868)*

this design be accepted at once to govern the preparation of detailed drawings for the sites recommended by the Magazine Committees. [11]

The Portsmouth Committee was undecided whether the additional cordite magazine should be constructed at Priddy's Hard (where cordite was currently being stored in C Magazine) or Wycor Marsh. If the present practice of the War Department was to be followed, there would be no objection if it were to be built at Priddy's Hard. If there was an existing danger from the Priddy's Hard magazine, it would undoubtedly be increased or doubled by the addition of the cordite magazine, and the committee members were divided on this point. It would cost somewhat less to build at Priddy's Hard even with the provision of an extra pier for cordite traffic, and the work could begin

immediately. On the other hand, Wycor Marsh would have to be acquired, entailing possible delay; furthermore, a separate establishment would have to be kept there, creating a large expense for maintenance. The committee considered that the Admiralty should make the final decision. As regards the new laboratory, the course was now clear and agreed on by all concerned. The Director of Naval Ordnance commented:

'Looking to the facts that 3½ years have now elapsed since [the] Board decided that additional magazine accommodation was required, and that it is two years, [and] all but one month, since the Chatham Committee recommended the acquisition of the piece of land near Upnor which we have not yet got possession of, it is submitted

7.11 Drawing showing the replacement of most of the original laboratory at Priddy's Hard by a shell store and mine store. *(From PTM/3110)*

7.12 The west elevation of the mine store, looking towards the shell store of 1879. To the left is the gable end of the rolling way that supplied the earlier laboratory (see figure 3.11). *(Jeremy Lake)*

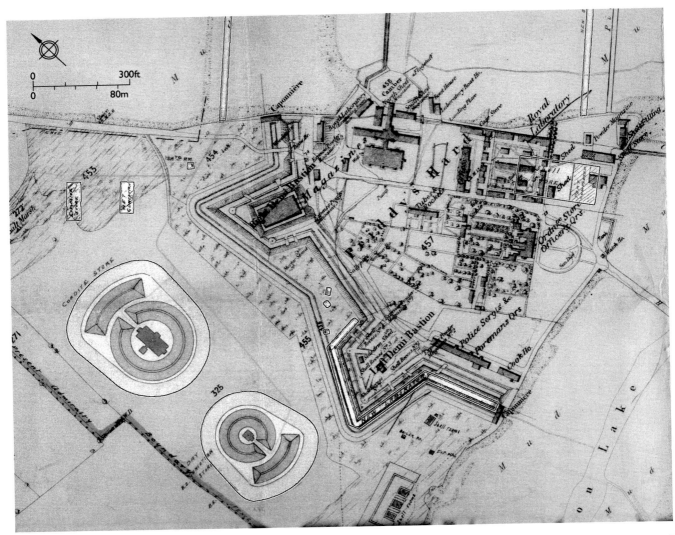

7.13 Highlighted are the proposals made for the storage of cordite and wet guncotton and the further modernisation of Priddy's Hard. Anticlockwise, from top right: additional shell pier; new shell store; new powder pier; wet guncotton store; explosives store; cordite magazine; and a dry guncotton store. The largest additions comprise the dry guncotton store and the cordite magazine, both marked out by their distinctive curved earth traverses. (From TNA ADM 116/868)

that the arguments against the further delay which would be entailed if the Wycor site were accepted are conclusive.'

Aside from cordite, storage was also required for guncotton (both wet and dry), filled shells (21,000 square feet) and mines (22,000 cubic feet). Another decision, to extend the examination of shells both in commission and in the Fleet Reserve had resulted in an additional requirement for three shell filling rooms. On Pease's recommendation, construction began on a new filled shell store and a mine store close to the shell pier.[12]

The Portsmouth Committee drew a sketch to show the suggested arrangements for Priddy's Hard. This displayed the general principles by which Priddy's Hard was to be redeveloped, but the placing of the cordite and guncotton magazines was to be altered in the actual dispositions. The design adopted for dry guncotton magazines was a diminished version of the cordite magazine. By October 1898 the new buildings had been designed and a plan of the depot produced to show the new magazine complex: buildings to hold cordite, dry guncotton, an explosives store, a store for wet guncotton and three new shell filling

rooms. The additional QF magazine was indicated as completed. Additional railways were shown running from the new powder pier to supply these buildings, and from the cordite magazine, cutting through the ramparts to the new laboratory. A rail connection was also established through the east caponier to connect with lines running from C Magazine along the east side of the depot. This railway established completely new traffic flows and made the original north–south route along the eastern side largely redundant. The original transit system had supported operations in the now obsolete laboratory buildings, which were selected to be used for the additional shell store and the mine and countermine store. The new tramways, like those being rebuilt and extended at Bull Point, were of 1-foot 6-inch gauge, though the wider gauge shell tramways were retained.

Growing pressures

Despite all these additions and remodellings, this phase of the development of Priddy's Hard was far from over. The relentless growth of the fleet rendered inadequate the original provision for magazine accommodation made in the Loan

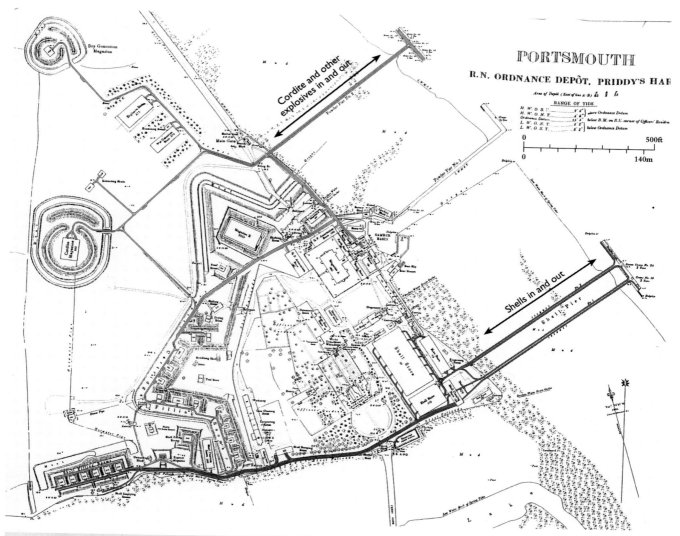

PORTSMOUTH

R.N. ORDNANCE DEPÔT, PRIDDY'S HAR

Cordite and other explosives in and out

Shells in and out

7.14 The transit system of Priddy's Hard at the beginning of the 20th century. The Powder Line is pale grey, the shell tramway darker. This plan shows the cordite and dry guncotton magazines as executed. *(Adapted from PTM/2470)*

7.15 One of the Priddy's Hard cordite magazines of 1905–6, photographed while used as a detonator store during the 1950s. Note the earthen traverses, breached by the 2-foot 6-inch tramway. The truck visible in the doorway had brass wheels. *(Priddy's Hard Archive 1998.4.216)*

Financial position in 1900

Expended 1 April 1895 – 31 March 1898	£55,630 (nearly)
Expended 1 April 1898 – 31 March 1899	£49,211 (nearly)
Total expended to 31 March 1899	£104,842
Estimated expenditure for 1 April 1899 – 31 March 1900	£116,896
Remaining for financial year 1900–1901	£184,982

Parliamentary Paper, 1900. Statement of estimated cost and expenditure on Naval Works.

7.16 Mosaic aerial view of Priddy's Hard, taken in the late 1940s. This can be read in conjunction with the phased plan in Appendix A (pages 238–9). Clearly visible are the distinctive outlines of the cordite magazines of 1898–9 and the extent of the building work associated with the First World War. Note the trees within the late 18th-century site, to the left (west) of the shell filling rooms of 1886–7 facing Forton Mill Lake, which represented the first expansion of the site outside the 18th-century ramparts.
(Priddy's Hard Archive, 1998.4.89)

Works Act – as indeed it was for everything else. Between 1895 and 1905 Naval Works Acts were passed every year save 1898, 1900 and 1902. On 1 April 1897, even before the first measures to improve ordnance storage had been completed, the value of stock on hand was: naval stores (£3,000,605); victualling stores (£1,117,258); naval ordnance stores (£9,142,423). So far no enormous sums had been spent at Bull Point and Priddy's Hard, and there had been little opportunity to spend much at the Medway. Out of the total 1895 estimate of £485,000 for magazines, the position in 1900 was expected to show that over £180,000 was available (see above). It was originally hoped that the completion date of the initial projects would be 1901–2. But all this was expected to change. It was clear that whatever happened more money would have to be spent on acquiring land, and the problem of Upnor and Chattenden would have to be tackled somehow in spite of all the War Office's obstructions.

A further bill was presented by the third report of the Committee on Magazine Accommodation at Devonport. The requirements for accommodation at Bull Point were revised to 127,000 cubic feet in addition to that available. After the first cordite magazine had been built, further accommodation of 18,000 cubic feet would be required in the form of QF ammunition storage, adjacent to the present group of QF store buildings.

All these proposals were accepted in April 1900, the work to be started as soon as possible at a cost of £69,250, a saving of over £10,000 on the original estimates. In the end, the shifting room came out at £1,900, as the number of staff was continually growing. By May 1900 the number of staff at

The principal items of the Bull Point expansion (1900–01)

	£		£
New jetty	13,752	Alterations to tramways	7,100
Wet guncotton store	2,081	Shifting Room	1,300
Mine & Countermine store	2,328	Tinmen's Shop	1,650
Covering in shell base	5,713	Boiler House	3,700
3- & 6-pdr QF store	3,684	Dry guncotton store	750
6-in to 12-pdr QF store	5,806	Additional QF storage	2,000
Cordite magazine	7,370	Alteration to Building 26	410

ADM 1/7549/B

7.17 The shell store was an iron-framed building with brick walling and an open well-lit interior plan served by the rail system. *(NMR BB94/10310)*
Below is the view southwards towards the shell store of 1879, with the mine store on the left and the shell store of 1899–1903 to the right. The distinctive architectural style was developed by the Admiralty architects after the take-over from the War Office in 1890. *(NMR BB94/10305)*

the two main sites were noted as: Bull Point – 250 men, with 200 changing their clothes and 240 provided with pegs and boxes in the shifting room; Priddy's Hard – 270 men, with 187 changing their clothes and 284 pegs in the shifting room.

A further batch of buildings was to be designed at the same time for Priddy's Hard, which reinforced the recent provisions of the Portsmouth Committee: a shell painting room, shell emptying room, shell scraping room, buildings for the conversion of dangerous ammunition and a further extension of the new shell store. The old laboratory was reduced almost to its present fragmentary condition and no longer used as danger buildings.[13]

The Boer War showed up a raft of inadequacies on the part of the army, and in March 1900 George Goschen, the First Lord, noted, not without satisfaction, 'the inability of the War Office to conduct the war without trenching on the reserves [of ammunition] of the Navy.' The Department of Naval Ordnance had made a detailed study of the ammunition stocks, and Goschen was determined that the naval reserves should be such as to cope with all eventualities. A total of £932,000 would put all right, £600,000 to be spent in 1900–01, part of the expense being

to hasten the introduction of cordite. This work was approved, but on 2 July 1900, the Permanent Secretary of the Admiralty, Sir Evan Macgregor, wrote to the Treasury to notify them formally that the continuous growth of the navy and the progress made in guns and ammunition had shown that the total estimate was insufficient and needed to be revised upwards in the following year. A new Works Loan Bill was to be introduced in 1901, the question of providing additional ordnance accommodation having become very pressing since Goschen's increased reserves of ammunition and other ordnance stores were approved. A portion of this additional accommodation could be most rapidly and economically provided by extending certain buildings currently being built, work on which had been suspended pending decisions, but it was also necessary to spend a sum of about £30,000 on undertaking works not included in the original estimate. The Loan Bill of 1901 was to increase the sum allotted to magazines to £870,000, out of which the huge proportion of £170,000 was estimated for excavating a new magazine out of the rock at Gibraltar (see pages 111–12).

With the Loan Work expenses increasing every year the Treasury tried to economise by cutting

7.18 This view of part of the Priddy's Hard laboratory complex was taken from the 'dirty area' bridge across the ramparts, which led to the 'Common' and the ladies shifting room, in May 1994. From left to right: one of the cartridge filling rooms (converted to a detonator testing room during the Second World War); a wash house and toilet from the 1920s; and a toilet block of 1899 converted to a ready use magazine when the new building next door was constructed. *(Explosion! Museum of Naval Firepower)*

7.19 Above: The laboratory complex and the remodelled fortifications seen from the top of E Magazine in about 1950. In the left foreground is the shifting room of 1897, and in the centre the rebuilt proof house (see figure OA.41). The line of roofs in the distance are the shell filling rooms of 1886–7, while to the right is the First World War-era cartridge filling section known as the 'Common'. The letters 'SWS' on the shelter on the rampart denote Static Water System. *(Priddy's Hard Archive 1998.4.180-181)*

7.20 Below: Two of the cartridge filling rooms in May 1994. The building on the left was a shell examination room (formerly a component store), while that on the right had been the last one used to handle gunpowder, cartridges for 3-pdr saluting guns being filled there. *(Explosion! Museum of Naval Firepower)*

7.21 Right: Another May 1994 view of some of the cartridge filling rooms at Priddy's Hard (see also figure A.28). *(Explosion! Museum of Naval Firepower)*

7.22 Above: The southernmost shell filling rooms in about 1950, clearly showing the electric 2-foot 6-inch gauge railway and the trucks used to transport large shells. This was taken up and replaced in the 1960s by diesel tractors. *(Priddy's Hard Archive 1998.4.184)*

7.24 Interior of the 1906 shell store at Bull Point. *(From HRO 109M91)*

down on essentials, such as attempting to block the renewal of the Civil Engineer-in-Chief's salary for another five years. Austen Chamberlain minuted:

'I should like very much to take a gentleman like Sir F. Mowatt [Permanent Secretary to the Treasury] through the offices of the Civil Engineer-in-Chief & Director of Works, & then over the Naval Establishments at Portsmouth & Plymouth. At the present time I think the Treasury have no conception of the magnitude of our task; & if the Permanent Secretary & the head of the Branch dealing with our work were personally conducted round these establishments, I believe that Treasury criticism would be much less frequent...'

The Treasury gave in and sanctioned continuance until April 1905. Chamberlain wished not only to retain key staff but also to invest in expertise for the future. In June 1900 he again minuted: 'With the experience of five years of sudden expansion to guide me, I give my opinion for what it is worth that <u>we must begin to recruit & train officers now if we do not wish a breakdown five years hence.</u> We can fill the lower grades fairly rapidly; but unless we train young men now we shall find it impossible to fill the more responsible places later on.' [Chamberlain's underscore] Higher salaries were needed to attract and retain capable men. He broke another lance, successfully, with the Treasury in October 1901 when he was initially blocked in his wish to agree a salary of £900 a year (rather than £800) for Lieutenant Colonel Exham at Portsmouth. The Treasury, after Exham had threat-

ened to resign, conceded £1,000. This was to be Chamberlain's last contribution as Civil Lord to the recasting of the physical infrastructure of the navy. He was promoted Financial Secretary to the Treasury and, in the style commonly attributed to a politician, identified himself wholly with the interests of his new department, a particularly easy thing to do when it was seen to have the highest status. In his new role of poacher turned game-keeper he turned down the Admiralty's proposition of May 1902 to modernise the machine tools in the dockyards through setting up a depreciation account.[14]

A great many improvements were still to be done. At the end of 1900, new rooms for filling cordite cartridges (based on the pattern of those at the new laboratory at Priddy's Hard which were protected by concrete traverses) were designed for Bull Point. However, despite all the recent additions and improvements, Pease was told in August 1901 that the Bull Point shell stores were full, and

7.23 Opposite, bottom: the same view as figure 7.22, but taken after the closure of Priddy's Hard. The outer boarding of the buildings was removed as part of the decontamination process, to make sure that no traces of explosives remained within the walls. None were found. *(NMR BB94/10316)*

7.25 Below: Bull Point, the QF ammunition store of 1899–1905. *(Jeremy Lake)*

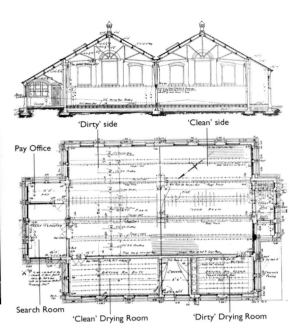

'Dirty' side   'Clean' side

Pay Office

Search Room   'Clean' Drying Room   'Dirty' Drying Room

7.26 The shifting room at Bull Point. *(Plan and section adapted from DML fiche 038124, photograh by Jeremy Lake)*

7.27 The cartridge filling rooms at Bull Point in 1999. Most of the buildings have gone, leaving the traverses. Compare with figure 7.29, opposite. *(Jeremy Lake)*

it had been necessary to utilise the receipt store. The congestion was so great that shell filling frequently had to halt until storage could be found. The Ordnance Officer at the depot submitted the idea of using *Eclipse*, which had been cleared of explosives in August 1898, as a temporary magazine for filled shells. A retrograde step like this showed how the efforts to modernise the depots were still falling short. The main cause of congestion in the shell stores was the growth of filled shell stock at the depot in line with the increase in the numbers and classes of ships belonging to the station, and to the larger number of QF guns now used (QF guns were invariably supplied with a larger number of rounds per gun than BL guns). Increased space was also required

for the deposit of shells from ships for triennial examination, and from ships that were cleared of explosives for dockyard refit or examination. The question of providing further permanent accommodation on shore was duly submitted. The inadequate condition of the mooring facilities at Devonport itself was shown by the fact that the largest ships able to lie alongside the coal hulk for the port, *Himalaya*, were the *Admiral* class of battleship (now obsolescent) and cruisers of the *Blake* class. If Bull Point was still inadequate, things were worse at Priddy's Hard in spite of all the new accommodation, transport systems and piers; for on 11 November 1902, an armour-piercing shell exploded in the new filled shell store, and the whole question of the depot's future reappeared.[15]

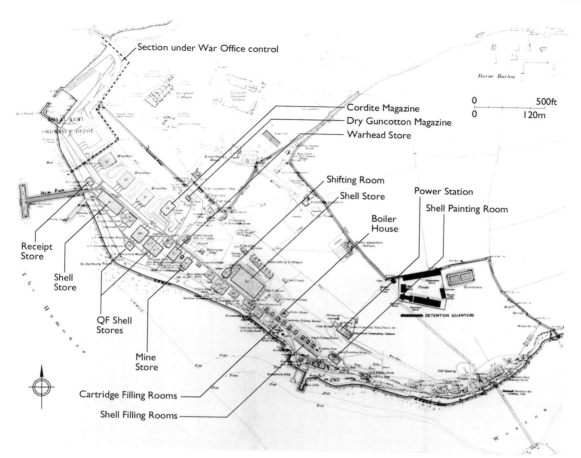

Section under War Office control

Cordite Magazine
Dry Guncotton Magazine
Warhead Store

Shifting Room
Shell Store

Power Station
Shell Painting Room

Boiler
House

Receipt
Store

Shell
Store

QF Shell
Stores

Mine
Store

Cartridge Filling Rooms

Shell Filling Rooms

0   500ft
0   120m

7.28 Bull Point as redeveloped in the early 20th century, with a new tramway system. The new powder pier is to the left. *(Derived from plan held by MoD[N] Library)*

7.29 The new cartridge filling rooms at Bull Point, in 1950, showing the tramway system in use. To the rear is the electrical generating house of 1904-6. For the same view today, see figure 7.27, opposite. *(From HRO 109M91, PH/72)*

Chapter 8 A Fresh Start

The accident at Priddy's Hard was to finally determine the future pattern of ordnance storage at Portsmouth. But the mishap was only one of many. The BL and QF projectiles and cartridges turned out to be prone to deterioration, sometimes in alarming ways, though some proved to be worse than others. This was not foreseen and ammunition, particularly after the introduction of cordite, was thought to be becoming safer to handle and store; a Fleet Circular of 30 April 1892 laid down that explosives were no longer to be removed from ships when in harbour for repairs, unless the local Commander-in-Chief thought it desirable to do so. Ammunition was also to remain on board if the ship was placed in a dry dock for a limited period, arbitrarily taken as ten days. In 1895 the Admiralty decided to adopt the high explosive lyddite as the filling both for 4.7-inch and 6-inch QF shells (see page 129). These shells, which were about to be issued to the Channel Squadron in March 1896, were made of forged steel, and of more complicated construction than any former projectiles. Lyddite needed to be detonated by a chain of ignition; the fuze detonated an initiator of gunpowder, which then set off an exploder of picric powder, which in turn detonated the lyddite (see figure OA.10). Filling with lyddite was beyond the resources of Priddy's Hard and Bull Point at that time, and the shells were supplied to the depots filled and fuzed. They were to be issued and transported in boxes, the fuze being protected from damp by an adhesive covering.

The decision to examine a proportion of the filled shells held on ships in Reserve every three years (see page 129) had to be reconsidered by the summer of 1896, as it was found not only that shells deteriorated rapidly aboard the ships, but that the laboratory staff, constantly engaged on the examination and repair of these shells, could not keep up with their principal tasks of filling shells and cartridges. The situation was becoming serious, as it was quite impossible for the Ordnance Factories to cope with the entirety of naval demands. Colonel Pease submitted that the shells for Reserve ships should be held in store at the depots. However, Captain Kane, the Director of Naval Ordnance, thought this would cause serious delays in mobilisation. This was an awkward question of priorities, but operational expediency was considered of overriding importance and Pease's suggestion was turned down. Here was another reason underlying the expansion of the depots,

both in terms of buildings and staff. In these circumstances Pease proposed abandoning the practice of a percentage examination of ammunition on ships as this invariably resulted in landing the lot, after a high rate of failure in the samples. The quantity of ammunition condemned in this way must have given food for thought, but there does not appear to have been any real concern. The immediate need was for more men at the depots for filling, examination and rectification.[1]

Explosions and their aftermath

On 29 November 1897, at Bull Point, a 4-inch armour-piercing shell stored in a box with two others broke spontaneously, ignited the bursting charge and burnt out the fuze. The filling of these shells was immediately suspended there and at Priddy's Hard. The explosion was not violent, restricted mainly to the box, and a large number of boxes remained undisturbed. The slight effect was ascribed to the shell breaking up before the bursting charge ignited. The Inspector General of Ordnance attributed the spontaneous splitting to internal stresses set up in the steel during the hardening process, and recommended that in future the charge be placed in a bag and the shell carefully examined for cracks before filling. There should have been no surprise in this; Palliser shells (though cast-iron, not steel) had been notoriously prone to cracking. It was recommended that in order to give time for any fault to declare itself the shells should not be filled within three months of manufacture. The Admiralty played safe and made the period six months, shells cracking during that period to be paid for by the manufacturer. A total of 767 of these shells were in store at Bull Point and 1,817 at Upnor. By the end of March 1898 the bag bursters were being sealed and filling was proceeding. Although the explosion had caused no damage, it had led to agitation in Plymouth, and the Town Clerk asked for assurances that the same, or worse, could not happen again. The secretary to the Commander-in-Chief, Admiral Fremantle, replied: 'the Admiral cannot say that the same thing may not recur, he desires me to assure you that there is no ground for apprehending any greater harm than occurred last time, which so far as life and property was concerned was nil. Needless to say that the reports which were circulated by the press were the most alarming feature of the affair.' The Town Clerk did not think much to this reply, pointing out that the recent explosion at Toulon Arsenal had done nothing to allay any fears about the proximity of Bull Point. The magazine at Lagoubran, a suburb of Toulon, exploded on 5 March 1899 (the Admiral replied to the Town Clerk in April) and a first enquiry attributed the cause to sabotage. Further enquiries came to the conclusion that the oldest batch of smokeless powder held there had spontaneously exploded. Fremantle attempted to placate the Town Council by assuring them that the manner in which British government magazines were designed and constructed, and the precautions observed in them, were, 'the best which modern science and high practical experience has yet been able to devise, and are calculated, as far as humanly possible, to avoid accident.' The Toulon explosion may have been the work of politically motivated men, evil beings, 'from which, owing to the conditions fortunately enjoyed in this country, we may hope to be exempt.' The pot was stirred further by 'An Engineer' writing to the local paper, who believed that the recent loss of the *Maine* at Havana and the Toulon disaster were due to chemical decomposition of the new explosives. He also maintained that 'The ugly powder hulks above Saltash Bridge, lately brought there to the disgust of the local residents' were a real danger, and could be detonated by an explosive bullet fired by a malcontent. None of this pacified the Town Clerk, who now wanted to be informed of the exact quantities of explosives held at Bull Point; and told the Admiral that it might be the duty of the Town Council in the interest of public safety to ask for the removal of the magazines from an area that was being rapidly developed as a residential district. Fremantle replied that he was not authorised to give such information. The Town Clerk then asked for the matter to be laid before the Admiralty, and Fremantle sent the file of correspondence to them, commenting,

'If people encroach within a limit which excites their timidity, they have only themselves to thank … I doubt if the civil population has any idea of the extent to which explosives are transported about the harbour, between the ships and the magazines; but they might reasonably be alarmed if this traffic had to be carried on overland by means of the railway to isolated distant depots …'

The Admiralty, naturally, backed up Fremantle and Bull Point continued to expand.[2]

Dangerous working practices did, however, exist, and in 1898 it was discovered that base fuzes at all three depots had been damaged by contact with the points of other shells through incorrect storage. That could be easily corrected; far more alarming was the explosion, in June of that year, of two 12-pounder AP shells in the shell room of the new second-class cruiser *Eclipse*. Drastic measures

were taken: the projectile was abolished. More unwelcome news came in October. After trials of ammunition supply on the brand-new Second-Class protected cruiser *Diadem*, Priddy's Hard reported that only a small proportion was useable.

Any faith in the total harmlessness of stored cordite was dispelled in December 1899, when the first cordite explosion took place on board a ship. A 6-inch QF shell, in a box of four, exploded on the battleship *Revenge*, the second flagship of the Mediterranean Fleet. Cordite had not yet replaced gunpowder as the propellant for all big guns; in March 1900 the Admiral commanding the Channel Squadron complained that it was nearly two years since the cordite charge for 13·5-inch guns had been approved, and yet two ships of his Squadron (*Resolution* and *Repulse*, sister ships of *Revenge*) were still supplied with powder. The lyddite-filled shells were clearly regarded with some degree of suspicion. Although they had been issued to the Channel Squadron, they were never fired, and the Admiral submitted that when the opportunity for firing at a rock arose, the modest total of two rounds of lyddite shell per gun should be fired. 'Unless this is allowed in peace time, the chances are against their being used in war, as the men are having instilled into them a belief that they are dangerous to handle.' That summer it was decreed that two per cent of the lyddite shell of ships in commission and reserve was to be landed annually for examination.

Further mishaps were reported. In February 1900 a 6-pounder QF exploded while in the floating magazine *Jumna* on the Medway. It was in a case with eleven others being returned for examination, which did not explode. The probable cause was a defective fuze of obsolete pattern. In September 1902, 6-inch and 4.7-inch QF cartridge cases made by the trade had split when fired with full cordite charges. No more were to be fired with such cases, which were to be landed as soon as possible and replaced by Woolwich

8.1 Spontaneously combusted 4.7-inch cartridges from the Second-Class protected cruiser HMS *Fox* (see page 181). The central cartridge set the others off – note the bulged mouth. *(TNA ADM-116/1025)*

cartridges or trade cartridges manufactured after 1 January 1896. The cordite charges were to be transferred from the condemned cases to serviceable ones as soon as possible. The replacement of powder charges by cordite was a costly business; the bill by the end of 1900 would be £262,000 for 13.5-inch calibre, £56,000 for 12-inch, £25,200 for 10-inch and £84,200 for 9.2-inch. Fortunately, the 13.5-inch was becoming obsolescent. [It is a commentary on the relative importance attached to gunnery at the time that it was decided to ask for only £50,000 for this purpose in the next Navy Estimates.][3]

The explosion at Priddy's Hard in November 1902 consequently did not come out of the blue. Overall responsibility for ordnance storage now rested with Rear-Admiral Sir Sydney Eardley-Wilmot. Colonel Pease had retired in February, having been kept on after his due time in order to oversee the Department at a critical period. He had much to look back on; when demanding an increased pension he could state:

'Considering that when I took up my appointment, neither the War Office nor the Admiralty knew within £3,000,000 as to where they stood respecting the requirements of equipment, whereas now the Accounts are up to date, I may hope to be entitled to some credit and consideration for forming and pioneering the Naval Ordnance Store Department to its present admittedly satisfactory financial and store condition .... Two of the Magazine Stations contain the largest Laboratories in the World (Woolwich excepted). Since the formation of the Department over twenty million pounds of powder and cordite have been made up into Cartridges in these Laboratories, thousands of tons of combustibles have also been manipulated annually, yet there has been but one accident, viz: that of a man injuring his back through a strain when wheeling a barrow. The Naval Ordnance Stores, which comprise weights from 110 tons downwards ... and the general Stores, amounting to hundreds of thousands of tons during the past 11 years, have also been manipulated without accident.'

On his retirement a major organisational change was made; the Naval Ordnance Department and the Naval Ordnance Store Department were amalgamated and Pease's post of Surveyor-General of Naval Ordnance was abolished. Eardley-Wilmot became the first Superintendent of Ordnance Stores, being subordinate to and directly under the Director of Naval Ordnance. He had practical experience, having been appointed Senior Lieutenant on the torpedo school HMS *Vernon* in 1877, and losing a hand in 1879 when explaining the action of a fuze, which by some mischance was fitted to a live mine. The Priddy's Hard explosion was caused by yet another failure of an armour-piercing shell, but this time the detonation involved others in the heap and considerable damage was done, although nobody was killed. A major enquiry was held because of the accident; not into its cause, for that was unhappily by now familiar enough, but into the whole question of the suitability of Priddy's Hard as a Magazine Depot.[4]

Priddy's Hard undergoes scrutiny

In May 1903, a committee visited Priddy's Hard in order to consider its suitability as a depot. The committee agreed that a change should be made in the extent and manner in which Priddy's Hard was used as the Portsmouth Magazine. Currently 1,000 tons of explosives could be stored in only two magazines (E and the later cordite magazine) spaced only 183 yards apart. Distributing the explosives in smaller quantities of 50 tons in separate traversed magazines and with 100 yards distance between each would greatly minimise the risk (and meet new Home Office regulations), but there was insufficient room to do this, and local conditions precluded the possibility of extension. Therefore the committee recommended that the bulk of the explosives be removed from Priddy's Hard and stored under safer conditions on another site, in fact, the familiar recommendation made several times before, most recently in 1884 (see page 100). Previous committees had suggested a number of alternative sites, but this committee offered only two, Paulsgrove Chalk Pit and Wicor Marsh, with a preference for the former. While these matters of moment were under consideration, another landmark decision was made: the supply of pistols and swords was reduced, while that of boarding pikes was discontinued.[5]

The Admiralty generally approved the report, and the Magazine Committee (see pages 146–50) was reconstituted. They met in November 1903 and decided on Wicor as the site. Eardley-Wilmot proposed to limit the explosive to 1,000 tons in 20 separate magazines of 50 tons traversed and placed 100 yards apart. In view of the increasing importance of Portland as a defended anchorage and coaling station, storage should also be provided there if a suitable site could be found. Colonel Raban, still Director of Works, was in favour of providing accommodation at Portland on top of the hill, though no funds were available at present, and he was unable to say if £50,000, a sum apparently given as a bench-mark, would be sufficient for the new Portsmouth magazines until more work had been done on planning the scheme. In January 1904 the Board directed that the necessary steps be taken at once to acquire land at Wicor, with enough ground secured for Home Office regulations to be adopted, and the following month instructions were given to purchase about

184 acres at the best possible price, under £150 an acre. The land was bought for £20,200 but word of the confidential negotiations and their purpose had leaked out and initiated furious local opposition. By June, the Civil Lord, Arthur Lee (more famous for donating his home, Chequers, for the use of subsequent Prime Ministers, and helping to found the Courtauld Institute) decided to cancel the purchase and instead acquire land for a magazine site at Bedenham, between Foxbury and Frater Lake, for about £90 an acre. By a happy chance this land belonged to the same vendor who cancelled the former contract. This deal saved some £13,500 from the original scheme. Treasury sanction was given in August but by September a change of plan occurred, it now being considered that the 1,000 tons of explosives should be stored both at Priddy's Hard and the new site. Despite the completion of the sale at Bedenham in October 1904, and the decision to concentrate all work there, some twists to the plot now followed. In a sudden reversal of policy, on 4 March 1905, a Board conference was held at which it was decided that additional accommodation for 6,000 tons of explosives was required in England and in view of the expense of subdividing this into a number of small magazines (the Bedenham proposal for 1,000 tons, in twenty 50-ton magazines being estimated at £100,000) it was decided to abandon the Bedenham scheme. Instead the land would be let, and storage inside Portsmouth Harbour be limited to 300 tons, counting the present magazine as 100 tons and building two others in the vicinity. The bulk of the ammunition would be held either at a new central depot on a convenient site in the United Kingdom or by increasing storage at Lodge Hill and locating the remainder elsewhere. Money allocated to Hong Kong and elsewhere would, it was anticipated, suffice for this work. Nothing came of this ambitious plan for a mammoth depot, save the two additional cordite magazines at Priddy's Hard. These brought the depot to the stage of development in which it would enter the First World War.[6]

Rivalry on the Medway

An equally muddled situation was developing on the Medway. Work began on the Lodge Hill magazines on 7 September 1899. Alternative plans were prepared for cordite cartridge stores, offering a pitched roof or a virtually flat one; the former was selected. When the two additional cordite magazines were added to Priddy's Hard, the bets were hedged and one of each type of roof was supplied. In 1901 further parcels of land were acquired – Binghams Wood and Deangate Wood – and plans drawn up to tidy the rail and train routes, including connections to a proposed torpedo range at Teapot Hard.[7]

Admiralty and War Office rivalry was a major factor in the administrative morass that prevailed, and a joint conference sought to address the following issues:

1. Woolwich Arsenal to be vacated by the navy as a storage depot for explosives.
2. The Admiralty to give up storage at Woolwich and the naval share of the powder magazines at Purfleet.
3. The Admiralty would require other storage accommodation in lieu, either new buildings or War Office buildings transferred. These requirements could be partly met by transfer of the following army storage: army magazines at Chattenden, army magazines and storehouses at Bull Point.
4. The present gunwharf at Chatham being inadequate to meet the wants of both army and navy, the Admiralty proposed that either the navy should take over the whole of the gunwharf, and the army be provided for elsewhere, or that the navy should vacate the present gunwharf and be provided with a new gunwharf elsewhere.
5. Whether it was possible for the Army Gunwharf at Devonport to be removed to another situation, as the space and water frontage it now occupied would be of great value to the Naval Dockyard.

8.2 The cordite cartridge stores at Lodge Hill, showing the two alternative roof styles. The gabled version was adopted here. *(Adapted from a drawing held by Work Services Manager, Chattenden)*

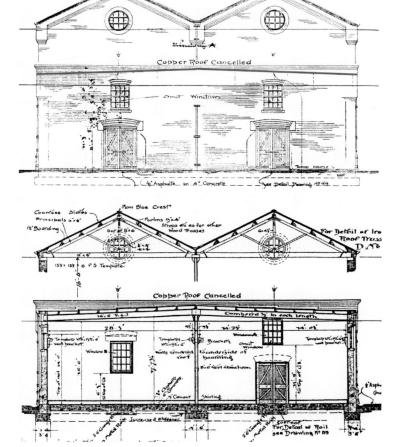

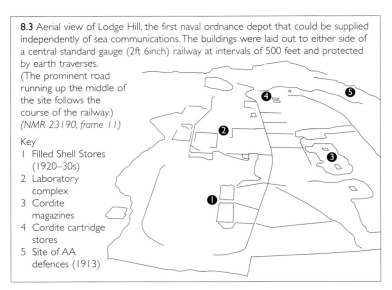

8.3 Aerial view of Lodge Hill, the first naval ordnance depot that could be supplied independently of sea communications. The buildings were laid out to either side of a central standard gauge (2ft 6inch) railway at intervals of 500 feet and protected by earth traverses.
(The prominent road running up the middle of the site follows the course of the railway.)
(NMR 23190, frame 11)

Key
1 Filled Shell Stores (1920–30s)
2 Laboratory complex
3 Cordite magazines
4 Cordite cartridge stores
5 Site of AA defences (1913)

The Admiralty's decision to release Woolwich came from a number of defects that they could perceive. There were conflicting interests in the establishment; requirements had entirely outgrown the existing facilities for expeditious handling of stores; traffic was congested at all times, and would be accentuated in event of war, which resulted in confusion, delay and waste of time and money. The traffic manager was not in a position to discriminate as to relative urgency, and there was some difficulty in berthing vessels and wharf business generally. It was also not desirable to make all shipments of naval explosives from the Thames. Such naval shipments as were necessary could be made from Lodge Hill and elsewhere. The Admiralty did not propose to continue storing at Woolwich large reserves of filled ammunition, but felt that it would still be necessary to retain storage accommodation for loose explosives to feed the factories and storage for filled ammunition awaiting shipment to other depots. The following new arrangements were suggested. The bulk of the cordite from trade, all of which was currently delivered at Woolwich, would be delivered at out-stations where it was required for filling, with samples only sent to Woolwich for firing proof. Small arm machine gun and aiming rifle ammunition, empty cartridges, empty shell, packages for ammunition etc could be delivered straight to out-stations, with only trade samples sent to Woolwich.

A long-running struggle for possession appeared to be settled by the agreement that the Admiralty should take over Chattenden, including all buildings and railways, though a certain amount of accommodation would have to be reserved to meet army requirements. The War Office refused to make any concessions over Bull Point or Devonport Gunwharf. The latter suited army requirements admirably and the only possible solution suggested was the surrender by the navy of the portion of the Royal William Victualling

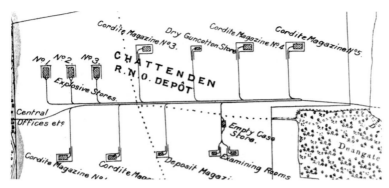

8.4 Lodge Hill as originally laid out, 1904. The buildings were laid out to the north and south of a central railway at intervals of 500 feet and protected by earth traverses. Note Deangate to the right, which became the site of the laboratory. Note, also, the name given to the site on the plan. *(From TNA T 1/10565B)*

8.5 One of the cordite magazines at Lodge Hill. This photograph was taken after the Second World World, when the original 2-foot 6-inch gauge track has been replaced by standard gauge. *(From HRO 109M91, PH/66)*

Yard set aside for ordnance matters, which was clearly unacceptable to the Admiralty. A final dispute over Chattenden was still to come. In July 1905 a further conference was held to discuss the army's claim, not in the original agreement, for payment for the Upnor–Chattenden railway. The Admiralty argued that the transfer of the Chattenden magazines, with the necessary means of access, was in exchange for the storage given up at Purfleet, with its necessary means of access. The magazines could not be used without the railway and if the army claimed payment for the railway the exchange was not a fair one; the navy might equally claim for its share of the pier and short length of line which were the means of access to Purfleet magazines. The War Office representatives pointed out that the railway was not only the means of access to the magazines, it was used for training Royal Engineers in railway work. This had not been mentioned in 1903, as at that time it was planned to remove the Royal Engineers' establishment entirely from the Medway to a new site on Salisbury Plain, but this plan had been scrapped and now the deal was regretted. The matter was sent for arbitration to the Treasury, who judged the War Office's claims to be invalid.[8]

Building at the Medway sites

By 1904, the Medway, despite having been the most backward in the past, emerged as the most advanced of the three naval Ordnance Depots. This was due to the advantage of Lodge Hill, a large, flat, undeveloped site not inhibited by the presence of residential buildings. The possibility of future difficulties had been made evident by the land slippages at the adjacent property of Chattenden, but the relief of having an area to build on at all, let alone a large area, must have overridden all other considerations.

When designing the new buildings at Lodge Hill, the plans partly made use of the principles governing the design of a magazine depot advanced by the 1865 Committee (see pages 81–2), although updated to meet an age in which cordite had largely replaced gunpowder. The cordite cartridge stores (see page 170) were untraversed buildings; the nine cordite magazines that eventually materialised were traversed, but the design had been altered from the type evolved at Crossness and adopted at Priddy's Hard. The geology of the Medway area made the provision of wet moats an impossibility and so rectangular traverses surrounded the buildings, which were given extremely low-pitched copper roofs, the metal being placed on 1-inch boarding on wooden purlins carried on steel beams. A magazine for returned ammunition and a dry guncotton magazine, similarly traversed, were also provided. These magazine enclosures were spaced out on either side of a 2-foot 6-inch gauge line, which connected with the Chattenden magazines and the Upnor railway. In September 1903 the first landslip occurred, at the traverse to No. 3 Magazine, and it was necessary to reform the gradient at 1 in 4 instead of 1 in 3. By the end of the year all the administrative buildings had been completed. By April 1904, five cordite magazines had been completed; Nos 1 and 2 held bulk cordite, No. 3 BL cordite cartridges, No. 4 BL and RML powder cartridges, and No. 5 BL cordite cartridges. The dry guncotton store held, in addition to dry guncotton, exploders, lyddite charges and tonite (another blasting explosive). The deposit magazine for explosives received from ships was also completed. Three explosive stores held QF ammunition in brass cases.

At the old sites in the Medway complex other developments were taking place concurrently. At Chattenden, out of the five store magazines one and a half were, as agreed (see page 172), reserved for cannon cartridges on deposit for the Army Ordnance Department, the remainder holding naval cordite, gunpowder cartridges and loose gunpowder. The ancillary buildings comprised a dry guncotton store, a wet guncotton store, and nine cartridge stores; the laboratory was using one

8.6 Above: The laboratory at Lodge Hill in 1930. *(From HRO 109M91, PH166)*
8.7 Below: Lodge Hill, 1930. From left to right; the standard-gauge transfer shed, rail traffic broken seal examination room, and the empty package store. *(Royal Engineers Library)*

of the cartridge stores as a temporary examination room, one held naval QF cartridges, one QF cartridges on army deposit, the others naval explosives not under magazine conditions. There were a few laboratory workrooms. At Upnor, A Magazine held small arms and machine gun cartridges and small-calibre QF cartridges; B Magazine held RML, BL and QF cartridges from 6-inch to 12-pounder. The small dry guncotton store, larger wet guncotton store, and stores for cartridges, fuzes, tubes and detonators had been joined by the filled mine store and filled shell store, which had been built on the recently acquired land. The castle and its environs were used for miscellaneous non-explosive stores. There was a small laboratory for examining filled mines, warheads, lyddite shell, and proving. There were no longer any facilities for shell filling or emptying.[9]

The location for replacement shell filling facilities was still undecided. At a conference in October 1903 two alternatives were proposed. The Superintendent of Stores advanced a scheme for making the Thames the main base for shipping. [This may well have been revived in August 1907 when a scheme was under consideration (although not adopted) for supplying ammunition to the fleet in wartime by means of a rail connection between Lodge Hill and the Thames at Higham Bight, with the terminus at the Submarine Mining Pier, Shornmead.] Were this plan to be adopted, then Lodge Hill would be the best place for the filled shell laboratory and additional shell stores; should it be turned down then the position was to be on the high ground behind the proposed torpedo range at Teapot Hard. There was no question about the laboratory buildings that were to be used for cartridge filling, these were to be an integral part of the complex at Lodge Hill, and were to be traversed. The cost of the laboratory alone was estimated at £46,000, which was reduced to £20,000 in June 1904 by omitting the traverses (demonstrating the relatively enormous cost of earthworks). By the time the schedule for the

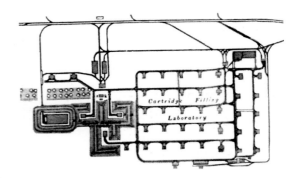

8.9 Lodge Hill Laboratory in 1912. Note to the left the three traversed expense magazines, one of the traversed cordite magazines and the shelter belt of trees.
(Derived from plan held by Works Services Manager, Chattenden)

Naval Works Loan Act of 1905 was drawn up (see opposite) the sums committed to the Medway far outstripped those spent on Priddy's Hard. The new laboratory shared the same design of frangible buildings as Priddy's Hard (though the buildings were clad in corrugated iron instead of timber) but its layout owed nothing to that site, where the fortuitous presence of the old fortifications enabled extensive traverses to be provided at relatively low cost. Instead, the rational – though close-grouped – layout adopted in the late 1890s at Woolwich for the untraversed filling rooms for cordite cartridges and lyddite shells was taken as the model. Despite an explosion in the lyddite establishment in June 1903, which killed fifteen people, the Superintendent of Building Works, still Colonel Ovey, stated that the buildings were so placed that with certain exceptions the men employed in them were practically safe from the effects of a possible explosion in an adjoining building, the exceptions being certain expense magazines and shell filling buildings. The expense magazines for cordite were constructed with very light roofs and no explosion with violence in them need be feared. Ovey did not think that even if unlimited money and space were available for a complete reconstruction of the danger buildings any real extra security would be obtained: the gain

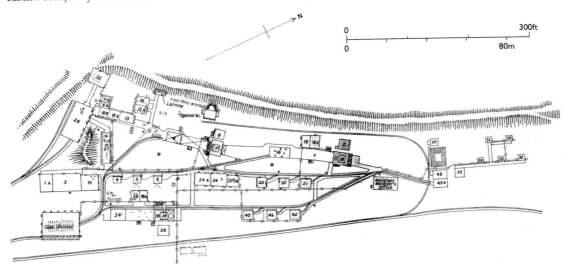

8.8 The lyddite establishment at Woolwich Arsenal. *(From TNA SUPP 5/148)*

Budgets for the Medway in 1905 Loan

Lodge Hill

	Estimated cost in £
Purchase of plots	20,728
Purchase of Ellis' Farm	11,000
Repairs to Lodge Hill House	552
Earthworks	21,010
Magazine buildings	41,628
Boundary fences	10,828
Reservoirs &c at Chattenden Farm	2,349
Connecting W.D. Well	780
Railways & Water Main inside enclosure	10,540
Quarters for Police & Workmen	21,000
Transfer platforms at magazines	1,650
Planting trees	203
Temporary buildings	155
Police canteen, billiard & reading rooms	1,400
Purchase of land for railway	3,300
Heating various buildings	3,140
Subsidiary buildings	12,000
New Laboratory	20,000
Paths inside enclosure	5,980
Adding to & renewing old Police Quarters	1,460
TOTAL	**161,000**

COL 18/2

Upnor

	Estimated cost in £
Converting residence to office	426
Wrought iron fence	442
Tinsmiths & Carpenters Shop	102
Filled Shell & Mine Store	12,665
Railways etc.	2,507
Bollards & piles to River Wall	411
Repairs to Shell Pier	338
Truck & Barrow shed	503
Spark catchers	19
Purchase of Littlers Land	18,772
TOTAL	**36,185**

of the increased distances between buildings would be offset by the increased difficulty in effective supervision. However that might be, the lyddite filling establishment was rebuilt at Tripcock, near Plumstead, where far greater precautions were taken in the protection of the buildings. As there was no intention of filling anything other than cordite cartridges at Lodge Hill, the Colonel's reassurances were accepted and the saving in money caused by doing away with traverses thought a fair trade-off. Work began on the new laboratory in January 1905.[10]

In 1905, attention shifted back to Upnor, as a consequence of the abandonment of the whole Teapot Hard scheme, which had comprised two distinct projects: the construction of a tramway

8.10 The existing railway connections from the Medway Ordnance Depots and the proposed branch to Teapot Hard. *(Adapted from TNA T 1/10565B)*

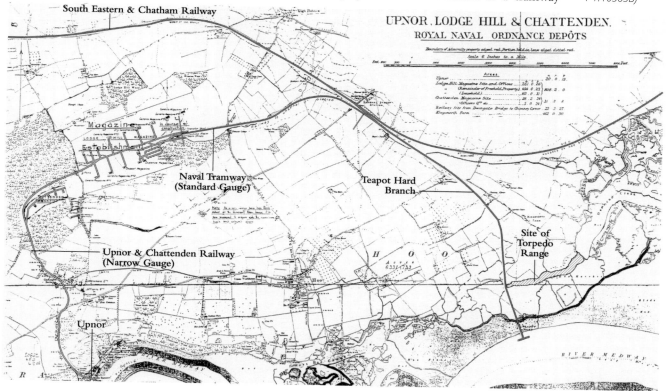

177

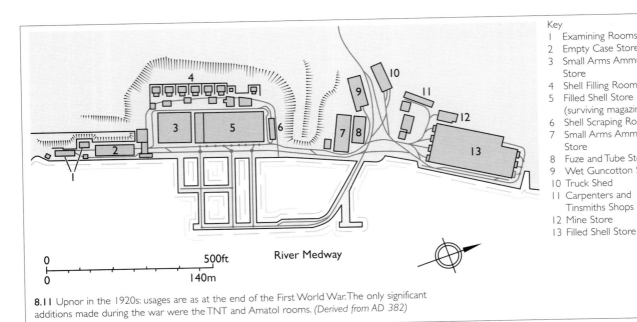

Key
1 Examining Rooms
2 Empty Case Store
3 Small Arms Ammunition
   Store
4 Shell Filling Rooms
5 Filled Shell Store
   (surviving magazine)
6 Shell Scraping Room
7 Small Arms Ammunition
   Store
8 Fuze and Tube Store
9 Wet Guncotton Store
10 Truck Shed
11 Carpenters and
   Tinsmiths Shops
12 Mine Store
13 Filled Shell Store

River Medway

0 ——— 500ft
0 ——— 140m

8.11 Upnor in the 1920s: usages are as at the end of the First World War. The only significant additions made during the war were the TNT and Amatol rooms. *(Derived from AD 382)*

8.12 Upnor shell filling rooms (to the right) in the late 1940s: the view would have been virtually identical in 1910. Note the castle visible through the winter trees in the background. *(From HRO 109M91, PH/66)*

8.13 Below: Upnor in 1930, viewed from across the River Medway. In the centre are the magazines, with the canteen and boiler house behind them and the main offices and shell store to the right. Beyond lies Beacon Hill, while in the foreground are lighters tied up at the jetty and to moorings. *(Royal Engineers Library)*

8.14 Another late 1940s view of Upnor, this time looking downriver from atop the northern tower of the castle. Again little would have changed from 1910, although the four-masted barque moored in the background was a newer addition; the training ship *Arethusa*, ex-*Peking*, she was at Upnor from 1933 until 1973. *(From HRO 109M91, PH/66)*

8.15 Upnor in 1930, showing the main entrance (left of centre), with the store shifting room and wet guncotton store to its left and the truck shed (with curved roof) and carpenter's shop to its right. The Georgian house was built for the 1820s boat yard and demolished in 1964. *(Royal Engineers Library)*

from the depot at Chattenden via Sharnal Street Station on the South Eastern and Chatham Railway to a pier at Teapot Hard on the Medway; and the formation of a torpedo range near Teapot Hard. The first project was considered essential to provide for the rapid issue of ammunition from the magazines to ships lying in the Medway during mobilization and for the transport of torpedoes between Woolwich and the then proposed torpedo range at Teapot Hard. The completion of the tramway between the magazines and Sharnal Street Station put the depot into direct communi-

179

cation with the whole railway system of the country – a service of great importance. The mobilisation issue was, however, made far less important by a change in policy made in February, which will be discussed later. Then, on 16 March, the Admiralty decided not to build the torpedo range at Teapot Hard, and the other reason for the line therefore fell to the ground. It was found after careful consideration that the modified requirements could be met at much less expense by improving the existing facilities at Upnor, and the pier and railway connection with Chattenden. At Upnor, the powder pier would be connected directly with the Chattenden railway by construction of a new viaduct with provision of additional barge berth; railways inside the depot would be rearranged and a passing place provided outside the entrance; new shell filling rooms would be provided and other minor works would take place. The shell filling rooms followed the pattern originated at Priddy's Hard and subsequently repeated at Bull Point. At Chattenden, a new siding on 4-foot 8½-inch gauge railway would be constructed outside the east gate of the new magazine enclosure; a new transfer shed and platform would be formed at the junction inside east gate of the 4-foot 8½-inch and 2-foot 6-inch railways; a new pathway would be created between the naval

magazine enclosure and that transferred from the War Department. It was also proposed to put the Upnor–Chattenden railway into working order. The 8th Railway Company, RE, finally ceased working the railway on 1 April 1906, and handed it over. For all this a further £25,000 was allotted in the Naval Works Loan Bill to cover the years 1905–7. It was announced in the Navy Estimates for 1908–9 that the laboratories at Upnor for shell filling and Lodge Hill for cartridge filling had been brought into use. [11]

The extent of storage accommodation now available at Lodge Hill, together with its connection at Sharnal Street with the main railway system, enabled the Medway magazines to move to the heart of the distribution system for naval cordite, largely replacing the Woolwich area. From 1910 all trade cordite was delivered at Lodge Hill. After acceptance it was then sent to Woolwich to be made into filled cartridges, which were returned to Lodge Hill for storage. Further laboratory facilities were needed to reduce the remaining dependence on Woolwich, and additional laboratory accommodation was also required for examining and repairing cordite cartridges. In April 1910 the traditional dependence on water transport for the movement of explosives was overturned when an agreement was made with

8.16 Another view of Upnor in 1930, looking north-east and showing the north-west end of the examining room (left) and empty case store (right) beyond. *(Royal Engineers Library)*

the South East and Chatham Railway to move cordite and powder between Waltham Abbey and Lodge Hill once the lighterage contract between Waltham Abbey and Upnor expired at the end of the year. By July 1911 four more store magazines intended for BL cordite cartridges were added at Lodge Hill, the other magazine accommodation remaining unaltered. The laboratory workrooms were by then arranged in three sets, each set comprising one cordite cutting room, three cartridge filling rooms, and one packing room (fifteen buildings in all), connected to each other, to a transfer shed at each end of laboratory site, and to two expense magazines on the south-west side by a 'clean' wooden platform 18 inches from the ground. A railway of 1 foot 6 inch gauge ran on the platform for carrying work to and from the workrooms and transfer sheds, where it was shifted to powder trucks of 2 foot 6 inch gauge for conveyance to the magazines. The shift of importance away from the old locations took definitive form on 24 November 1911, when the office staff from RNOD Upnor was transferred to Lodge Hill. The impressively scaled depot was, however, still too small, as the size of battleships and their guns (quite apart from the great increase in size of the navy as a whole) continued to grow. In August 1912, to relieve congestion, 24,700 cartridges, together with 310 filled 12-inch shells, were sent to Priddy's Hard, which was also to take 34,500 cartridges from Bull Point.[12]

Problems of capacity at Portsmouth

The ordnance storage situation in the Portsmouth area had been transformed and now had a greater capacity than Lodge Hill. That situation had come about without the succession of U turns that had been seen many times before. The new explosive (cordite) raised old concerns. The two additional cordite magazines (see pages 170–71) were completed in 1906, the boiler house being extended to cope with the additional heating required. It became apparent during the year that the material was not as safe as had first been hoped, when no less than four explosions of cordite in magazines took place in India. One explosion occurred in the magazine of the second-class cruiser *Fox*, caused by spontaneous ignition within a box of 4.7-inch QF cartridges (see figure 8.1). These were stored four to a box; one apparently ignited and set off two others. A photograph taken for the subsequent enquiry shows the initial ignition to have bulged the mouth of the cartridge case. At Hyderabad, powder kept in the same magazine as cordite exploded, causing great destruction.

It was at once decided that powder and cordite were not to be kept in the same magazines at naval depots, and in May 1907 it was ordered that all cordite Mark I, dating before April 1905, be destroyed. BL cartridges could be drowned in deep water by ships, but QF ammunition had to be returned to depots for disposal. It now seemed – again – that excessive quantities of explosives were being held at Priddy's Hard. In April 1904, despite the findings of the 1903 enquiry (see pages 170–71), C Magazine held 80 tons, E Magazine held 625 tons, the cordite magazine held 625 tons, and the dry guncotton magazine held 62½ tons. The Committee on Magazine Storage in the Portsmouth District (see pages 146–7) was reconvened, reporting in February 1908. Storage accommodation had to be provided inside Portsmouth Harbour for 1,200 tons of cordite, composed of loose cordite for use in filling cartridges at Priddy's Hard, and filled cartridges for rapid issue. The committee members endorsed the earlier decisions that large quantities of explosives should not be stored at Priddy's Hard and that the depot should be a ready use magazine only. The four magazines there, if restricted to 50 tons storage in each, would enable 200 tons of cordite

The recommended distribution of cordite around Portsmouth

Service	Priddy's Hard, tons	*Carnatic*, tons	Marchwood, tons
Ready supply for replenishments of ships in Commission	100	100	
Ready supply for Gunnery Schools	50		
Filled cartridges for examination & repair	50	50	
Filled cartridges for ships building & repairing		50	100
Loose cordite for filling	100		
First replenishment for the fleet		300	
Second replenishment for the fleet			300
Other reserves			550
Merchant cruiser outfits			70
Special Service Vessels			150
Surplus cartridges			200
TOTAL	**300**	**500**	**1370**

COL/20

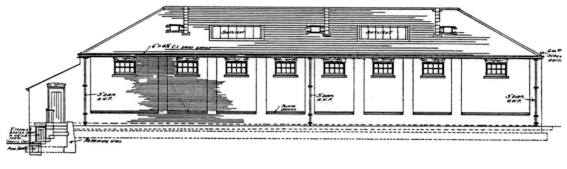

8.17 Elevation and section of a Bedenham magazine. *(From PTM/3674)*

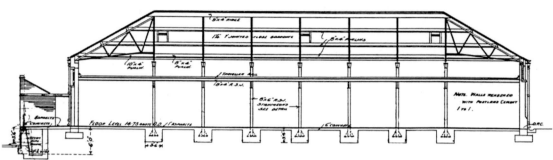

8.18 Below: plan and section of a Bedenham magazine, showing traverses. These magazines were intended from the first to be rail-connected, negotiations with the London and South Western Railway beginning early in 1910. *(From PTM/3677)*

to be housed. The remaining storage inside Portsmouth Harbour consisted of *Carnatic*, moored off Frater Point. The Admiralty had decided in 1904 that a magazine on shore should urgently replace this hulk, then containing 1,725 tons of explosives.

Bedenham, already Admiralty property, was unanimously recommended as the site for a new magazine depot. The site had many advantages: the

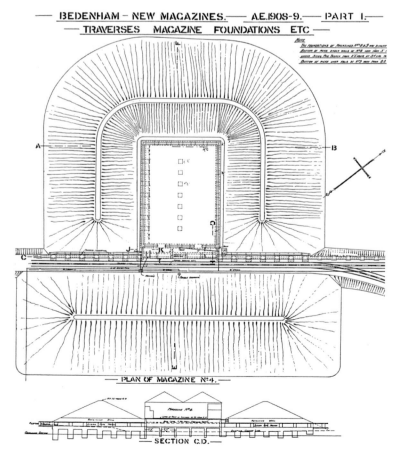

area of land available meant that the explosives could be divided up into comparatively small quantities, thus securing greater safety; there was a good water frontage and facilities could be made for the rapid receipt and issue of ammunition if it were provided with a pier capable of berthing a Woolwich steamer and lighters; and, finally, it could – and should – be connected with the London and South Western Railway and thus be linked up with the general railway system of the country. This would enable supplies to be despatched by rail to Southampton or any other shipping port. It would also enable supplies to be received by rail direct from contractors or from Woolwich.

Although it was desirable at Priddy's Hard to limit the quantity of cordite in any one building to 50 tons, owing to its proximity to the dockyard, this amount might be increased at Bedenham in view of its relatively remote situation. The proposed land magazines within the harbour at Portsmouth would comprise four 50-ton magazines and the new magazine at Bedenham of 1,000 tons, to offer a total of 1,200 tons.

The development of Bedenham, if approved, would take a considerable time and temporary arrangements would need to be made for the safe storage of the cordite that had to be retained within Portsmouth Harbour. A distribution list was drafted and approved (see page 181). However, the issue of the first and second replenishments of the fleet in time of war could not be carried out as rapidly as desirable. Increasing pressure was being brought on the Portsmouth Depot by the demands for ammunition from ships at Portland. The gross tonnage of magazine stores shipped to Portland from Priddy's Hard during each of the last three years had risen from 604 tons in 1904–5

8.19 One of the Bedenham magazines nearing completion. *(From TNA ADM 195/46)*

to 1541 tons in 1906–7. This method of supply was most uneconomical, steamers and lighters being sent only partially loaded. The committee consequently recommended that a small depot for ammunition and ordnance stores be established there for the replacement of practice expenditure of the Channel Fleet. Within a few days Sir Inigo Thomas, the Admiralty Secretary, wrote to the Treasury outlining the proposals, but this scheme was to come to nothing.[13]

Ammunition directives call for further changes

As has been noted, the Teapot Hard scheme was dropped partly because of new arrangements for ammunition supply. In January 1905, Rear-Admiral Sir Sydney Eardley-Wilmot had proposed a drastic change in the issue of ammunition to ships. It had been usual for many years past to keep all supplies in England made up and ready for immediate issue. This had resulted in very heavy expenditure of money in consequence of the constant changes in armaments of ships and alterations in patterns of components. The staff at the naval Ordnance Depots was constantly overhauling ammunition to keep it up to pattern, and large quantities had to be scrapped when ships were removed from the effective list, or when patterns were changed. Eardley-Wilmot proposed that in future all outfits (the prescribed store of ammunition to be kept on a ship) were to be kept filled. It was understood that as all effective ships would have nucleus crews, their outfits would be on board and landed periodically for examination and to be brought up to pattern. A proportion only of the reserves at home depots was to be kept

made up, the balance being kept in the shape of components. Eardley-Wilmot suggested that a minimum of twenty-five per cent of the stock might be kept filled. This would necessitate arrangements (rooms and staff) at the depots to meet large filling requirements in times of emergency, but he assumed that these could readily be

Tonnage of cordite carried by HMS *London* in 1914

12-inch	6-inch	12-pdr	Small Arm, Machine Gun and Blank	Total tons
67.2	59.4	3.0	3.0	132.6

Another 26.5 tons had been loaded since war broke out.

Shell
Weight of bursters in tons

	Lyddite	Common	Other	Total
12-inch	4.0	13.0		17
6-inch	1.6	5.0		6.6
Smaller			3.0 (estimate)	3.0
TOTAL	**5.6**	**18.0**	**3.0**	**26.6**

Weight of projectiles

	Tons
12-inch	139.6
6-inch	149.9
12-pdr	5.0
TOTAL	**294.5** (calculated wrongly in original)

Guncotton

	Tons
Dry guncotton	.132
Wet guncotton (in 16¼ lb tins)	.422
Warheads	1.47
TOTAL	**2.024**

ADM 116/1370

provided. The Director of Naval Ordnance concurred with Eardley-Wilmot's suggestions, except that he thought fifty per cent of the reserves of 9.2-inch ammunition and above should be kept filled. Consequently, it was unnecessary to provide for the rapid transport of such large quantities of ammunition as previously envisaged in times of emergency, and the shipment of explosives on mobilisation would also be greatly reduced. The Commander-in-Chief at the Nore was advised of the new arrangements on 19 February 1905.

Nevertheless, it was still considered vital to keep a considerable stock of filled cartridges in the Portsmouth District, so that all was in readiness for immediate shipment, in case of war. The development scheme for Bedenham had been dropped partly because of this decision that the ammunition required for vessels in Reserve, all those that retained nucleus crews, was to be carried on board the ships instead of being kept in the shore magazines. However, by 1908 the circumstances had again changed in some important aspects:

The three major depots by 1913

At Priddy's Hard, C Magazine (capacity 80 tons) was no longer used and E Magazine was used for cordite (it had a capacity of 625 tons, but only 100 tons was accepted). Of the three purpose-built cordite magazines, one had a capacity of 625 tons (100 tons being allowed), the other two with a normal capacity of 50 tons (100 being allowed in emergency). The dry guncotton magazine could take 62½ tons, and *Carnatic* (with a capacity of 1,725 tons) was still in use, 500 tons being allowed. The remaining storage accommodation and laboratory facilities remained largely unchanged. The accommodation at Bedenham has been seen above (see page 182). At Marchwood, in addition to the magazines there were three explosive stores, used for QF ammunition, and the shoe houses were used as temporary isolation magazines.

At Bull Point, considerably greater quantities were stored. No. 3 Magazine held 375 tons of cordite and 190 tons of powder (in spite of the ruling of 1906 – see page 181) and Nos 2 and 3 held 580 tons of cordite. The dedicated cordite magazine held 500 tons. *Newcastle* was still present in spite of all previous decisions to do away with her. With a capacity of 92,000 cubic feet, she housed an unspecified number of filled cartridges. The only significant addition since 1904 had been an additional filled shell store, on the model of the one recently completed at Upnor (see page 176). At that site the only magazine listed was one of the cells of B Magazine, in use for deposited ammunition. The laboratory housed shell emptying and six shell filling rooms, a proof room and examining rooms for warheads and filled mines. The old filled shell store held 27,450 filled shells, loose and in boxes; the new filled shell store held 143,740.

At Chattenden, each of the five store magazines had a maximum capacity of 281 tons. Two held BL cordite cartridges, 6- to 4-inch, and were usually full, with an actual tonnage of 160.

The other three magazines contained BL and RML gunpowder cartridges and gunpowder in bulk, packed in powder cases, boxes and barrels, and were also usually full, with an actual tonnage of 140. Lodge Hill was principally used for storing cartridges, laboratory operations in connection with cartridges, and reception and storage of trade cordite. Gunpowder was no longer held. The three cordite cartridge stores had a maximum capacity of 1,100 tons each, and were usually full, but the approximate tonnage of actual explosives was 240 tons of cordite cartridges for calibres of 6- to 12-inch. Three of the nine store magazines held BL cordite cartridges for calibres from 4- to 13.5-inch, packed in brass powder cases and cartridge boxes. Their maximum capacity was 1,000 tons, and they were usually full, the approximate tonnage of actual explosives being 600. Two others held bulk cordite of all sizes, packed in wooden cases, and were again usually full, with an actual tonnage of approximately 620. The deposit magazine had a maximum capacity of 240 tons, and was generally reserved for the isolation of doubtful cordite cartridges, so the quantity stored varied considerably, although it was usually about 25 tons. In time of pressure it was used for BL cordite cartridges of 4- to 13.5-inch, or bulk cordite, taking approximately 105 tons of explosive. The precise use of the other four store magazines was not recorded. The dry guncotton store held dry guncotton, exploders for lyddite shell, tonite (see Glossary) charges and dynamite, packed in boxes and packing cases. The maximum capacity was 80 tons, with 10 tons of actual explosive. The three expense magazines held cartridges in hand for repair and cordite required for current laboratory operations. Up to 1 ton was stored in each magazine. The filled truck shed was for holding up to 20 loaded powder trucks overnight; if full, it held approximately 35 tons of BL or QF cartridges or cordite.

RM 10, COL 18/1

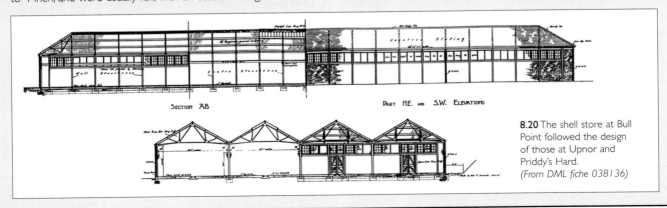

Section AB   Part N.E. and S.W. Elevations

8.20 The shell store at Bull Point followed the design of those at Upnor and Priddy's Hard.
(From DML fiche 038136)

- As part of the arrangements for rapidly meeting the urgent requirements of the fleet in wartime it had now been decided to keep a considerable stock of filled cartridges in the Portsmouth District in readiness for immediate shipment.
- Special service vessels at the Home ports being constantly in the basins had to land their cordite to be stored on shore.
- The requirements of magazine accommodation had increased owing to ships carrying guns firing charges, which had to be stored in properly constructed magazines, instead of ammunition, which did not need to be stored under strict magazine conditions.

Consequently, the Bedenham scheme was authorised to proceed forthwith. It was estimated that the magazines would take some two and a half years to complete. Final drawings for the magazines were completed by February 1909. The extremely wide traverses adopted were reminiscent of those suggested by the 1865 Magazine Committee (see Chapter 5), and the design incorporated provision for a standard gauge railway to supply the magazines. The magazines were derived, with different roofing arrangements, from the pioneering cordite cartridge stores at Lodge Hill (see page 171). Plans for buildings for the examination and repair of BL and QF cartridges were drawn up at the same time; the office buildings, boiler house and facilities for the staff were all contained within a square traverse at the end of the row of magazines. In 1910, negotiations were opened about the railway connection.

Marchwood was about to become marginalised; the Admiral Superintendent at Portsmouth Dockyard reported adversely on the security arrangements there, but the Superintendent of Stores did not think it worth spending any significant sum there: 'the new Magazines at Bedenham should be completed as rapidly as possible and then Marchwood will only be used for reduced quantities of surplus and obsolescent ammunition which will not be of great importance from a security point of view.' In 1912 a second set of magazines was built, parallel to the original ones, so repeating the general design of Lodge Hill (see figures 8.3, 8.4 and Appendix A). By October 1913, the depot was completed, the ten magazines

having a normal capacity of 200 tons each, although this could be increased to 300 tons.[14]

Troubles with ammunition continued, and an additional workload was placed on the depots by the withdrawal of some of the earlier issues. By 1914, the amount of cordite carried by a typical pre-Dreadnought battleship was fairly substantial (see HMS *London* tonnage, page 183). Subsequent classes of battleship shipped much heavier outfits, placing a considerable workload on the depots in the preparation, storage and issue of this ammunition.[15]

On the eve of war, the deficiencies that had been so alarming twenty years earlier had been corrected. At the end of 1913, the three naval depots offered substantial facilities (see opposite). By July 1913, 190 rounds were provided for each heavy gun. For ships in home waters, 80 rounds were on board with the remainder held in reserve. The cost had inevitably been greater than the original estimates, for dockyard works as well as magazines, and the Naval Works Acts were duly amended. Those of 1895–1901 fixed the maximum period of repayment of terminable annuities at thirty years from the passing of the 1895 Naval Works Act (see pages 145–6), but by the Naval Works Act of 1903 the maximum period was set at thirty years from the date of the 1903 Act. The £1,186,000 borrowed for magazines in 1903 under the earlier provisions, was to be repaid by annuities of £78,363, the last payment due on 1 November 1924, while the additional £1,031,000 borrowed in 1903 was to be repaid by annuities of £53,864, the last payment falling due on 8 December 1932. In 1905 the estimated bill for the new magazines was £1,335,000, with expenditure to 31 March 1905 being £208,199, and that for 1905–6 and 1906–7 being £297,100; completion was expected in 1909–10. To put this in perspective, the figures for the Keyham extension were a £4,500,000 total, with expenditure to 31 March 1905 being £2,831,229, and that for 1905–6, £424,250, that for 1906–7, £768,000; completion was expected in 1908–09. *Dreadnought*, completed in December 1906, cost £1,783,883; the *Iron Duke* class, completed in 1914, averaged £1,891,122. In the face of these figures, the new magazines were a good investment.[16]

Chapter 9 **The Test of War**

In 1914 the regular army was organised into six divisions of all arms and one cavalry gun division. The cavalry division was composed of around 9,000 all ranks, with twenty-four 13-pounder guns and twenty-four machine guns. The other divisions were composed of around 18,000 all ranks, also with twenty-four machine guns and seventy-six guns. Fifty-four of these were 18-pounders, 18 were 4.5-inch howitzers, and four were 60-pounders. The fourteen territorial divisions were equipped with obsolescent guns. The consumption of ammunition by these guns was so great, and completely unforeseen, that by the end of September Sir John French, Commander of the British Expeditionary Forces sent to Europe in August 1914, was concerned about the situation. In stark contrast, the navy mounted a much larger number of guns, of greater size, with a thoroughly established system of magazines distributed around the world. The war was to bring changes to the way in which naval ammunition was stored and distributed in the United Kingdom, but these developments were as nothing compared to the challenges faced and overcome by the army.[1]

The First World War brought about a staggering increase in the production of projectiles and explosives. For the first time, the demands of the army were to outstrip those of the navy, for nobody had foreseen the prodigious expenditure of shells at the Western Front. These missiles were virtually all manufactured and filled by private contractors, and their efforts were documented in the official history of the Ministry of Munitions, a work for which the Admiralty refused to supply information.[2] The initial inadequacy in the supply of shells for the army and the means by which the situation was remedied is another story. The crisis was not one of failure to provide sophisticated storing and handling environments, which were not needed for the millions of land service shells eventually churned out. These were simply stacked in warehouses or in the open awaiting shipment to France, where they were stored in massive ammunition depots to the rear of the armies.

Overseas depots

By 1918 six ammunition depots had been created: Audruicq, Zeneghem and Dannes in the Northern Lines of Communication; Blargies,

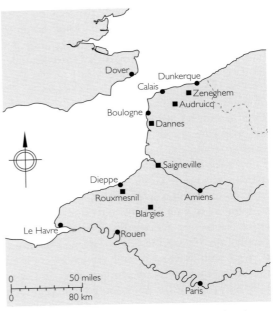

9.1 The depots established in France by 1918, showing also the principal cities and the Channel ports.
(Map by Stephen Dent)

Rouxmesnil and Saigneville in the Southern Lines of Communication. The layout of these depots had, under the pressure of war, undergone a forced evolution in 1915. In that year, Audruicq was constructed to receive ammunition landed at Boulogne, and another depot was built at Grand Quevilly, near Rouen, to take the ammunition shipped to that port (and currently being stored in warehouses in the town). The Quevilly base consisted of five steel-framed sheds covered with corrugated iron, and was brought into use in March 1916. Some of the ammunition that had been temporarily stored in the Rouen warehouses was being moved into the new depot when, through a faulty fuze, a destructive explosion occurred. Only 600 tons of ammunition was in the new depot at the time, so the loss was trifling, but 20,000 tons were in the old depot, and an explosion there would have caused enormous damage. The ammunition supply was temporarily rerouted to Boulogne, as much as possible sent from Rouen to the armies, and the remainder sent to Quevilly. The post mortem on the accident recommended that explosives be distributed among a large number of depots, each holding no more than 2,000 tons, with no buildings closer than 70 yards apart. But in the circumstances it was quite impossible to act on these recommendations.

As in previous years, a major incident was responsible for a rethink of the layout of these huge depots; in this case the total wrecking of Audruicq by an air raid on the night of 20 July 1916. A single bomb put the whole establishment out of action for several months, the fire being carried from shed to shed by the loaded wagons, and £3,500,000 worth of ammunition was destroyed (though this was less than half the value of what would be fired off in a busy week). Four different types of risk, corresponding to different types of ammunition, were identified. When complete rounds were packed in wooden boxes, the ignition of a round would set the adjacent boxes on fire and destroy the whole stack; wherever possible, the cartridges should be detached from the shell and packed separately. For heavy gun ammunition, the danger lay not in combustion but in the explosion of the shell and the distance to which fragments could be projected; live shell had been picked up two miles away. Trench munitions had very thin containing walls, so an accident was likely to detonate the whole mass virtually instantaneously, causing an immense shock wave. Chemical and incendiary projectiles had their own specific dangers.

It was decided that it would be best to segregate the different types of ammunition into separate areas. The separation of the magazines at Bedenham had been 350 feet, the lines of magazines being 500 feet apart; but those were heavily traversed buildings. Each depot was to be of a standard size, accommodating a total of 35,000 tons of ammunition: 16,000 tons boxed ammunition; 12,000 of component ammunition; 3,500 of trench ammunition; 2,000 of chemical and incendiary ammunition; 1,500 of small arm ammunition. Quevilly and Boulogne were abandoned as depots, their locations being too dangerous; Blargies, just completed, could not be modified to conform to the new plan, but massive sandbag traverses were provided, and Audruicq was rebuilt as closely as possible to the revised requirements.

The total of 35,000 tons was not, however, to remain the norm for these massive stores. By 1917 no less than 10,000 tons of ammunition was arriving every day, with Dunkirk providing additional harbour facilities. A standard pattern for a depot was finally agreed on in June 1918. Each group of sheds was to be 300 feet clear longitudinally of the adjoining groups, with a separation of 1,200 feet between parallel lines of groups. Extensive use was made of traverses both within and without the buildings; sandbags on their own had been found to be unsatisfactory for this purpose, as they rotted quickly, and the preferred construction was of corrugated iron, supported by a strong wooden frame and filled with earth or sand. Cartridge sheds and fuze and tube sheds were provided with splinter-proof roofs; these were of low pitched

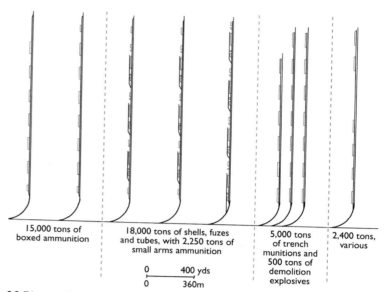

9.2 Diagram of a standard pattern base ammunition depot to hold 38,650 tons. All movements were carried out by narrow gauge railway. *(Adapted from The Works of the Royal Engineers in the European War, 1914-1919, Work under the Director of Works [France], Chatham, 1924)*

Labels within diagram:
15,000 tons of boxed ammunition
18,000 tons of shells, fuzes and tubes, with 2,250 tons of small arms ammunition
5,000 tons of trench munitions and 500 tons of demolition explosives
2,400 tons, various
0   400 yds
0   360m

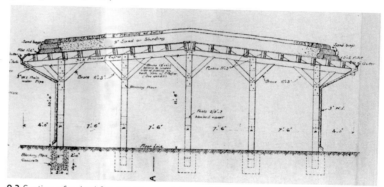

9.3 Section of a shed for cartridges or tubes and fuzes. Note the sandbags at the edges of the roof to retain the protective layers. *(From The Work of the Royal Engineers in the European War, 1924)*

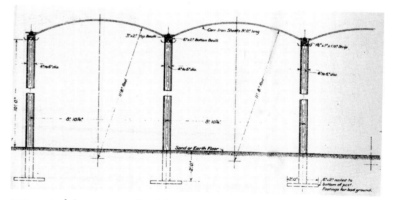

9.4 Section of a shed to house shells: the roof is light corrugated iron. *(From The Work of the Royal Engineers in the European War, 1924)*

corrugated iron covered with 15 inches of sand and aggregate. Heavy shells were roofed in with light corrugated iron. The final accommodation at each of the depots comprised:

	Tons		Tons
Audruicq	44,000	Zeneghem	49,000
Dannes	65,000	Blargies	64,500
Rouxmesnil	49,000	Saigneville	60,000
		TOTAL	331,500

Trials of war

Weaknesses in matériel were disclosed early in the First World War. In December 1914 a 9.2-inch gun was destroyed when firing lyddite common shell with full charges on the armoured cruiser *Achilles*, causing considerable damage to the mounting and gunhouse. The shell was probably a Mk.III, recognised as a weak design. All of these and earlier marks were ordered to be withdrawn. Some worrying trials had shown that prematures occurred in lyddite shells that had been filled with certain batches of Waltham Abbey picric acid. The 13.5-inch lyddite common shells had given four prematures out of eleven; the 12-inch lyddite common shell one out of eleven. No prematures, however, had been reported with those filled with trade acid. All 13.5-inch and 12-inch shells filled with Waltham Abbey acid of certain dates were disembarked forthwith. A source of danger was revealed in January 1915, when a sheet of flame was seen while a gunloading cage in *Princess Royal* was being raised; the fire was caused by powder spilling from a broken igniter. After the Battle of Jutland, Admiral

Beatty's complaints included doubts about the safety of nose-fuzes in common HE shells. The Department of Naval Ordnance agreed that there was a possibility of a lyddite-filled shell fitted with the No.13 fuze detonating, if hit fairly. However, a new shell filling was coming into use. This was trotyl (later known as TNT, see Glossary), which supplemented and eventually superseded lyddite as a shell filling. All trotyl-filled shells were fitted with the No.45 fuze, which had a sealing device and did not pose the same risk. Orders were consequently given to withdraw all heavy lyddite-filled common shell as soon as possible. At firing practice in August 1916, the light cruiser *Aurora* of the Harwich Force fired seven shrapnel shells for exercising AA control and testing fuzes. The shells had been kept on deck since the ship was commissioned. Five out of seven failed, and the matter was reported to Lodge Hill. All fuzes of 6-inch and 4-inch shrapnel similarly stored on the ship were returned to Lodge Hill and replaced by new ones sent from Woolwich.[1]

The difficulties caused by the absence of a shore-based Ordnance Depot to supply the main forces at Scapa and Rosyth

9.5 The battleship HMS *King George V* pictured on a fine morning in Portsmouth Harbour, with Priddy's Hard faintly visible through the mist beyond her bow. Built at Portsmouth Royal Dockyard, *King George V* was completed in 1912 and served throughout the First World War, being sold for scrapping in 1926. This view gives a good idea of the size and power of her 13.5-inch guns. Along the side of the ship's hull are stowed anti-torpedo nets, while the object in a frame overhanging the quarter is a common service lifebuoy: four copper balls connected by a light metal framework and launched by a trigger release. (*Priddy's Hard Archive 1998.3.2*)

were considerable. After Crombie came into operation (see pages 190–91), the armament reserves for replenishment after fleet actions were disposed between the three stations.

During the war, the average expenditure of ammunition per outfit (total ordnance supplied) by ships of all descriptions was:

⅕ of outfit for heavy guns
⅓ of outfit for 6-inch and 7.5-inch guns
¼ of outfit for light guns
¼ of outfit for 15-inch turret guns

These figures give some idea of the workload sustained by the Ordnance Depots.[2]

[1] ADM 137/4050, ADM 137/4051, ADM 1/8463/176, ADM 137/2081
[2] ADM 137/4052, ADM 1/22864

If the quantities held at dumps behind the front line were added, the total weight of ammunition in France amounted to half a million tons. Compared with these massive improvised depots, the old formal magazines used by the army were almost an irrelevance; Weedon appears to have been used solely for the storage of small arms and no information about the uses of Purfleet has been located.[3]

Ammunition transportation in the UK

The navy was also in an unexpected situation. Its three great depots had all been brought up to date and had the potential for expansion; but, as they had been developed in close relationship to naval dockyards located to face French and Dutch opponents, they were in the wrong place for a war against the Germans. No permanent bases calculated to meet the challenge of a fleet from across the North Sea were to be fully operational for some time (the first ship docked at Rosyth in March 1916) and the Grand Fleet was mostly based at the remote anchorages of Scapa Flow and Cromarty Firth, far from any sources of supply. These improvised bases were to be the chief instruments in denying the command of the North Sea to the German High Sea Fleet, and it was essential that ordnance stores be provided there in quantity. So as not to hold ammunition in quantities that would limit the effectiveness of the fleet if lost, it was at once decided to discontinue the use of supply ships for ammunition. One or more smaller ships, holding quarter outfits for each squadron, were to be used as depot ships. Called ammunition ships, they were to be supplied by ammunition carriers operating between the Grand Fleet's base and the naval Ordnance Depots. In October 1914 the Commander-in-Chief of the Home Fleet recommended that additional ammunition carriers be loaded with a quarter outfit and kept at Pembroke as a reserve in case of a fleet action. This would also reduce the quantity held at Upnor, which was thought vulnerable to bombing. The ships were eventually moored in the Hamoaze at twelve hours' notice. Because of the real danger of submarine attack, the ships were unloaded in July 1915 and sent empty to Inverness, where they eventually reloaded their cargoes, which had been sent on by rail. From thence the ships went to Invergordon, on the Cromarty Firth, where they remained until required. During the first year of the war large transports were loaded at Priddy's Hard (the tonnage of ammunition shipped is not known) and certainly at the other depots as well. In total, 23,000 tons was despatched from Priddy's Hard in smaller ships during that period, but after that the shipping of ammunition from the southern ports was halted because of the submarine menace, with only mines being embarked.

For the first time, the traditional method of transport and distribution of naval ordnance was completely upset, and the railways came into their own, sometimes assisting in unexpected ways. Explosives had hardly figured in pre-war goods traffic, and the railway companies consequently owned very few copper-lined gunpowder vans. In this wartime emergency, standards were relaxed and the use of temporary gunpowder vans was authorised. Any iron or steel inside them had to be covered up with leather, cloth or sheet lead. Fortunately, most of the explosives and projectiles did not require specialised vehicles. Gunpowder vans (standard or improvised) had to be used for cartridges filled with gunpowder, CE, dry guncotton and picric acid and its derivatives, except when in metallic cases or cylinders. However, picric acid and its derivatives could not be placed in lead-lined improvised vans. Ordinary closed vans, locked, were suitable for amatol, cordite and cordite cartridges, while ordinary trucks, well sheeted, would do for wet guncotton, mines, shells, BL and QF ammunition.

With transport by ship no longer an option, all ammunition was railed to Inverness, which became a major distribution centre, and was forwarded by ship from there to Scapa and the other anchorages. A branch line was built from Inverness Station to the harbour, where extensive sidings were constructed to hold ammunition wagons. This had been a remarkable improvisation; a message arrived at Inverness in May 1915 ordering the immediate construction of the branch, as several ammunition trains had already been despatched from the south. The line was completed in just ten days. Great security surrounded all these operations; several German spies were arrested in the town, some being executed. In August 1916, Inverness and all stations on the Highland Line beyond were declared a Special Military Area, where identity cards were required for access. These arrangements continued for the rest of the war, and, together with the equally vital coal trains, put a great strain on the largely single-lined Highland Railway, parts of which had to be doubled to cope with the traffic. Bedenham and Lodge Hill, as we have seen, were already connected with the national railway network, and Bull Point was shortly to follow. The transport of ammunition by rail, which was vital, was nevertheless often hindered by the wasteful use of wagons by the Admiralty, War Office and the Ministry of Munitions. On one memorable occasion 28 lbs of gunpowder was sent from Purfleet to Catterick in a wagon of its own. In addition to this primary function, however, the railway workshops were also important manufacturers of projectiles and fuzes, and as well as producing them, rectified an enormous number of cartridge cases returned from France (over 30 million 18-pounder cases alone). The Lancashire and Yorkshire Railway devised a rectifying machine that enabled an output to be maintained far beyond that available by the manual methods (see Glossary). Quite apart from these functions, the railway system served to provide temporary magazine accommodation. A landslip in December 1915 made the Folkestone–Dover line unusable as a through route for the duration, and the 1,392-yard Shakespeare Tunnel was made available as the ultimate in bombproof storage, sometimes housing well over a hundred trucks of explosives – an expediency which anticipated later developments.[4]

Wartime developments at the UK depots

A proper land-based magazine was provided for the naval dockyard established in Rosyth at

9.6 The scale of work involved in rectifying cartridge cases is shown by this sculptural pile awaiting treatment at Doncaster Railway Works. *(National Railway Museum)*

Crombie, four miles upstream on the banks of the Forth, on a site bearing many topographical similarities to Bull Point. Land was acquired in early 1913 for a branch line to connect with the North British Railway. A 2-foot 6-inch gauge internal rail network was also provided. The depot opened in May 1915. It had six cordite magazines (each with a capacity of 47,763 cubic feet), three shell stores (two of 30,500 square feet and one of 32,100), thirteen cartridge rooms, two cordite cutting rooms, six filling and examining rooms, a shell painting and scraping block of buildings, twelve shell filling and examining rooms, and three TNT melting rooms – in short, an establishment comparable with those serving the older dockyards. The stocks held there were to be sufficient to provide, together with those held afloat, a duplicate outfit in reserve. Replenishments were sent from Crombie to Inverness for shipment, Crombie being replenished from the southern depots. It was soon supplied with a large store magazine establishment at Bandeath on the south side of the Forth, 30 miles from Rosyth and 25 miles from Crombie. A standard gauge line connected all thirty-six magazines and seven shell stores to the main line. Each magazine held 300 tons of explosives, and was divided into two bays by a concrete traverse. The shell stores, each holding 5,000 tons and measuring 155 feet by 152 feet, were divided into four bays by concrete traverses. Additional shore bases for non-Grand Fleet ships were established at Harwich, Dover (with a sub-depot at Dunkirk), Liverpool, Buncrana and Milford Haven. At Harwich, Dover and Liverpool part of the stores were kept afloat. A great deal of railway traffic was concerned with the movement of mines, particularly after the decision to lay the enormous (and in the end virtually useless) Northern Barrage minefield between the Orkneys and the Norwegian coast. Mine depots were estab-

lished at Bedenham, Immingham and Grangemouth (the main base for minelayers). Issue of mines began at Immingham in February 1917.[5]

The losses suffered at Jutland at least had the benefit of easing the workload of the Ordnance Depots. At the Battle of the Dogger Bank in January 1915, *Lion* fired 243 rounds of main armament, *Princess Royal* 271, *Tiger* 355, *New Zealand* 139 and *Indomitable* 136. All this had to be replenished by the ammunition ships at Rosyth, where the shore-based Ordnance Depot at Crombie was shortly to come into operation. At Jutland, 1,235 x 15-inch shells, 1,424 x 14-inch and 13.5-inch and 1,511 x 12-inch shells had been fired, and the battle-cruisers *Queen Mary*, *Indefatigable* and *Invincible*, with the armoured cruisers *Warrior*, *Defence* and *Black Prince*, were sunk. These losses meant that the reserves of 13.5-inch, 12-inch, 9.2-inch and 7.5-inch shells had improved, as the demand for them had materially decreased, but there was a deficit of twenty-two per cent per outfit for 15-inch shells, carried by the *Queen Elizabeth* and *Revenge* class battleships, none of which had been lost. Writing immediately after the war, the Director of Armament Supply considered that if better standardisation of ammunition had existed, the battle would probably have had no effect in decreasing reserves. That lesson was not learnt and ships in the Second World War still carried a great miscellany of guns, with all the ensuing complications.

Unfortunately, very few records survive to give a picture of the development and functioning of the Medway and Plymouth Depots during the war, and no official history was published to shed light on the matter. On the Medway, the site of Upnor was too cramped to allow any significant additions, while at Lodge Hill a massive new shell store with an available capacity of 265,200 cubic feet was added. Otherwise, the design had been so

9.7 A late war view of British battle-cruisers on the Firth of Forth. From left to right, HM ships *Australia*, *New Zealand*, *Indomitable* and *Inflexible*. Each carried eight 12-inch guns. *(Conway Maritime Press)*

9.8 The new cartridge filling rooms at Priddy's Hard as completed. *(From TNA ADM 195/46)*

9.9 The additional facilities provided for Priddy's Hard in the summer of 1915. The buildings in black are the principal later wartime additions. *(Adapted from PTM/2481)*

effective and the accommodation so extensive at Lodge Hill that only extensions to the laboratory were made. Bull Point, by contrast, paralleled Priddy's Hard in the number of additions to which it was subject, although on a reduced scale. The dry guncotton magazine was given extra (and apparently unique) protection by the addition of a steel trussed roof to cover the traversed area, and facilities for annealing cartridge cases were extended. The shell filling rooms were adapted for filling with trotyl, and a shifting room (see Glossary) for trotyl and shellite workers was added. A now very essential connection with the Great Western

Railway was made in 1916, and a transfer shed provided. The war ensured the survival of *Eclipse* and *Newcastle*, and these ancient hulks survived the war, not being put up for disposal until 1921 and 1929 respectively.[6]

Much more is known about the Portsmouth area, for the Naval Ordnance Supply Officer at Priddy's Hard compiled a summary of the works there for an official history, which was never completed. By 1914 the Portsmouth Gunwharf had ceased to accommodate filled shells. It was solely concerned with the storage of guns and the manufacture of spare parts necessary for their maintenance, the foundry being extended for this purpose in 1902. A thousand mines were also in store. Priddy's Hard, no longer a deposit magazine, was engaged in the filling and repair of cartridges and shells, the repair of packages and cartridge cases and the storage of shells. The newly completed Bedenham had ten magazines holding 4,000 tons of cartridges, and the seven magazines at Marchwood held 6,000 tons of gunpowder and cartridges. The facilities that had been created so recently were to prove an easily expandable base capable of meeting demands greater than any predictions. The first requirement was for increased laboratory capacity. At Priddy's Hard, the six shell filling rooms and the twelve cartridge filling rooms in the ditch of the old fortification were employed in repairing defective ammunition and filling; all these shells and cartridges were mostly destined for gunnery schools. Manufacture of BL and QF drill cartridges was undertaken on a large scale; this involved a good deal of experiment in conjunction with the gunnery school HMS *Excellent* to guide the designs for the new types of large guns. No attempt was made to replicate the elaborate earthen traverses of the relocated laboratory, but the topography of the site meant that the symmetrical arrangement adopted at Lodge Hill could not be followed. Instead, the twelve additional cartridge-filling rooms, in two sets of six, were at forty-five degrees to each other and connected by a new tramway to the cordite magazines. These were all completed by the summer of 1915. A further set of six rooms for filling smaller QF cartridges was built between the cordite magazines

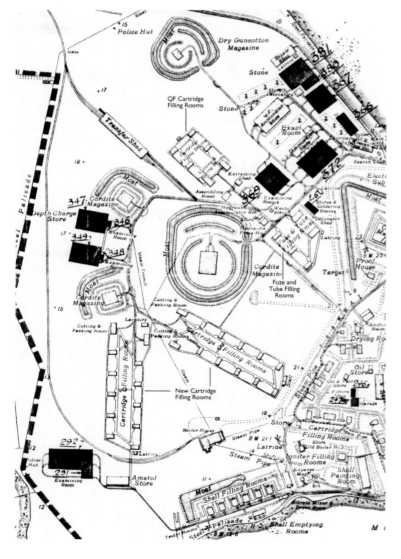

and the dry guncotton magazine, together with a building for examining them. Because of the inability of the Royal Laboratory at Woolwich and the trade to supply the urgent requirements of the fleet, five rooms for filling and packing fuses and tubes were also added. The increased production of QF ammunition called for increased storage space, and the explosives store and wet guncotton store of 1898 were used for this purpose. Two old case stores adjacent to the old covered rolling way were rebuilt and adapted as rooms for cleaning and rectifying brass cartridge cases. The rolling way had become redundant and part of it was incorporated into the lacquering room. In the summer of 1915 a set of three trotyl melting rooms were built at Priddy's Hard to serve the 1886/7 shell filling rooms, and one of these is the only surviving building of its type. By working day and night, a filling rate of as much as 60,000 lbs of the explosive per week was achieved at Priddy's Hard. A hydraulic press house for pressing tetryl pellets was also required and built at the same time. Trotyl was relatively cheap to produce, at about half the cost of lyddite, but required the scarce raw material toluol. This situation was mitigated by the fact that it could be mixed with relatively inexpensive ammonium nitrate (which cost a quarter of the price of trotyl) to produce the explosive amatol, which, however, was relatively insensitive and required a special exploder system. As a consequence a large amatol store was built and one of the trotyl melting rooms used as an amatol mixing room. The shell emptying rooms were adapted for

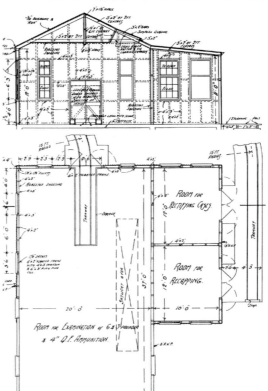

9.11 Above: The examining room for 3- and 6-pounder QF ammunition just completed at Priddy's Hard in July 1915. (From TNA ADM 195/46) Left: It is uncommon for both a drawing of an ordnance building and a photograph of it on completion to be preserved. The plan shows the division of the building into two sections, one involved in dismantling and inspection, the other in reassembly. Each has a separate tramway. (From PTM/2875A)

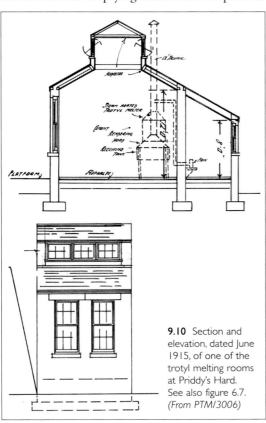

9.10 Section and elevation, dated June 1915, of one of the trotyl melting rooms at Priddy's Hard. See also figure 6.7. (From PTM/3006)

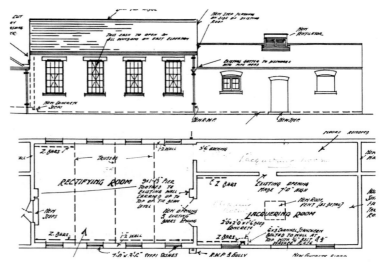

9.12 Case stores adapted as rectifying and lacquering rooms at Priddy's Hard. Note that part of the old rolling way is incorporated as part of the structure. These were rebuilt in 1915; the left-hand one was rebuilt again in 1938. (From PTM/2838)

9.13 The exterior of the rectifying shop at Priddy's Hard, now demolished. This was where fired brass cartridge cases, metal cartridge and shell boxes came to be repaired before they were reused (wooden boxes were repaired by the chippies). The rectifying of brass cartridge cases was divided into two operations: men hammered the cases back into shape over formers; women re-lacquered them. A standard gauge railway runs across the front of the building. (*Priddy's Hard Archive 1998.4.198*)

filling mines by the installation of presses and guncotton cutting equipment; the tramway system was further enlarged as a consequence, a connection being established between the shell emptying rooms and a mine store for 2,000 mines, with its own examining room. At Priddy's Hard, horned mines were assembled and detonator carriers filled, the requirements of the fleet for some forty mines and sinkers weekly being met, and some 1,000 countermines were filled here before these

9.14 An explosive paravane. (*TNA ADM 137/1889*)

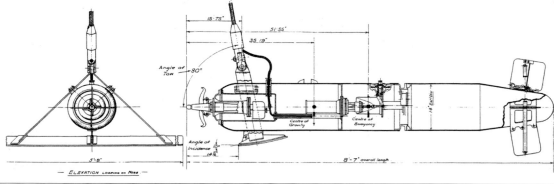

9.15 The arrangements for filling and storing mines at Priddy's Hard as of 1916–17. The standard gauge railway line was originally built to supply the boiler house with coal; it was then additionally used for the despatch of mines. (*Adapted from PTM/2485*)

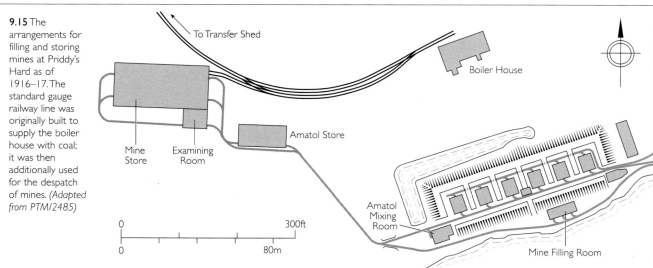

operations were transferred to Bedenham.[7]

These additions to Priddy's Hard were thus mainly led by the development of chemical explosives. Other buildings were required to store new weapons systems. When aerial bombs were first introduced they had been located in the shell store, but in 1916 a large store for 550 lb and 530 lb bombs was built between the two smaller cordite magazines. A store for depth charges stood beside it. Undersea warfare accounted for more additions. An explosive variant of the paravane (towed float that supported minesweeping cables) designed by Lieutenant Burney for anti-submarine use was a speciality of Priddy's Hard, where the fillings were to hand. Empty paravanes were delivered from the trade and filled with TNT, prepared for trials and rectified afterwards. The original paravane facilities were on a very small scale, a mere addition to the old cottages (see figure 3.10), with a testing hut placed at the south end of a nearby reservoir. By the summer of 1916 this work had so expanded that a set of large workshops was added along the approach road from Hardway. This was necessary as the explosive paravanes, like the bombs, had been stored and handled in the shell store, which although very substantially enlarged by the appropriation of 13,000 square feet of open space lying between it and the mine store, was soon found insufficient. The insertion of roof trusses between existing buildings to provide low-

9.16 Depth charges being prepared after the Second World War at Ernesettle (see pages 208–10). Note the foreman behind the barrier, his status denoted by a trilby hat. *(From HRO 109 M91, PH/72)*

9.17 The firing point structure at the western end of the Horsea Torpedo Range, built on Little and Greater Horsea Islands in the north-eastern corner of Portsmouth Harbour in 1889. The two-decked firing point at the narrow end of the range held two above-water torpedo tubes and one underwater tube. Inside the building was a steam winch which raised and lowered the submerged tube. The 850-yard lake, extended to 1,115 yards in 1904, is the principal survival on the site, which is now the home of the Defence Diving School. *(Priddy's Hard Archive 1998.3.116)*

9.18 Two interior photographs of the Royal Navy Torpedo Depot, Malta, in 1945. Above: Workers in the gyroscope assembly workshop at Misida Creek Depot. Below: The north corner of the main torpedo workshop at Kalafrana Depot. Although the men are dressed for working in Mediterranean conditions, otherwise these scenes are very much typical of the bustle of activity to be seen at all the depots. See also pages 110-113 and figures 6.15 and 6.16. *(Priddy's Hard Archive 2002.223.24 & 2002.223.35)*

cost covered spaces was well practised in the dockyards; the idea was also used for a timber store between A and B Magazines. The non-explosive minesweeping paravanes, probably a better investment than the anti-submarine variety, were soon added to the stores and needed additional separate accommodation. The non-explosive variant was entirely built by commercial firms, the agricultural machinery business of Ruston & Proctor producing equipment so reliable that by the beginning of 1917 they were issued without a sea test. At Bull Point a large sub-depot building for paravanes was designed in November 1917; as a road vehicle maintenance unit it survives today, the only remaining structure intended for paravane work.[8]

The hulks replaced

None of the paravane buildings remain at Priddy's Hard. The First World War structures that do remain owe their presence to a curious process of evolution. In June 1908 the captain of HMS *Excellent* reported that the *Vernon* hulks (see page 97) were worn out – a cry heard many times before – and a replacement shore establishment was required. The captain had heard rumours that a portion of the Ordnance Department was shortly to be transferred to a new site and, if so, room might be found for the new *Vernon* buildings on the ground to be vacated. He proposed to retain *Warrior*, moored at the end of a new pier, take over the powder pier and build barracks on the ground behind, utilising the explosive store and wet guncotton store as lecture rooms. The Commander-in-Chief forwarded the suggestion to the Admiralty, suggesting cheaper alternatives: part of the naval barracks, or Whale Island. Nothing came of this, and the hulks remained in use, but successive captains of *Excellent* persisted. In July 1910 it appeared that the choice of site for the new *Vernon* lay between Horsea and Frater, it being understood that the use of Tipner, Priddy's Hard and the gunwharf was out of the question (although the gunwharf would undoubtedly be the best place). In 1913 the matter was raised again. The hulks were on their last legs, with the exception of *Warrior*, which 'will probably last for many years yet', a correct judgment from the captain of *Vernon*. The captain thought the naval portion of the gunwharf was a good site, but had the drawback that *Warrior* could not be laid alongside, and as a consequence Horsea seemed the best site.

The pressures of war finally got things under way, and in September 1916 Rear Admiral Phipps Hornby (invalided home from the Dardanelles and now engaged on torpedo work) submitted that: 'the appropriation of the New Gunwharf to the requirements of the Mining Service may be definitely approved in principle, and Priddy's Hard

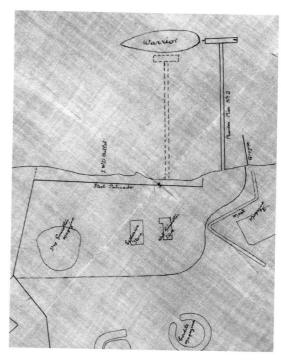

9.19 The proposal to locate *Warrior* at Priddy's Hard and adapt part of the site for the *Vernon* establishment. (TNA ADM 179/31)

decided upon as the site for erecting such new shops and storehouses as may be necessitated by the Ordnance Department surrendering the gunwharf. These buildings to be constructed on the semi-permanent basis.' The Commander-in-Chief, Admiral Sir Stanley Colville, concurred.

The gunwharf was clearly the best site for *Vernon*; and although it now held principally guns and their accoutrements, mines, sinkers and bombs, these could all be housed elsewhere. All guns of 4-inch calibre and above could at once be stowed in the dockyard and QF and machine guns placed in a new store there. Bedenham was intended as a mine store, so it was suggested that all mines be placed there, along with bombs. The arrangements for these were chaotic. For example, the gunwharf had large sheds under construction for stowing bombs that came from factories in the centre of England and were then returned to London for filling. Moreover, the present arrangement of three establishments belonging to the naval ordnance was uneconomical, their separation from each other by water causing delays, unnecessary transport and duplication. Admiral Colville cited the following example. A cordite case arriving from a ship was landed at Priddy's Hard; if damaged, the case (in most instances) would have to be sent over to the gunwharf to be repaired, which would be quite unnecessary if the repair shop were at Priddy's Hard.[9]

Transhipment of ammunition and stores was constant from one establishment to the other. It was clear that Priddy's Hard should be connected with the main railway system – the Admiral had already officially urged that in wartime this train service was all important, owing to most of the ammunition being sent to the fleet by train; in

9.20 Water transport.

Above: The camber at Priddy's Hard after 1950, with depot motor vessel *Sten* in view. *Sten*, along with *Dagger* and *Dirk*, appeared at the depot in 1950 after the Bedenham explosion, to patrol the ammunition barges moored in groups between Priddy's Hard, Bedenham and Portchester. At the time the belief was that the explosion had been caused by sabotage, and the vessels' initial job was simply to keep the public away. As time passed and tension eased they began to be used to transport workers between the depots. The doorway on the left is the end of the rolling way from the 1777 magazine. When gunpowder was no longer used for filling shell and cartridges the camber was used for repairing barges and small armament vessels. The air raid shelter in the centre background is still extant, as is one of the few remaining pieces of decorative steel railing in the foreground. *(Priddy's Hard Archive 1998.4.214)*

Below: A motor fishing vessel at Forton Jetty, Priddy's Hard, in the 1950s. These vessels were taken over by the Admiralty during the war to run ferry services to and from the various naval establishments; one continued to perform the complete circuit of the harbour into the 1960s. Behind the jetty is the Forton Creek rolling bridge, the centre section of which was made of wood on rollers and could be rolled back by two men to allow access to the creek. This was replaced by the Millennium bridge in 2000. In the background are air raid shelters, with the steel tanks (given concrete outer skins to protect them from shrapnel and incendiaries during air raids) of the naval oil depot to the right. *(Priddy's Hard Archive 1998.4.213)*

9.21 Left: a view looking towards the shell stores at Priddy's Hard showing, in the foreground, a transformer box, and in the distance the gable end of the rail transfer shed, a flat-roofed surface shelter built in 1939–40 for protection of personnel from air attack and later used as a bicycle shed. *(Stephen Dent)*

9.22 Above: this shifting room was built in 1897 to serve the new laboratory complex. The doorway visible was the 'dirty area' entrance reached from the sally port through the ramparts, while the 'clean area' exit to the laboratory rooms was at the far end. *(Stephen Dent)*

9.23 The windows of the QF store of 1896/7 were deepened when it was converted into a carpenters' machine shop for the Experimental Mining Depot in 1915. *(Jeremy Lake)*

peace it would also be an enormous advantage and economy. The current operation of shipping everything by water between Priddy's Hard and Bedenham, required frequent handling of cargoes, a very large fleet of lighters and a large labour bill. Considerable transhipping work had been entailed at Bedenham, stores having to be transferred from railway trucks to barges for delivery at Priddy's Hard and vice versa. In one year, 65,000 tons had been brought in or out of the depot by this means or by carrier. The Admiral was confident that an unbiased small committee would prove that the Ordnance Department could easily give up the gunwharf and be housed at Priddy's Hard and Bedenham, with the guns and mountings relocated in the dockyard. The Superintendent of Ordnance Stores found that erecting a tinsmiths' and a painters' shop at Priddy's Hard, and adapting an existing building to form a carpenters' shop, would meet the immediate requirements of the Experimental Mining Department.

At a conference on October 28 it was proposed that the tinsmiths' and carpenters' shops at the gunwharf be reprovided at Priddy's Hard. It was also suggested that the Army Gunwharf could be moved to Hilsea, freeing the whole site for naval purposes. The new empty package store had to be built first to release the other buildings, which would take about two months. The tinsmiths' and painters' shop was a new building, the two sections of which were differentiated by their roof construction (the tinsmiths' shop had steel trusses). The carpenters' shop was a conversion of an empty case store, which was originally the second QF shell store of 1896 (see figure 9.23). The travelling

crane was no longer required and was moved to the new adjacent empty package store, while the original high windows no longer gave adequate lighting and were extended downwards, the work being executed with remarkable attention to detail. The original QF shell store had similarly lost its function, and was then in use as a components store. A drastic change of use befell the laboratory boat house, which became part of a complex around the south end of the camber adapted for rectifying brass cartridge cases. The plant available at the depot was transferred to these buildings, which were converted into a set of seven annealing rooms with the necessary high-pressure gas ovens. Storage accommodation for these cases was provided by the covered space created between the shell store and the mine store. The latter building

9.24 The time-honoured methods of providing additional covered storage space by inserting trusses and adding lean-tos were resorted to at Priddy's Hard during the First World War. (Adapted from PTM/2485)

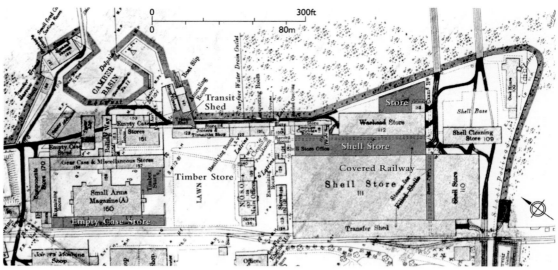

9.25 The tinsmiths' shop at Priddy's Hard. It was adapted in 1929 for handling torpedoes along a standard-gauge line set under new porches, which were removed when the railway was taken up. The tall doors were added to receive the torpedoes and runways handling them into the building. (NMR BB94/10346)

had also changed its function, now storing warheads for torpedoes. In September 1917 the provision of a standard gauge railway from Bedenham to Priddy's Hard was included in the Priddy's Hard scheme, together with a store for inflammables. As part of the decentralisation of the dockyard generating plant, provision was made for a substation at Priddy's Hard, while a landing shed was built on the camber by the old powder pier. The introduction of the railway necessitated the demolition of most of what was left of the entrance and the related old fortifications; it also required two transfer sheds, one by the shell store (whose construction destroyed a portion of the remaining part of the original laboratory) and another lying alongside exchange sidings for the transhipment of materials to the tramway system. A further branch led to a coal dump for the boiler house lying behind the shell filling rooms; this line also had a spur running into the new mine store, which, as another consequence of the shifting of

explosives storage to Bedenham, was converted to a shell painting room and a supplementary transfer shed for shells.[10]

The necessities of the time caused the introduction of female labour into the depot for the first time. Women worked all the power sewing machines for making up empty cartridges and overalls, and did a great deal of filling work on all types of cartridges, small and medium shells, fuzes and tubes, generally working separately from the men. Segregated facilities, including latrines and a Matron's group of buildings, were provided for them. As a first expedient, a shifting room was converted into a shifting and dining room for women, but plans for a separate dining room were drawn up in June 1916, and the building then reverted to its former single use.

The additions to Priddy's Hard caused by the replacement of gunwharf facilities were only a limited substitution, and in December 1917 the first plans were drawn up for a comprehensive set

9.26 Women first worked at Priddy's Hard at the end of 1915. By 1918 there were 71 women on the clerical staff and 781 labour staff, of which 38 were employed in the gunwharf, repairing, storing and issuing gun barrels. Men and women generally worked separately. This posed portrait shows the overalls, trousers and caps worn by women workers, however the front of the overall would have been buttoned up to the neck when working. *(Priddy's Hard Archive NAM 1435)*

9.27 Shell section workers, probably around the end of the First World War. The building behind is the laboratory office, one of a row of buildings originally built in the 1860s as messengers', foreman's and police quarters. *(Priddy's Hard Archive 2002-573)*

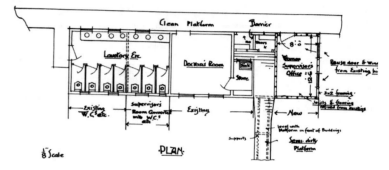

of gunwharf workshops immediately to the north of Priddy's Hard. The ending of the war meant that haste was not essential and construction was not completed until 1920. It was also decided that the powder pier of 1876 should be demolished, though for similar reasons this did not take place until 1921. The New Gunwharf had a far more limited function than its predecessor, which as has

been seen was once a universal provider, more important in the scheme of things than Priddy's Hard. Now its functions were restricted to the repair of guns and their breech mechanisms; the largest buildings on the site being stores for accoutrements and mechanisms, the work being performed in a Blacksmiths' Shop and a Fitters' Shop. A rifle range was provided for testing small

9.28 The Matron's room at Priddy's Hard, extended in 1917 from an existing latrine. *(PTM/3270)*

9.29 The array of magazines at Bedenham in 1918, with their railway system. Note the additional row of magazines to the top of the plan, added in 1912. Also shown are the two QF stores of 1917; B Magazine of 1916; and, to the right, the pier for the receipt and despatch of ammunition and explosives. To the left the railway branches out to the Gosport–Fareham line and the branch to Priddy's Hard, established in 1916 – prior to which water was the only means of transfer between the two depots. *(Adapted from PTM/3639)*

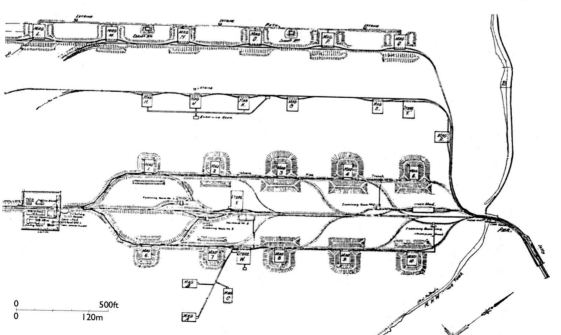

0   500ft
0   120m

9.30 A plan of the Portsmouth Gunwharf, by this time HMS *Vernon*, incorporating both the Old and New Gunwharf sites, and now entirely under Admiralty control, as drawn up in 1920. The New Gunwharf (figure 2.1) projects seawards to the south of Old Gunwharf, which stands on land successively reclaimed from the sea, forwards from the line of Gunwharf Road, and the site of the late 12th-century dock. Surviving buildings are: the Grand Store (also known as the Vulcan Block) and the Customs House, which date from 1811 (see also figure A.40 in Appendix A); the Infirmary, which dates from 1835 and housed wounded Royal Marines; the shell store of 1856; the gate of 1803; and parts of the boundary wall. See also figures 2.1, 2.2, 2.3, 2.4, 5.5, 5.25 & 5.26. *(TNA ADM 179/38)*

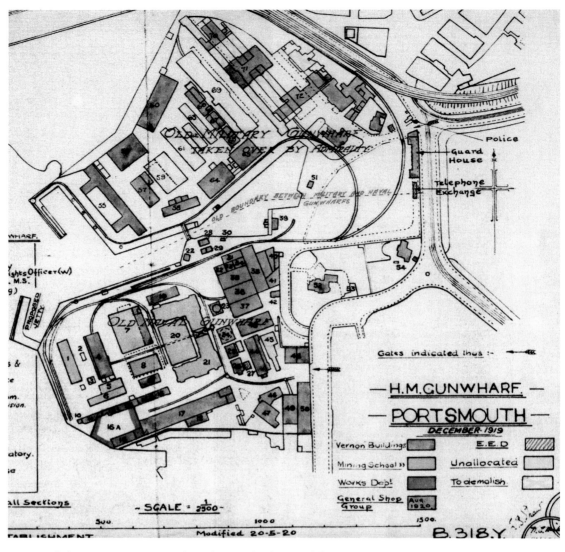

arms, and the site was connected to the standard gauge network.[11]

Bedenham's capacity was vastly expanded because of its increasing stores of mines and bombs, but its planned layout ensured that the ad hoc layout evolved at Priddy's Hard was not repeated. As a first measure, three additional cordite magazines capable of storing 3,000 tons were erected in the magazine area in the summer of 1916. These were temporary structures, built of wood and clad in corrugated iron, and survived until 1930. During 1917 and 1918 a further ten magazines, holding a total of 12,000 tons of cordite and BL ammunition, and three magazines, with a capacity of 5,300 tons of QF ammunition, were erected. The original accommodation was used to its fullest extent, creating a massively increased total available capacity of 28,300 tons against the original 4,000 tons. By the end of the war, further magazines were under construction to hold an additional 2,400 tons and a storehouse and truck shed were pressed into service for the storage of 1,000 tons of QF ammunition. In 1917, at the adjacent site of Frater Lake, a new depot was constructed to accommodate two bomb stores,

and five mine and shell stores for 6,000 mines and 50,000 tons of filled shells. This depot was still incomplete by March 1920, when the Treasury was informed that it required £318,000 to be completed as designed. From December 1917 a special train ran once a week from Bedenham to Grangemouth, the trains being made up of thirty wagons, each carrying eight mines. All this accommodation, however, was still insufficient and some 20,000 tons of filled shell had to be handled and stacked in the open; they were stowed outside with a view to minimising the effect of explosion in the event of an air raid, with powder-filled shells and empty shells being used as traverses, although later many sandbag traverses were built. Nor was this enough; to provide further accommodation for cartridges two large floating magazines were fitted up and taken into use for the storage of 7,000 tons, being supplemented by large ammunition barges. During the year ending 30 September 1918, 205,000 tons of explosives were carried by rail in and out of the depot. The pier work for the same year amounted to 132,400 tons, of which 67,000 was destined for or sent from Priddy's Hard.

By contrast with the enormous investment

THE TEST OF WAR

made in the Portsmouth Harbour area, Marchwood was relegated to a secondary role and no facilities were added. During the last two years of the war its magazines were emptied of ammunition and used for storing low-grade cordite, which was repacked and issued for land service or otherwise disposed of. Latterly 250 tons were handled daily against the previous maximum of 100 tons. The size and workload of all these depots increased dramatically during the war, as can be seen when comparing the staff in 1914 with those on the payroll in 1918. The numbers at the gunwharf rose from 320 to 880, at Marchwood from 21 to 103, but by far the greatest increase was at the Priddy's Hard–Bedenham complex, where the complement of 533 men had grown to 2,298, of which no less than 695 were women. There was now accommodation available for 150,550 tons of explosives instead of 29,630.[12]

Wartime development of less established depots

It was not only the established depots that experienced vast expansion. Temporary magazines to house the increasing production of propellants and high explosives waiting to be sent to the Filling Factories were soon required. Reigate Caves, formerly used as bonded stores, with an average height of 8 feet, length 125 feet, and numerous side chambers for occupation, were converted for the purpose in September 1915 and used until September 1918. During this period 12,049 tons of propellants passed through the magazine, which at times held 2,400 tons and seldom fell below 1,000 tons. Even better protection was provided by the old salt mines at Northwich, located at the bottom of a 300-foot shaft, and about 20 feet high.[13]

Such suitable expedients were strictly limited,

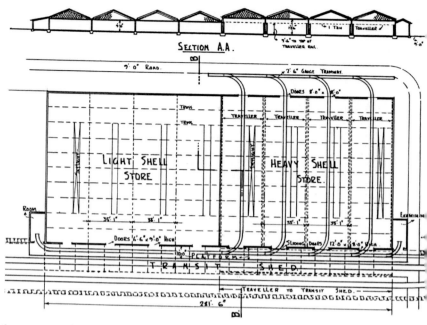

however, and the provision of conventional magazine buildings was costly, though a few had to be made. The principal improvisation, resorted to on a large scale, was the adaptation of brick kilns, which were lying unused with house construction suspended during the war. These were often rail-connected, not near heavily built-up areas, and, at least in the early years of the war, had labour to hand. At the end of December 1916 there were forty-five magazines in commission, containing on average 750 tons each. By the autumn of 1917 at least £6 per ton of explosives, or a total of approximately £400,000, had been saved by these shifts, but there were no more suitable premises, and the output of propellants and high explosives was increasing. The Director of the Department of Explosives Supply (DE) reluctantly concluded that purpose-built magazines would have to be provided. Not only were there only some four or

9.31 Additional shell stores and their rail system provided for Bedenham. (PTM/3664)

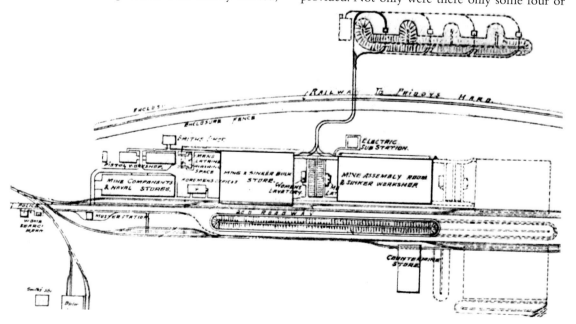

9.32 The Mine Depot built at Frater, just south of Bedenham, in 1917. (Adapted from PTM/3639)

9.33 This mosaic image is created from a series of direct vertical aerial photographs taken in 1947, part of a countrywide programme. The areas of the three depots of Bedenham (initially planned as a storage area, hence the building layout), Frater and Elson are shown on the plan, together with the locations of the principal buildings, the road and rail links, and Frater Creek which separates Bedenham from the other two depots.

See figure 9.29 for the magazine area at Bedenham.
(*Priddy's Hard Archive 1998.4.169*)

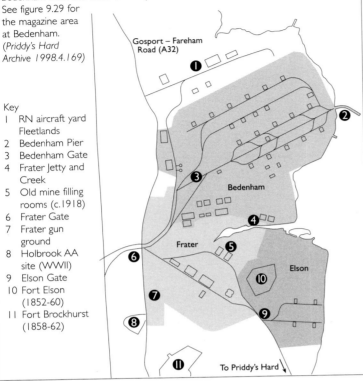

Key
1 RN aircraft yard Fleetlands
2 Bedenham Pier
3 Bedenham Gate
4 Frater Jetty and Creek
5 Old mine filling rooms (c.1918)
6 Frater Gate
7 Frater gun ground
8 Holbrook AA site (WWII)
9 Elson Gate
10 Fort Elson (1852-60)
11 Fort Brockhurst (1858-62)

Shell development post Jutland, 1917

The quality of the shells supplied before 1917 was generally disappointing, the failure of many to explode on hitting the target partly contributing to what Jellicoe termed the 'unpalatable result' of Jutland, and a Shell committee was set up to devise superior fillings. Lyddite suffered from a liability to form explosive substances, picrates, and was sensitive to shock, so had proved unsuitable for penetrating armour. Shellite (see Glossary) was evolved as a less sensitive filling, but had the disadvantages of being liable to form sensitive compounds and to retain moisture, which caused deterioration in exploders and fuzes with which it came into contact. However, it could be melted on a water bath at the low temperature of 80 degrees centigrade, making it particularly suitable for poured fillings. In January 1915 it was decided to adopt trotyl to supersede lyddite as the burster for common HE shell of calibres 9.2-inch and above, and filling with trotyl commenced, probably at Upnor. Trotyl, or TNT, had about the same power as lyddite and shellite, but could only be exploded with a gaine. This was a device adopted for initiating detonation of HE shells in conjunction with a powder-filled fuze, as HE fillings could not be detonated by gunpowder. No. 2 Gaine was a steel cylinder containing a fairly large quantity of CE or Composition Explosive (see Glossary), the Service term for tetryl, a nitro-compound too sensitive for use as a shell filling, and which could not be melted or cast in large quantities, but was ideal as part of an exploder system. Above this was placed a large fulminate detonator, and above that again a small quantity of gunpowder. The gunpowder was ignited by the fuze, and in its turn caused the fulminate detonator to disrupt and initiate detonation of the CE pellets, which communicated the detonation to the shell filling.

ADM 186/174, TH29

five suitable premises available, with a potential capacity of no more than 7,600 tons, but at the termination of hostilities all the brickworks would have to be emptied for the 'Homes Fit for Heroes' building programme.

New magazines would need to meet the following requirements: isolation; railway connection, by then exceptionally difficult to find; suitability from a military point of view; cheap handling at site; easy distribution to filling factories. The accommodation required by the end of the year was to provide for stocks expected to be on hand by 1 April 1918: 100,000 tons of propellants and 50,000 tons of high explosives and miscellaneous combustibles. The maximum gross capacity of the present magazines, including those in preparation, was 119,400 tons, and so provision had to be made for a further 31,600 tons. To meet this target the Director proposed: eleven new buildings to carry 2,000 tons each (22,000 tons); one new building at Pembrey to carry output during test (2,000 tons); temporary accommodation yet to be found, four to five places (7,600 tons); this gave a total of 31,600 tons at a cost of £176,000. But this was probably an underestimate, for in October 1917 it was decided that too large an amount of propellant was destined for the magazines, which meant that extra stores were required, and the whole proposition might actually cost approximately £200,000. The magazines were to be built to a standard design, 330 feet by 92 feet, in breezeblock, cement coated on outside, with corrugated asbestos roofs and wooden floors.

The first sites were selected at the end of the month, at Gloucester, Pembrey, Ratby West, Ratby East and Desford. By 17 November 1917, the foundations at Gloucester were in, and three bays had been erected. Desford was abandoned, with Lanemark selected as a suitable replacement site to meet the needs of Scotland. By the end of the month Dalston and Curthwaite were added to the list, both well placed for receiving surplus output from Gretna. At the end of the year, two further sites were chosen: Marsh Gibbon, on the Bletchley–Oxford railway, and Ridgmount, on the Bletchley–Bedford line; Normanton Hill was added to the list in January 1918. But the situation of ammunition storage was still far from ideal. At the beginning of February there were sixty magazines in commission and the average contents had risen to over 1,730 tons each. The number would be increased to seventy-seven when the current building programme had been completed, which at the present average contents would give a total capacity of 133,200 tons. However, in March 10,000 tons of propellants would be arriving from the United States, not shown in the official estimates of the programme laid down for shipments. Unfinished magazines would have to be pressed into service, using the completed end of the build-

ing. The Director of the DE thought that for safety purposes the average holding should not exceed 1,000 tons and even at this reduced quantity the risks taken were very great; the former average of 750 tons should be the aim as soon as circumstances permitted. Adding to the difficulties, the possibility of air raids was increasing weekly, and it was quite impossible to reduce the stocks carried by magazines within the vulnerable areas; in addition, demands were being made that the storage at Gretna be reduced by 6,000 tons at the earliest possible date.

The Director estimated that the final demand would be accommodation for 150,000 tons, giving an average of approximately 2,000 tons in each magazine, even when all the proposed new magazines were in commission. The forecast was for a slight reduction of propellants, but an increase in high explosives (HE). The official estimates were highly misleading, showing a countrywide total of 66,000 tons of propellants at the end of February when the true figure was approximately 77,000 tons, with an additional 2,000 tons held at Woolwich and 4,000 tons at filling factories; in all, this was 17,000 tons above the official estimate, not even including the deliveries from the United States. In addition, large quantities of propellants were likely to be returned by the navy, the Admiralty intending to transfer 4,000 tons by June, and holding a further very large quantity for reworking. The position clearly indicated that a further building programme in addition to the twelve magazines now in course of erection seemed inescapable; the only hope of relief was the possibility of persuading the American Government to store a proportion of their production in the States. By April 1918 the sites at Verwood, Dinas Mawddwy, Fontley and Plas-Bennion were under preparation and ten were being built, although progress was very slow, and work on magazines at Hardwick and Ellesmere was about to commence. The time taken for the disposal of the enormous quantity of unwanted munitions meant that these 1918 magazines were retained for several years after the war, but by 1926

only Hardwick, Ellesmere, Pembrey and Northolt remained, and those were being cleared. The traversed magazines at Pembrey appear to have been retained. A permanent Central Ammunition Depot, on a very large scale, was built at Bramley, between Basingstoke and Reading.

With the termination of hostilities, the staffing returned to peacetime proportions, and many of the depots established during the war were closed down and the buildings sold. Crombie and Bandeath were retained, even though the future of Rosyth Dockyard was in doubt. There was plenty of work to be done, as there were large quantities of time-expired cordite and other redundant munitions to be disposed of; for example, no capital ships armed with 12-inch guns (all the dreadnoughts and pre-dreadnoughts) were retained, and their ammunition became useless. The great depots in northern France (together with some German ones) were engaged for several years in breaking down the huge dumps of shells and cartridges and the vast amounts of ordnance salvaged from the battlefields. After the war this work was done and the buildings taken over by civilian contractors, most notably the English-managed firm of F. N. Pickett et Fils. Post-war disarmament saw the army shrink to its former size, and the newly established Royal Air Force struggle for survival. The navy, which had been by far the largest in the world, dwindled, never to regain that position. It must have appeared to the Treasury that expenditure on ammunition storage was never again to reach the proportions it had assumed under the Naval and Military Works Acts. They were wrong, and the reason lay in the vulnerability of Ordnance Depots to attack from the air, as demonstrated by the example of Audruicq (see page 187). Even before the war, the Admiralty were concerned about the defence of Lodge Hill against even the feeble threats which might then be posed; within a short space of time this was to be a real menace, and the Treasury was forced into a struggle against the insistent and apparently endless demands of the Armed Forces, and in particular the Navy.[14]

Chapter 10 Going Underground

After the First World War, the ordnance storage needs of the Admiralty were determined by the classes of ship retained and the need for strategic reserves for purposes other than fleet actions. The battleships and battle-cruisers armed with 12-inch and 13.5-inch guns were fast approaching obsolescence and there was no point in renewing their stocks, while the armoured cruisers with 9.2-inch and 7.5-inch guns were being sold for scrap. In peacetime 2,000 tons of cordite would be needed per year for practice, giving a turnover of the complete stock in ten years, so no further provision for the post-war fleet was required. The Admiralty cordite factory at Holton Heath, established during the war, could make 150 tons of cordite a week, allowing the completion of one outfit of cartridges for the whole post-war fleet in 15 months. However, there was a deficit of 6,000 new type 15-inch shells. For the fleet, each vessel was to have two outfits, together with a central reserve for subsidiary operation, such as bombardments. In September 1920 it was decided to keep a further reserve for arming auxiliaries and merchant ships.[1]

Impact of the Ten Year Rule

All this seemed a gross overprovision to Sir Eric Geddes, probably the least liked ever (by his naval colleagues) First Lord of the Admiralty, an office which he held during the closing stages of the First World War. In August 1921 he was appointed chairman of a committee set up to recommend cuts in national expenditure. Their findings, though pleasing to the Treasury, were distasteful in the extreme to those who suffered as a result. The Geddes Committee considered that Holton Heath was overproducing cordite; it deemed the current output of 30 tons a week excessive and as the fleet had only expended about half its outfits of ammunition during the war, the reserves were also excessive. As a consequence, cordite production was halved in 1922. Apart from Geddes' recommendations, there was a further incentive to the Treasury to limit expenditure: the Government had adopted the Ten Year Rule, which adjured the Services, in preparing their Estimates, to assume that no war (apart from colonial exploits) would take place for the next ten years. This assumption was to be renewed year by year until 1932.[2]

10.1 The entrance to one of the Ernesettle magazines. *(HRO 109M91, PH/72)*

10.2 Ernesettle, looking north. This 1947 view gives a good idea of the layout of the site at the conclusion of the Second World War. The locomotive (a Southern N class) hauling freight in the background is most likely on the morning Okehampton run to Plymouth Friary, rather than anything to do with Ernesettle, which had a siding operated from Bere Ferrers signal box. Out on the river Tamar are destroyers, escort vessels and landing craft laid up after the end of the war. The open area in the background has been further developed as RNAD Ernesettle since 1945. (Plymouth Naval Base Museum)

Despite the unpropitious climate – Rosyth was reduced to a care and maintenance basis in 1925 – the air threat (to magazines rather than ships) continued to preoccupy the Admiralty, which in 1925 began slowly to re-provision storage facilities for naval ordnance. In that year four magazines were completed at Ernesettle, a site lying on the other side of the Tamar Bridge from Bull Point and the nearest suitable site for tunnelling. These were single-cell tunnels cut directly into the shale of the hillside, with a total capacity of 1,240 tons. The stone was heavily charged with water, so new constructional techniques were adopted. The tunnels were lined with concrete, and within them were built the magazine buildings themselves. These were formed by internal brick walls with corrugated asbestos cement roofs, to cut out seepage of subsoil water through the concrete lining. It was fortunate in the event that only a small investment had been possible, for by 1932 water was found to be coming through the concrete arch, and was then discharged by the internal corrugated roof into cavities on each side, affecting the brickwork, which began to disintegrate. However, in the autumn of 1927 the underground magazines appeared to have been a success, and in the draft estimates then being prepared £93,000 was proposed for additional underground storage at Bull Point (the name Ernesettle was not used to give the impression that no new depot was in contemplation). This did not materialise, for the Admiralty now had a more important struggle on their hands. There was no immediate need for new magazines, but there was for cordite.[3]

In December 1927, the First Lord, William Bridgeman, wrote to Winston Churchill, then Chancellor of the Exchequer, that much of the cordite had recently developed 'disquieting symptoms', which made a reduction of its service life a necessity. A large proportion of the old cordite manufactured during the war would need to be scrapped anyway. This led to a depletion of reserves.[4] Bridgeman consequently proposed an extra £220,000 for cordite. The Treasury immediately sprang into verbal action, as they believed the Admiralty were dismissing their own findings; in 1924 cordite production had been doubled from Geddes' recommended figure, and there was now in stock over 10,000 tons, valued at £300 a ton. The Admiralty now wished to scrap 6,000 tons of this and introduce yet another new type of cordite (Cordite S.C., or solventless carbamite – see Glossary), 'which they will proceed to manufacture with feverish haste with no guarantee that that in its turn will not be wasted.… Such behaviour is quite irreconcilable with the Government's present naval and financial policy which the Admiralty are supposed to follow'. Another Treasury official noted that the Admiralty had an advantage that was hard to undermine; when they could claim that men's lives were in danger, it was not easy for the Treasury to force an economy, and clearly could not oppose the removal of all doubtful cordite from ships. But the proposal to replenish reserves in full over the next four years was a different matter, another example of the navy's refusal to acknowledge the Ten Year Rule, and the Treasury was entitled to press for the cost to be spread over at least

eight years. The Admiralty argued back, and Bridgeman proved to be a very supportive First Lord. It was pointed out that in a discussion on 1926 Navy Estimates Churchill had accepted the policy of having two outfits of ammunition for each ship as being sound and reasonable. The present stock of 11,500 tons was based on this, and there was very little surplus. The annual production had been increased from Geddes' recommendations by 1,000 tons in 1924 and 1925 partly due to additional destruction for safety purposes of certain cordite manufactured by the trade during the war. So far from continuing to increase, it had been decreased in 1926 and 1927 to 1,000 tons. The annual practice expenditure of ammunition between 1921–25 had been approximately 1,950 tons and from 1926 and onwards was about 1,250 tons due to reduced allowances for target practice. In all years more ammunition had been fired off than the amount manufactured, the balance being met from the surplus stocks held in 1921. Far from being an extravagant rate of production, about 4,000 tons of surplus cordite had been expended and not replaced. Production would need to rise from 1928 to 1932 because of the shortening of cordite's shelf life and the necessary destruction of wartime cordite.

The Treasury's suggestion of spreading the replenishments over eight years instead of four had to be seen in the light of the following facts. The manufacture of Cordite M.C. (see Glossary) at Holton Heath had been discontinued, and production had switched to Cordite S.C., which was capable of being more rapidly produced and promised a longer life. By April 1928, the factory would be capable of producing 1,500 tons a year per shift. The normal war output of 2,500 tons a year per shift would not be reached until 1932 and then only if money was approved in 1929 Estimates. The years 1928 and 1929 would inevitably be heavy replenishment years due to the large stocks of cordite that would be over the ten-year approved age. The Admiralty considered that prolonging the replenishment period to eight years would give an inadequate rate of replacement given the capacity of the factory during the years 1928–32. Furthermore, the amount actually proposed for 1928 could not be decreased without the outfit actually on board being below that authorised for certain guns. The Treasury appear to have lost this particular battle, but one concerning much greater sums was just a few years away.[5]

Admiralty versus Treasury

The Ten Year Rule was allowed to lapse during 1932, allowing more realistic planning to take place. After the ineffectual conclusion of the second London Naval Conference in March 1936, in which the Japanese had withdrawn from the proceedings, refusing to allow the scale of their fleet or the size of their ships to be bound by treaty limitations, the biggest naval building programme in England since 1918 was authorised. This was to be financed by a sequence of Defence Loans Acts, which undermined Treasury control of expenditure. Shortly before the first Act received royal assent in March 1937, a paper was prepared in the

Treasury outlining the working of the Naval and Military Works Acts of 1895 to 1905. It was extremely hostile to the whole principle of financing by means of loans, which it termed 'an invitation to wasteful and grandiose schemes'. The New Standard of Naval Strength proposed by the Admiralty on 29 April 1937, was certainly grandiose. It proposed a new fleet of 20 capital ships, 15 aircraft carriers, 100 cruisers, 198 destroyers and 82 submarines. The original estimate was for £104 million a year over and above the normal Navy Votes. As part of the package, the Admiralty wanted up-to-date, which meant underground, storage for its ammunition. In the circumstances the Treasury reaction was understandable: 'The Navy are not suffering from undue modesty at the present time. In addition to their proposals for a new standard of naval strength, they submitted proposals last week for a new cordite factory to cost £⅔ millions, while this week they produce a demand for additional underground storage of naval ammunition reserves at a cost of £5 millions. Perhaps it is just as well that the Session is coming to an end.' The Treasury accepted that the present arrangements for overground storage of naval explosives were unsatisfactory, but did not believe that expensive tunnelling was the answer.

The army and the air force had been faced with the same problem, and the Treasury tried, unsuccessfully, to persuade them that it could be solved, not by underground storage, but by storing filled ammunition in relatively small dumps dispersed over a large area. The Treasury were made aware that the cost of the extensive internal transport systems required to draw efficiently on widely scattered deposits would vitiate the whole point of the plan. In the end the Air Ministry and the War Office were solving their problem by buying up disused quarries and fitting them up as ammunition storage. The Ernesettle magazines had caught the army's interest during the late 1920s, as the

large depot built at Bramley, near Basingstoke, was open to aerial attack. By 1930, all Area Commands had submitted lists of possible sites for underground storage. The quarries in the Corsham area seemed to be the most promising, and in August 1935 Treasury approval was gained for the purchase of Ridge and Tunnel quarries for £35,000. This was the kind of sum of which the Treasury approved. Partly in order to cater for air force requirements, a further quarry at Monkton Farleigh was purchased in May 1937. A quarry wholly for air force use was acquired at Chilmark, in Wiltshire, in June 1936. Four more were to be acquired, but, as will be seen, only Chilmark proved to be successful. Though the initial cost of the quarries was attractive to the Treasury, their adaptation was 'pretty expensive', and by July 1937 the latest estimates of £2½ million far exceeded those first submitted. Nevertheless, it appeared that this was still going to be a good deal less expensive than the method proposed by the Admiralty at Plymouth (Ernesettle), Rosyth (Crombie) and Milford Haven (a completely new depot) of constructing tunnels especially for the purpose of ammunition storage. The Admiralty claimed to have found no suitable quarries or caves. The Treasury suggested that the Defence Policy and Requirements (DPR) Committee ought to do no more than agree on the desirability of doing something, while the Admiralty should investigate a smaller scheme. This would at least ensure that nothing was done for a satisfactory period. This proposal was minuted, probably by Sir John Simon, the Chancellor of the Exchequer, who showed his distaste for the way things were shaping up: 'However meritorious the purpose, we have to face up to the question whether or no business methods of examination are to be discontinued. Short-circuiting such methods is now the rule, not the exception, & I shall be bound to ask the Government, if this goes on, whether Treasury control is to be abandoned, & Parliament so informed.' The DPR Committee authorised the Admiralty to prepare proposals and costs for 148 underground magazines. They were ready with a first instalment; a suitable site had been found at Dean Hill for sixty magazines. The Admiralty wished to proceed as soon as possible, the depot to be finished by 1942, at a cost of £2½ million. Meanwhile, temporary storage was required for 60,000 tons of ammunition and explosives. Some relief was provided by the decision to stow Reserve ships' outfits on board, which would release space for 5–10,000 tons of storage ashore. As a result, all new facilities proposed for the Chatham district were cancelled. A site suitable for the temporary accommodation of 30,000 tons had been found in West Cumberland at Broughton Moor; the balance was to be stored afloat. [6]

The Admiralty's escalating demands for

10.3 Nissen hut at Ernesettle, 1944, described on the original photograph as a 'secret building' for the US Navy. The figure is probably a 'Seabee' from the Construction Battalions of the US Navy; the objects piled to one side of the hut are concrete 'biscuits' used to build the embarkation hards used for loading landing craft for the invasion of Europe (the nearest such hard PP2 is situated just to the south of the Tamar Bridge, only a stone's throw from Ernesettle). *(Plymouth Naval Base Museum)*

ordnance storage since 1934 were striking. The need for additional storage had first become apparent in 1933, and increased very rapidly from 1935, when the provision of additional anti-aircraft ammunition began. By the summer of 1937, naval underground magazines existed or had been approved for: Ernesettle – twenty-two magazines, costing £703,000, completed; Crombie – six magazines, costing £149,000, to be completed by 1938; Milford Haven – nine (of which five were for mines), costing £872,000, to be completed in 1939; Fishguard – ninety, costing £3,450,000, to be completed in 1940 and 1941. Apart from Dean Hill, the Admiralty wanted further provision at Plymouth, Rosyth, Scapa Flow and Harwich. Magazines were already completed at Hong Kong (eleven magazines) and Ceylon (two), with two further magazines to be added at Ceylon in 1939; sixteen magazines were also to be built at Singapore, twelve in 1938 and four in 1939. This would create a total of 162 magazines. By the time a DPR sub-committee met on 22 July 1937, the Admiralty had reduced its requirements to 123 magazines. It was then the turn of the army to increase its demands. The War Office stated that the space available at Corsham and Monkton Farleigh was insufficient for the revised army requirements. However, the navy was still the chief offender when it came to wasting space. It was now Admiralty policy to hold two outfits for low-angle guns and three outfits for high-angle guns, the supply of which had increased greatly since 1933. The Treasury tried to persuade the Admiralty that provision on this scale was unnecessarily high, and again quoted the fact that during the whole four years of the last war, the navy generally only fired half an outfit, but to no avail. To the Treasury the difference in the cost of storage between Admiralty magazines and those of the other Services was perplexing.[7]

This extraordinary difference in cost between facilities that, in the Treasury's eyes, performed identical functions was due to the fact that the Admiralty employed overhead travellers in these underground magazines to manipulate their heavy shells, just as in the land magazines. This necessitated increased height, and excavation was the most labour-consuming part of the construction. The army shifted everything by hand, since their shells and cartridges were smaller. The Admiralty insisted that every magazine must be able to take any size of projectile, so every single one had to be made high enough to take a system of travellers. Furthermore, the maximum content of an Admiralty magazine was 500–600 tons of ammunition, with 200 tons of explosive content; in the War Office quarries 1,000–1,500 tons was allowed. The Admiralty insisted that their limitation was required for safety reasons, and pressed on with their plans. They now had in mind an underground depot to outstrip all others, at Trecwn, very close to Fishguard. The design was an improvement on the Ernesettle magazines, the condition of which was still bad in 1937. The Building Research Department of the Department of Scientific and Industrial Research had been consulted about Ernesettle, which recommended that the brickwork be demolished and replaced by a new lining built far enough from the concrete wall to enable a man to pass. A damp-proof course was essential, and the back of the internal lining should be covered with bituminous paint. Aluminous cement and clean silica sand were recommended, and it was suggested that future designs of underground magazines should be drawn up with these points in mind, which informed the designs for Trecwn. Rock from Trecwn was then sent to the Building Research Station to see if it would be usable for making concrete, so providing some means of economising. There appeared to be no reason to suppose concrete made with the rock would be poor, and by the end of the year concrete bricks made from Trecwn aggregate were sent for test. These were intended to form the arched lining of the Trecwn magazines, where very wet conditions were likely to be encountered, but they did not come up to permeability requirements, though as good as any concrete brick that had been tested. Bricks for reconstructing Ernesettle were sent for test in the spring of 1938.[8]

In April 1938 the First Lord, Duff Cooper, submitted for the Cabinet's urgent consideration the pressing need for underground storage of oil and ammunition. During his tenure of office he maintained, in his own words, 'a perpetual struggle with the Treasury, who never ceased, as they never have ceased, to maintain that the finances of the country were in a desperate condition.' In May 1938, the Treasury attacked from a new angle, attempting to reduce the cost of storage by regulating the production programme to coincide with delivery dates of approved ships, to decrease the rate of ammunition supply. They felt that the possibility of temporarily slowing down parts of the ammunition programme for the provision of reserve outfits should be considered. The Broughton Moor depot, which was only for temporary storage, was now budgeted at £650,000, and the Treasury felt that the Admiralty should adopt it for permanent use. Its size could be determined by the additional requirements of the Admiralty in the light of any future policy on the size of reserves. If only temporary storage was required, far less expensive proposals must be submitted than Broughton Moor. The Treasury's conclusion showed that the political climate as regards defence expenditure was beginning to change: 'Strictly speaking, we ought to tell the Admiralty that we cannot authorise expenditure on this temporary storage unless it can be found by equivalent savings on Navy Votes. In present circumstances, however, I don't think we can press this point very far.' This was minuted by Sir Alan Barlow, Under-Secretary to the Treasury: 'I do not believe that a programme of the size asked for represents the wisest use of the Admiralty's financial resources, or that their way of carrying it out is the cheapest. The WO say there are acres of empty quarries [at Corsham] near Bath. Admittedly Bath is less handy than Portsmouth, but they could surely store some at Bath, where the cost is ¼ or ⅓ of the cost at Portsmouth.' The Admiralty rebutted these points. In 1937, the Annual Report of the Research Department, Woolwich, had commented on the adverse effect of quarry storage where no air-conditioning was provided. The report also stated that the ammunition production programme was already regulated to coincide with the delivery dates of ships. The suggestion that the tempo of supply could be slowed down ignored the realities of the situation. In view of the necessity of maintaining continuity of employment for the available production facilities, and the impossibility of regulating and co-ordinating intermittent production of the many components, any slowing down of parts of the ammunition production was out of the question. The Admiralty then presented to the Treasury their current situation and requirements as regards ammunition storage (see Admiralty magazines, page 215). This would give a potential total of 124,840 tons of underground storage.

In response to this renewed statement of requirements, the Treasury returned to the point that converted quarries were a cheaper and equally suitable form of storage, quoting a War Office representative who stated that un-air-conditioned quarries were suitable for bombs and plugged shell, though not for fuzed shell. It was hoped that cordite could be stored satisfactorily just by warming the caverns. If air-conditioning had to be installed in Corsham and Monkton Farleigh, the additional cost might be £500,000. The Treasury were being disingenuous here; the month before this response to the Admiralty was written the army had decided that air-conditioning would be necessary, since with air-conditioning the period of satisfactory storage would be ten years, without it would be only three years. The Treasury refused to accept this and it was not until July 1939 that funds for this were made available. The Treasury concluded: '... it is quite problematical whether any of this reserve ammunition, on the storage of which millions are proposed to be spent, will be required. I think that the Chancellor should say bluntly that the case has not been made out & that a different type of plan must be prepared.' So he did. On 22 July 1938, Sir John Simon stated that the case for Dean Hill had not been made, though

he was prepared to allow the purchase of the land for Broughton Moor and the planning of the the scheme there, which could be adapted to permanent storage.[9]

Instability in Europe

The Czechoslovakian crisis in September 1938 was, however, to alter everything. Fears of a possible German air attack, made worse by absurd estimates of the casualties likely to be caused, made the exposed depots of Lodge Hill and Bedenham appear as extreme liabilities. This could only be solved in the short term by dispersing as much of the ammunition as possible. With Ministerial approval an extraordinary and unrecorded piece of railway logistics was performed, with the result that 29 miles of disused railway sidings and tracks in the West Country, Wales and Scotland were occupied by truckloads of naval ammunition, with no anti-aircraft protection and exposed to the dangers of sabotage. This expedient was resorted to again two years later (see pages 216–7). Duff Cooper resigned over the Munich Agreement and his successor, Earl Stanhope, was now in a much stronger position than his predecessors had been with regard to the Chancellor. He wrote to Sir John:

'Quarries do not provide satisfactory storage for reserves of naval ammunition. The fact that the navy lives over its magazines and that an explosion on board may lead to the loss of an 8 million pound ship and many valuable lives makes it essential that reserves of naval ammunition should be maintained in the highest state of efficiency and safety'.

The Admiralty had reduced the cost of Dean Hill (to £1,426,000) by planning to accommodate only thirty magazines, though the total cost of new build would remain almost the same, as it was now proposed to house the remainder of the requirement in a new underground depot further north:

'where experience during the recent crisis has shown that additional accommodation will be necessary to meet the demands of the Fleet in war.... I began my letter by calling our requirement of underground ammunition storage urgent. How urgent it is was unmistakably demonstrated by the recent crisis.... Towards remedying this disastrous state of affairs, the Dean Hill project is the first and most urgent of the permanent measures which must be taken.'

The original scheme at Dean Hill had provided for some laboratory work to be transferred from Priddy's Hard. This was now abandoned in the new plan of only thirty magazines, and the labora-

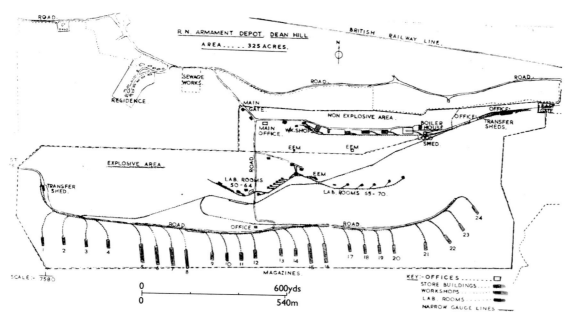

10.4 Sketch plan of Dean Hill, which was prepared for the information of new employees. (HRO 109M91, COL 18/2)

tory facilities were to be solely for the maintenance of stores on the spot, the main laboratory work for the District remaining at Priddy's Hard. A number of cartridge-filling rooms were also deleted from the plan. In the face of this, and the worsening international situation, the Treasury were forced to make a qualified retreat. The official who had been the Admiralty's principal opponent conceded that: 'I am very doubtful whether in present circumstances it is possible to secure any further reduction. The Admiralty, after all, can point to the fact that they have reduced their total requirements of magazines by 35 or so.' No further attempts were made to induce the Admiralty to use quarries. The War Office and Air Ministry no longer set such a good example, as the War Office were considerably reducing the amount of ammunition in their quarries, thus increasing the cost per ton. Furthermore, there was much force in what the Admiralty said about the necessity for ensuring the absolute efficiency and safety of ammunition since 'the Navy lives over its magazines'. Finally, the quarries were not suitably situated to meet the operational requirements of the fleet. The Treasury concluded: 'We have pressed the Admiralty as far as we can on this matter.'

On the question of holding the reserves of ammunition ready filled, the Admiralty remained quite adamant. The Admiralty representatives had given the Treasury to understand that the holding of ammunition unfilled would not mean any appreciable saving of magazine accommodation. It was now admitted that holding reserves unfilled would mean an approximate saving in underground storage space of forty to seventy per cent. However, if war were to break out, it was intended that within only a few days, seventy-five per cent of an ammunition outfit for the active fleet could be transferred into armament supply issuing ships. This meant that all the reserves must be held ready

filled. Of course, a very large proportion of the underground storage would be vacant in this situation and it therefore appeared as if the Admiralty were merely providing this storage to overcome the difficulties of the first few days of war. The Treasury asked whether arrangements could not be made for the ammunition to be transferred before an emergency, during the precautionary period for example. The reply was that, firstly, the transfer might not take place so quickly as expected, and secondly, the consequences of a successful unexpected attack would be so disastrous that the risk could not be taken of holding the ammunition in unprotected overground storage. The Admiralty representatives also said that in war time, production of ammunition would

10.5 Aerial view of Dean Hill, c.1990, looking east. The magazines are built into the north slope of the hill. (HRO 109M91, PH/67)

10.6 Above: Entrance to No.1 Magazine at RNAD Dean Hill. This magazine was later refurbished to act as an overnight store for convoys carrying nuclear weapons around the United Kingdom, and was enclosed within its own secure, fully self-sufficient compound. *(Nick Catford / Subterranea Britannica)*
10.7 Below: The light traverse laboratories at Dean Hill, each built of brick separated by concrete traverses and with overhead gantry cranes. The 2-foot 6-inch rail network connected to the Salisbury–Southampton line. Repair and refurbishment of ordnance took place in the earth-covered heavy traverse laboratories. *(Nick Catford / Subterranea Britannica)*

10.8 Dean Hill was administratively controlled by Priddy's Hard, and when the site was closed in 2004 this locomotive and its carriages were given to the museum, where they are now on display. The locomotive's engine allowed it to pull up to 203 tons at a top speed of 7 mph. The left-hand truck is a rare example of a 1940s carriage with a sliding roof as well as side doors, to allow both hoizontal and vertical loading. *(Stephen Dent)*

have to go on even if the fleet had not been engaged in any actions and that consequently the underground storage would soon be filled up again. The Treasury argument was dropped, and their representative was forced to write: 'I am afraid that the conclusion which we have reached regarding this proposal [Dean Hill] is that while the Admiralty are probably doing themselves pretty well, we can see no firm grounds on which we can hope to reject the scale or the standards of this particular proposal.' [10]

Finally, on 14 February 1939, Treasury warrants were issued for the compulsory purchase of the land at Dean Hill. The Chancellor had allowed this project to go ahead on the understanding that the number of underground magazines to be provided elsewhere was cut down by ten or twelve. The number was accordingly reduced to forty-two, and it was decided that these were to be at Benarty Hill near Loch Leven, a site with direct rail access to Crombie, 18 miles away. The depot, with fourteen double and fourteen single magazines, together with six magazines for mine charges, was estimated at £1,540,000. The Admiralty stated, hopefully, that with the construction of the Benarty depot all known requirements for the storage of naval explosives underground in the UK would have been met. There was to be no haggling with the Chancellor over this, and on 24 June 1939, the Treasury warrant for the purchase of the Benarty land was issued. Within a week, at a Treasury Inter-Service Committee meeting, arrangements for emergency accommodation were made. In 1937 the Great Western Railway had offered a redun-

10.9 The barrel of a 14-inch Mark VII gun being forged at Woolwich in 1938. The barrel is being extracted after heat treatment, in the presence of an inspector from the department of the Chief Inspector of Naval Ordnance, and also the press, with the intention of making a clear statement to Germany. (*Priddy's Hard Archive 2002.219*)

dant bore of Colwall Tunnel, in the Malverns, for use as a magazine, and this had been one of the locations to which trucks had been sent at the time of the Czechoslovakian crisis. It was now proposed to convert the tunnel into a magazine for mines, depth charges and HE shells, its use being foreseen (correctly, as it turned out) for five years, perhaps longer. It could be adapted for £25,000, and the proposal was adopted.

Admiralty magazines, existing, planned and required, in 1937

Overground magazines (existing)

	Number of magazines	Tons of ammunition
Chatham District	24	23,600
Portsmouth District	38	39,100
Plymouth District	9	10,100
12 Dutch barges at Plymouth		8,200
Copperas Wood	2	1,800 (Depth charges)
Crombie & Bandeath	45	33,900

Underground magazines (existing)

	Number of magazines	Tons of ammunition
Ernesettle	4 old type (under repair)	1,240
Crombie	6 (being stored)	3,600

Underground magazines (approved)

	Number of magazines	Tons of ammunition	Completion Date
Ernesettle	22 (10 double, one single)	13,200	February 1941
Trecwn	90 (31 double, 28 single)	54,000	Part by March 1940, rest October 1941
Milford Haven	7 (less than standard size)	3,000	December 1938

Further depots required

	Number of magazines	Tons of ammunition
Dean Hill	60	36,000
Crombie District	23	13,800

T161/1073

10.10 One of the magazines at Grain. Indistinguishable externally from any other Nissen hut variant, it is in fact a Romney, designed specifically for storage purposes. *(HRO 109M91, PH/79)*

Changing priorities for the Second World War

War was declared on 3 September 1939, and the search for temporary magazines intensified. The decline of a number of rural branch lines and their consequent closure to passengers meant that much more railway track was available for requisitioning than had been available during the First World War. By the end of September it was decided that 120 huts could be built beside the Dolphinton branch line, which ran between Lanark and Edinburgh, for ammunition storage. The following month the Admiralty decided that quarries could be used for storage after all, and that Pickwick quarry (near Corsham) could be made suitable for temporary storage of 10,000 tons of naval ammunition for a cost of £20,000. Sir Alan Barlow, the Under-Secretary to the Treasury, could not resist recording his pleasure at this 'Damascus road' conversion, which was followed by the acquisition of the nearby Goblin's Pit quarry for the storage of a further 5,000 tons, at a cost of £18,000.

Winston Churchill had assumed the office of First Lord at the outbreak of war and, probably because of his passion for quick results, on 21 November 1939, the Admiralty decided to abandon all schemes not likely to materialise before the end of 1940. Milford Haven, Dean Hill and Ernesettle were to be completed. The first stage of Trecwn (twenty-eight single magazines) was to be completed, and a further twenty-four single magazines completed by the end of 1940, the rest to be reconsidered in June 1940. [On 18 July 1940, it was agreed that the depot would be completed with eighteen double magazines.] The Benarty scheme was abandoned, together with a projected central Mine Depot at Ingleby Greenow. Unfortunately, it was agreed that twelve magazines at Singapore were to go ahead. The Treasury were now pleased with the Admiralty's attitude, which was seen as ' a really genuine attempt to confine their attention to work which may be expected to be of value during the present war.'[11]

In June 1940 another complete branch line was taken over. This was the Cleobury Mortimer–Ditton Priors line in Shropshire, which had been closed to passengers in 1938. This boasted no tunnels, and was acquired to serve the sub-depot for Priddy's Hard constructed at the

terminus, though all available space was used for storage as well. The depot was intended to hold 35,000 tons, at a cost of £379,000. Cartridge cases were cleaned in the disused engine shed at Cleobury Town. Ditton Priors was to remain a rail-connected Ordnance Depot until 1965, by which time it was described as 'geographically perhaps the least effective surviving RNAD in the country'. In October 1940 accommodation was dispersed from Priddy's Hard to Reading, Woolston and Thatcham (where a shadow gunwharf was set up, reverting to store accommodation in 1943). Railway accommodation was made use of at Fontley Tunnel (only a few miles away, between Fareham and Botley) and Frith End Tunnel. The Midhurst-Chichester branch line, not far away, had closed to passenger services in 1935 and was taken over in 1940. The line ran through two tunnels, at Cocking and Singleton, the latter having a capacity of ninety-eight wagons. These were provided with iron doors and naval guards. More sub-depots were established at Hawthorn Tunnel in the Forest of Dean, and Dover, all also originally opened with the assistance of Priddy's Hard.

As in the First World War, improvisations were resorted to everywhere. The magazines at Fort Elson were taken over in the early years of the war, and E Magazine at Priddy's Hard was used to house gunwharf spares. Undoubtedly the most desperate expedient was the use of the training ship *Implacable* (originally the French third-rate *Duguay-Trouin*, captured in 1805) between April 1941 and February 1943 as a floating magazine. Relief to the Tamar depots was given by a host of mostly unsuitable buildings: unused brick-kilns (not as plentiful as during the previous war, because of the wartime building commitments), china-clay sheds, quayside warehouses in the closest proximity to other buildings, and the tunnel of the abandoned narrow-gauge line built to serve Cann quarry near Plymouth, which was used to store depth-charges. The Upnor/Chattenden/Lodge Hill complex was reinforced by additional accommodation at Aylesford, Queenborough, Gravesend, Larkfield and Chatham. In 1941 Sheerness-based ships were served by twenty barges of ammunition lying in the Medway at distances of 2 to 7 miles from the port. This unsatisfactory situation was remedied by finding a suitable site for a magazine on Grain, at Cockleshell Hard, connected with Upnor by rail. This depot was estimated at £62,000, to include twelve magazines at £8,400.

The army also required accommodation to supplement that provided at Bramley. Three sub-depots, commenced in 1938 and completed by 1943, were created in the Corsham quarries with a combined storage capacity of 250,000 tons. The underground storage imposed some limitations and no doubtful or repairable ammunition could be stored there. Shortly before the war an additional Central Ammunition Depot was begun at Longtown, near Carlisle. Its design was to remain unique in the United Kingdom, the main storage being in semi-underground buildings with earthed-up roofs. Two additional CADs of wartime construction supplemented these. The first to be completed, in February 1942, was at Nesscliff, between Shrewsbury and Oswestry, and comprised 164 storehouses and 26 ammunition repair workshops spread over an area of 1,800 acres. It held some 200,000 tons. The second, in operation by October 1942, was at Kineton (the site of the Civil War battle of Edgehill). This was a much more compact site, holding 150,000 tons. Emergency accommodation had to be provided while these depots were being constructed, and sixteen ammunition sub-depots were eventually provided. These simply consisted of corrugated iron sheds with a capacity of 400 cubic feet placed on the verges of country roads and 30-foot strips of adjacent fields. Each of these sprawling locations occupied 100–120 miles of road and was served by at least two railway stations. They could be constructed very quickly: six were opened in July 1940. Their initial capacity was for 20,000 tons each, but by the end of the war the smallest held 50,000 tons and the largest 180,000 tons.[12]

The demand for naval ammunition continued to be insatiable, and in February 1942 it was forecast that by December 1943 there would be a shortfall of accommodation for 100,000 tons, and it was proposed to extend Broughton Moor. A brand new depot for 50,000 tons was planned at Beith, in the Clyde area, the cost provisionally estimated at £900,000. Another depot at the River Drift Clay Mine, Camerton, near Broughton Moor, was estimated at £20,500, and the facilities there were to include an HE examining room, a shell painting room, a shell scraping room and narrow gauge railway. The thirty-six large magazines established at Ditton Priors needed strengthening. By the end of August 1942, even with these facilities in place, it was expected that by the end of June 1944 there would be a storage deficiency of over 90,000 tons. Broughton Moor was to be expanded to take a further 6,500 tons and a new depot, similar to Beith, built at Welbury, to take 50,000 tons. However, delays to Beith and Welbury meant that a further subterranean quarry, at Beer in Devon, was pressed into use (see page 225). In 1942, because of bomb damage to Marchwood, Dean Hill was brought into use before its completion, with only twenty-four magazines. Though hampered operationally by the need to transfer between the narrow gauge and the standard gauge, and the lack of a suitable local workforce and accommodation, the location was otherwise convenient, and at the height of its operations, in

October 1944, 101 men and 228 women were employed there. With the ending of hostilities the use of large unprotected stores provided a vastly cheaper alternative, and by October 1945 a hangar at Castle Bromwich aerodrome formerly used for the assembly of Spitfires began to be taken over as RNAD Minworth. The demand for ordnance storage meant that many temporary stores were created overseas, often on sites that had been used during the First World War, but at the end of the war, many of these would be discarded (see Navy's global storage, page 222).[13]

Protection and war damage

The Second World War left its mark on the old depots in the shape of passive air-raid defences. These had two functions, the protection of the stores and the protection of the staff. Nothing could be realistically done about a direct hit by a large bomb, but incendiaries were another matter. Not powerful individually, if they rolled into the valleys of roofs or stuck in gutters then a conflagration might be started. This fate befell four of the Marchwood Magazines on the night of 19–20 June 1940; they and their contents were totally destroyed, and a fifth magazine was severely damaged in the following December. Four were rebuilt and brought into use again by January 1942. These magazines had not received the roof modifications that had been applied to selected buildings in the other depots (rather than pitched roofs, they had flat concrete roofs, on which the

10.11 The aircraft hangars at RNAD Minworth, one of the temporary sites that stored naval munitions immediately after the war. (ADM-1/28299)

10.12 The dry guncotton magazine at Bull Point, showing (above) the false roof applied for protection against incendiaries, and the blast protection for the entrance; and (right) the interior, with its original hot-water pipes. (Jeremy Lake)

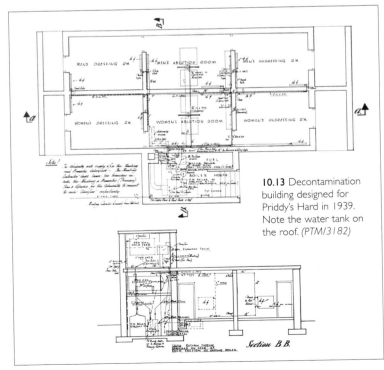

10.13 Decontamination building designed for Priddy's Hard in 1939. Note the water tank on the roof. (PTM/3182)

bombs could burn out harmlessly). Where the roof was of very low pitch, as at the dry guncotton magazine at Bull Point, a false roof was raised above it. Steel shutters were applied to the windows.

In February 1941, at the height of the air raids, the £100,000 allotted for protection of above-ground magazines was increased to £225,000. Much less now remains of the structures intended for the men and women. Trench shelters were designed in 1938, and in 1939 first aid and decon-tamination stations were built. Air-raid shelters, both above and below ground, were provided in considerable numbers (there were eleven above-ground shelters at Priddy's Hard, supplemented by the old magazines), but most have been cleared away or filled in. The fortunes of war dictated that these passive defences were not put to any serious test. A trifling raid on Lodge Hill took place on the night of 7–8 May 1942, when a solitary bomber released a stick of five bombs. Two fell on a field and farmyard at Chattenden, while the other three were on target. One failed to deto-nate, one fell 12 feet south of the depot and demolished part of the steel fence, while the third fell 28 feet from a cordite magazine, currently in use as a shell store. Part of an end wall was demol-ished and the adjacent walls cracked. Bull Point and Priddy's Hard escaped the devastation that was visited on Portsmouth and Plymouth, the raids on Portsmouth of 10 March 1941, only resulting in the burning out of the component store and severe damage to the tailors' and printers' shops. One cartridge assembly room was destroyed, as was No.9 Magazine at Bedenham.

The air force's underground storage facilities were much less fortunate, though enemy action took no part in their mishaps. Linley, in Staffordshire, was abandoned before completion because of serious roof falls. In January 1942 a large proportion of Llanberis quarry collapsed onto a train in the process of unloading, burying 75,000 bombs, only nineteen of which were damaged beyond repair; however, the buried 46,691 500-lb general-purpose bombs represented twenty per cent of the total stock available to the RAF. Mowlem's recovered all the bombs within nine months; the fault was laid at their door, for the collapse was attributed to their concrete not being up to specification and when cracks were observed they were attributed to minor defects rather than to major miscalculation. Harpur Hill, in Derbyshire, had been similarly constructed and was partly emptied for strengthening, but no confi-dence was placed in it. Worst of all was the fate of Fauld, near Tutbury in Derbyshire, which had the distinction, on 27 November 1944, of being the site of the greatest explosion in the history of the United Kingdom. Fauld was an old gypsum mine, which had been worked out around 1880, and had

10.14 Marchwood
in 1947, with
four magazines
rebuilt with flat
camouflaged roofs.
The fifth one hit, at
the top right, has
been demolished.
See also figures
2.40, 2.42 and 2.43
on pages 45–8.
*(New Forest District
Council)*

10.15 Below left:
A 1947 view of
Oerlikon gun cases
inside C Magazine
at Marchwood.
*(New Forest
District Council)*

10.16 Below: One
of the Marchwood
magazines after the
bombing of 19–20
June 1940, with the
remains of the
Oerlikon gun cases
that were stored
inside. *(HRO
109M91, PH/50)*

been excavated on the crown and pillar system, where large areas of inferior or worthless stone were left to support the overburden. The pillar beneath Upper Castle Hayes Farm was approximately 200 feet thick. At 11.10 a.m., 3,500 tons of high explosive were detonated, and some eighty people, civilian and services, were killed, the resulting crater being 900 feet long, 600 feet wide, and 100 feet deep. Castle Hayes Farm and its occupants vanished without trace. Structural damage was caused at 1½ miles and minor damage, through earth tremors, at 10 miles. This was a replay of Priddy's Hard in 1883 on a monstrous scale, for the subsequent Court of Enquiry held that in all probability the initial explosion had been caused by an airman chipping out the CE exploder from a 1,000-lb bomb, using a brass chisel. A witness, who had left the quarry before the explosion, had seen this happening. The recovery of the unexploded

bombs took about a year. As a consequence of this disaster, it was promulgated that no work could be undertaken on explosives anywhere than in a laboratory if the regulations required laboratory conditions. All unclassifiable repairable and unserviceable explosives had to be stored apart from serviceable explosives and 'must not, repeat not' be taken into underground storages.

The amount of effort expended in the protection of ordnance during the Second World War was prodigious and has now been well documented in McCamley's pioneering work (see Bibliography). An essential part of the war effort (though its role is not stressed in the mountain of books describing the conflict) – the storing, preparation and distribution of munitions to the three services – played a part in the bankruptcy faced by Britain at the end of the war. The doughty struggles of Treasury mandarins before the war had a real point behind them. The British economy could not afford a military effort on the scale required to win the greatest war in history. [14]

D-Day: Operation Overlord and the Hampshire depots

The D-Day landings, which began on 6 June 1944, involved one of the largest operations of military, naval and air power ever seen. Hampshire's geographical position, its road and rail network, and its historical naval importance meant that it was the perfect springboard for the invasion, and the county's Ordnance Depots played a pivotal role

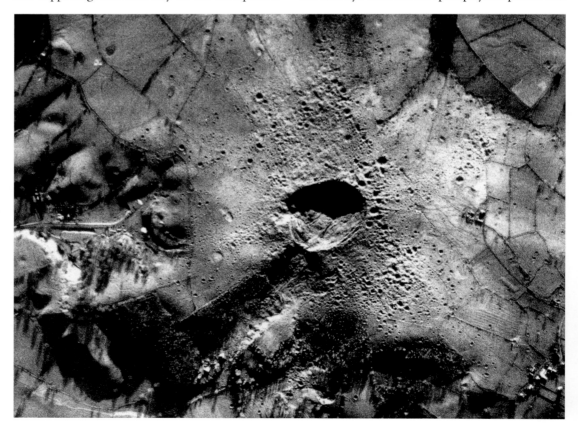

in the operation. Bedenham and Priddy's Hard were to act as principal suppliers of armaments, with back up and support provided by the other naval establishments at Gosport and Portsmouth.

An order from December 1942 had stated that Priddy's Hard would need to service and supply an initial fleet of eight cruisers and thirty-eight destroyers, with 900 tons lighterage demanded in addition to that already held. In March 1944 this was increased to 7,400 tons lighterage for one battleship, one monitor, nine cruisers and eighteen destroyers. Not only would this fleet require ammunition, but also its old equipment would need removal, examination and servicing.

The Home Guard

In May 1940 the Local Defence Volunteers (later named the Home Guard) were formed to help defend Great Britain against invasion. Within 24 hours of the first appeal, a quarter of a million men aged between 17 and 65 had volunteered. Eventually this citizens' army numbered a million and a half men. Many of the volunteers had seen active service in the First World War and so had experience of weapons and procedures that were to prove invaluable to the training of new recruits. As the Ordnance Yards were vulnerable to attack and sabotage, they led the way in mustering the LDV, issuing armbands (in lieu of uniforms which had not yet arrived) and initiating training.

After French capitulation in June 1940 Britain became a fortress, ready to repel an invasion. At the depots LDV units were strengthened and new officers appointed to form a Depot Battalion. The general duties of the Battalion included providing riflemen for anti-aircraft defence, crews for machine guns and defence against landing parties; however, all volunteers carried on with their normal work until an air raid was given, at which time they moved to their Battalion positions. Each depot had three platoons which formed the company, and the Area Commander's Office at Priddy's Hard was commandeered as general headquarters.

In July 1940 the LDV was renamed the Home Guard, after a suggestion from Sir Winston Churchill, and from then on the volunteers received the same training as the regular army. In September of that year the Dockyard Defence Volunteers was renamed the 18th (Dockyard Port) Home Guard Battalion of the Hampshire Regiment, which had a combined strength of 2,600 men. Under this reorganisation, an intensive training programme began, with all volunteers required to achieve an adequate standard in all areas of weapon use, observation and reporting, map reading, field fortifications and unarmed combat. More specialised training was provided to different units within the Battalion, including riflemen, machine gunners, bomb throwers, artillery and signals. Training periods were also undertaken for company exercises including battle drill and field manoeuvres.

Training and defence work continued until 1943, with the Home Guard fulfilling their duties in close cooperation with local councillors and other volunteers. Apart from trench digging, fence building and repairing essential communication lines, volunteers manned the new 'pillboxes' constructed within the depot. In addition to their military duties, the depot companies were also trained firefighters and bomb disposal units, working closely alongside the Depot's Passive Defence Organisation and the Royal Marine Police (see Guarding the Magazines, pages 76–9).

From The Royal Naval Armament Depot's of Priddy's Hard, Elson, Frater and Bedenham *by H.W. Semark (Winchester, 1977)*

10.19 No.3 Company, 32nd Hampshire (Connaught) Battalion, Home Guard outside the Gas Defence Station at Priddy's Hard Gunwarf in 1944. After the reorganisation of 1940 the Home Guard at Priddy's Hard consisted of sixty men in all. There were two twelve-man rifle squads, and twelve three-man machine-gun crews manning four Maxims and eight twin Lewis guns. A position for one of the latter is still extant on the roof of E Magazine. Training took place on Tuesdays and Thursdays. Thirty men were on duty each night, their main duties after 1940 being defending against air raids, and in particular the deadly 'butterfly' bombs. They were finally stood down in July 1944. (*Priddy's Hard Archive 1998.3.129*)

The navy's global storage at the end of the war

Permanent	Tons	Temporary	Tons
Western Mediterranean Gibraltar, Malta	25,000	**Western Mediterranean** Taranto	7,000
Eastern Mediterranean		Haifa, Gilbana, Amiriya, Mex, Lake Timsah, El Tina, Fort Agrud, Gebel-il-Ilwa, Aboukir	70,000
East Indies Trincomalee, Bombay	30,000	Colombo, Pulgaon, Madras, Vizagapatam, Cochin, Calcutta	29,000
Singapore	15,000		
Hong Kong	6,000		
Australia Sydney, Fremantle, Darwin	20,000	Sydney, Brisbane, Cairns, Darwin, Melbourne, Adelaide	37,000
South and East Africa Ganspan, Kilindini, Aden, Durban, Simonstown	41,000	Eritrea, Port Elizabeth, East London	55,000
Bermuda	3,000		
Canada		St Lazare and St Polycarpe	30,000
Great Britain	450,000		135,000
Total	**590,000**		**363,000**

Some of these were old facilities, dating back to the 18th century; a few were survivals from the First World War, such as Mex, 4 miles from Alexandria, where a widely spaced depot and laboratory had been built in 1916, while others were recent improvisations.

In the UK, the permanent storage capacity of 450,000 tons (with 135,000 tons held in temporary magazines) exceeded the foreseeable post-war requirements, with a good margin for unforeseen contingencies. The temporary magazines abroad would soon be discarded, for both financial and political reasons, as a glance at their locations makes clear.

ADM 1/18687 and Major-General A.Forbes, *A History of the Army Ordnance Services*, vol.III (London, 1929)

10.27 Below: NAV *Bedenham* loading for D-Day. Priddy's Hard was the main distribution centre for ammunition for Operation Neptune. The order to prepare for the Operation was given on 20 April 1944. NAV *Bedenham* blew up at Gibraltar in 1951 not long after the similar explosion at Bedenham. The cause was thought to be the same in both cases, faulty depth charges. (*Priddy's Hard Archive. 1998.3.156*)

Additional stores were essential to meet the demand (particularly of Landing Craft requirements) and in 1943 sites were approved at Portland and Newhaven. During the early months of 1944, curved profile, heavy-gauge corrugated iron huts (called elephant huts) were also constructed at Priddy's Hard, with intermediate dumps and groups of huts established at Shoreham, Southampton and Exbury. Extra stores, other than those requested by the Admiralty, were also utilised as a precaution. At most of the sites separate supplies of guns and gun spares were held for Defensively Equipped Merchant Ships (DEMS), Coastal Forces and Landing Craft.

Some 20,000 tons of ammunition had to be laid on for the bombarding force, while in addition fired cases had to be stored at the hards. Final details of requirements were not received until March to May 1944. At Priddy's Hard some 6,500 tons of ammunition was issued to the bombarding force vessels prior to D-Day, with sixty-nine lighters and two coasters preloaded at Portsmouth with bombarding replenishments and other ammunition reserves. By 1 May 1944, Gosport had produced 50,000 5-inch rockets for shore bombardment, of which 30,000 were allocated for LCT(R)s (Landing Craft Tank, Rocket) on D-Day itself. In the following week all support warships were re-ammunitioned. Mine assembly was carried out at the Mine Depot in Frater from March to May; the mines (totalling 3,560) were

10.28 The laboratory office staff photographed in 1945. There is a dedication, lines of verse and a number of signatures on the reverse of the original, as if given as a gift to a woman no longer working there or on sick leave. *(Priddy's Hard Archive 2002.184)*

10.29 Group photograph of workers from one of the non-explosive workshops at Priddy's Hard, taken outside what is now the entrance to the Explosion! Museum of Naval Firepower, sometime between 1945 and 1950. During the war the workers tended to keep to their own specific areas, with little communication or interaction between these, resulting in little idea of what was going on in general. Thus, although in the spring of 1944 most people knew that there was a massive armada of vessels gathering out in the harbour and in the Solent, at the time of the Normandy invasion itself many didn't realise that the ships had gone, and the first they knew of the actual landings was when ships began to return on the evening of D-Day, to land casualties, and to replenish stores and ammunition. An additional task carried out at Priddy's Hard at that time was the preparation of rockets for aircraft. Such was the volume of this extra work that at one point the Senior Armament Supply Officer said that it almost overwhelmed the staff. *(Priddy's Hard Archive 2002.1293)*

10.30 Ammunition being loaded and unloaded from barges at Bedenham pier and at Portsmouth. The images appear to date from after the 1950 explosion; before this there were six cranes on the pier rather than three. They must also pre-date the 1970s. In the 1960s boatloads of holidaymakers would come close alongside to watch this taking place. In the 1970s, however, the operation was considered too dangerous to undertake in the dockyard and was moved to a more remote jetty further up the harbour. The same barges and pier are still in use today, although the tugs are now diesel rather than steam. (Priddy's Hard Archive)

then distributed to coastal craft at Gosport, Dover, Plymouth and to RAF Bomber Command.

During the assembly period, the numerous craft (coasters, tugs, motor fishing vessels, self-propelled and dumb lighters) arrived to facilitate loading and unloading. Lighters were provided at a buoy off Agrangi for servicing tugs and off Durns Point for servicing DEMS at Cowes. Two 1,000-ton Armament Supply Issuing Ships (*Procris* and *Fendris*) were provided for the service of destroyers and coastal craft, and were berthed in the Solent. The bombardment vessels arrived at their South Coast sorties fully loaded but required considerable adjustment on arrival. The increased demand for anchorage for vessels requiring supplies and preparation led to the construction of further hards, floating harbours and slips around the Hampshire coastline. As D-Day approached and so many vessels were demanding space and supplies, it was necessary to obtain the Commander-in-

Chief's approval that only those ships with essential operational requirements for the invasion itself would be supplied.

A constant ferry service between Priddy's Hard and Armament Supply Issuing Ships on the far shore was maintained after D-Day to provide a continual supply of ammunition. Communication was maintained at all times. Ships on arrival were presented with an abbreviated code for signalling requirements of ammunition; lighters were provided with boards showing the class of ship for which they were loaded, and therefore the ammunition they contained. One of the problems that had to be overcome was that empty ammunition packages and fired cases needed to be removed before supply ships could be reloaded with new ammunition. Extra dumps were provided for the return packages and special parties (mainly of women) were drafted in to unload. Women formed more than half the total work force (of

Beer Quarry Magazine

Beer Quarry was a very old working of fine limestone that was used extensively in mediaeval times for ecclesiastical buildings of the south west. Although the north workings had been considered for use as a naval magazine in 1940, the matter was not pursued until the anti-invasion ban was lifted in 1943. Since 1940 the quarry, which had for some years been operating on a very low level, had been cleared of rubble and its adaptation on the lines of Pickwick Quarry, Corsham (see page 216), was expected to be a simple matter. In May 1943 the storage position for explosives was causing considerable concern as a result of slow progress at the new RNAD Beith due to shortage of labour, and a delay in obtaining concurrence of the Ministry of Agriculture and Fisheries for the site of another new 50,000-ton depot in Yorkshire (Welbury), where construction would not start until June of that year.

Although cuts had been made in the output of gun ammunition, the net increase in stocks at home was still averaging over 10,000 tons gross a month, mainly because of large quantities of Fleet Air Arm stores (which grew relentlessly during the war), rockets, special stores for Combined Operations and new types of anti-aircraft and anti-submarine weapons. At the present rate of intake there was only sufficient storage available to last until about the end of June 1943. In these circumstances Beer offered a quick-fix solution, readily adaptable for the temporary storage of a limited range of explosives (depth charges, shell); the work required consisted mainly of draining, provision of internal roofing to protect against drips, and the erection of a few huts for use as offices, mess room, laboratory rooms, and other minor purposes. It was hoped that the work would take only about three months, with a portion of the quarry ready for storage in about a month. A labour force of about fifty would be required. When alterations were complete the quarry was expected to accommodate about 15–20,000 tons of ordnance.[1]

The adaptation of Beer became even more of a priority on 15 July 1943, when the site at Welbury had to be abandoned due to last minute objections by the Ministry of Labour. Additional works were soon proposed, to include a shifting room for eighteen persons (two-thirds women), a store office, painting and scraping rooms at entrances, and canteen requirements revised to 120 persons. The explosives were to come in and out by road from rail terminals at Seaton or Seaton Junction, where a police hut and possible messing facilities would need to be provided. The depot commenced operations on a reduced scale in mid-

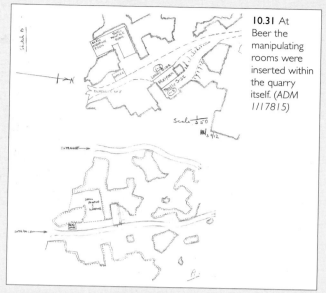

10.31 At Beer the manipulating rooms were inserted within the quarry itself. (ADM 1/17815)

October 1943, but by December further works were required.[2]

After the quarry was returned to its owners, quarrying resumed on a greater scale than before the war, with relatively large quantities being extracted, mainly for church restoration purposes. A future Master Mason of Exeter Cathedral, Peter Dare, served his apprenticeship there – he was told it had been used as a mushroom farm during the war. An adjacent quarry is now open as an attraction during the summer months.

---

[1] When the detailed planning was done, the work comprised:
a) Levelling and draining
b) Provision of corrugated sheets to drain away roof seepage where necessary
c) Main office and police office to be provided inside entrance
d) Two laboratory rooms to be provided inside entrances; A small police hut at road entrance
e) Fencing round the owners' crushing plant in front of the quarry
f) Grill doors for quarry
g) Latrines
h) Lighting inside entrances for loading and unloading lorries
i) Lighting and heating in police hut, offices and laboratory rooms
j) Diesel tractors and trollies
k) Charging plant for magazine lanterns and portable lighting sets
l) Canteen for 150 persons (two sittings)
Shell scraping and painting facilities might also prove to be required, but there was plenty of space. The Beer scheme, estimated at £22,000, seemed a very reasonable solution.
[2] ADM 1/17815

3,000) at Priddy's Hard at this time, having been first recruited at the outbreak of war. Although the staff numbers at the yard had increased dramatically for the war effort, and the volume of work was so unremitting, they were kept in their own areas and so had little chance of discovering the full extent of the massive international operation. Working double-shifts or round-the-clock during the build up to D-Day, the workers at the Ordnance Depots are the reason that the fleet was so well prepared.[15]

...

In the changing face of warfare from the mid-20th century onward, the depots would no longer be called upon to perform the same historical roles. Many of the depots went on to play their part in the Cold War (and so to continue to stretch the economy) and store nuclear weapons, which brought completely new factors into the design of magazine accommodation. Although a number of sites remain in use as missile, torpedo or mine depots, out of the three Ordnance Yards at the major dockyards only Bull Point remains in use by the Ministry of Defence (see Appendix A). The depots at Upnor and Priddy's Hard have long since closed and their sites been partially redeveloped, although the castle at Upnor and many of the buildings at Priddy's Hard remain open to the public as museums.

The Legacy of the Ordnance Yards

Jeremy Lake and David Evans,
with contributions to Priddy's Hard by
Rob Harper, Gosport Borough Council

Following a comprehensive review of Britain's dockyards conducted by English Heritage during the late 1990s, and new research focused on the Victorian period[1], it became apparent that very little was known about the ordnance yards, despite being at the forefront of Britain's dominance as a sea power since the late 1700s. It was clear that research needed to be undertaken immediately in order to inform a wider public understanding and initiate conservation of the sites where appropriate. Priddy's Hard was the focus of much of this concern, as only the Georgian magazine and associated structures were protected at a national level, and additional buildings had been rejected for listing by ministers in the early 1990s. Above all, the lack of an informed understanding of the development, character and significance of the site was also presenting obstacles to an agreed approach by the site's many stakeholders to sustainable development proposals and funding options. There were similar concerns expressed by the Ministry of Defence and others concerning Bull Point. The decision was taken, therefore, to initiate a documentary survey of the key sites that existed prior to 1914, and to evaluate them within their broader thematic and international context.

The gunwharves were all subject to a comprehensive survey by English Heritage's Listing Team in the mid 1990s, as part of the evaluation of the naval dockyards. The most complete of the surviving gunwharves is located at Morice Yard, within the naval base at Devonport, Plymouth. The 1720s site replaced the short-lived Old Gunwharf at the head of Stonehouse Pool. Still bounded by its original perimeter wall, it comprises storehouses flanking a now-infilled basin, behind which is the magazine of 1744, and a series of terrace walls which rise dramatically up to the slope to the fine Baroque-influenced terrace of officers' housing. The principal surviving additions comprise a fine carriage store and associated house of 1776–7, and three store buildings added in the 1840s. The gunwharf at Portsmouth, founded in 1662 and disposed of in 1998, has been substantially redeveloped as a leisure and shopping complex. Part of the gunwharf activities, that of gun repair, moved to a purpose-built extension to Priddy's Hard in 1918. The new development incorporates three listed Napoleonic period buildings, including The Grand Store, halved in size by bombing in the Second World War, and the magazine of 1856. The gunwharf at Chatham, the site of the first dockyard founded in 1547, was subject to extensive demolition after its closure in the 1950s. The principal visible remains are the early 18th-century storekeeper's house and offices (now the Command House public house) and a former ordnance store built in 1805 and decommissioned in the 1950s. It is now being incorporated as a waterfront development within the proposed Chatham Naval Dockyard World Heritage Site.

The survival of many of the ordnance yard sites mentioned in the text has been equally if not more patchy. Their evaluation for the purposes of statutory protection have depended firstly on the commissioning of research on individual sites and structures, and secondly on an understanding of their wider technological and historical context. The focus of attention for statutory protection through listing or scheduling have been the most outstanding individual survivals (Tipner, Great Yarmouth, Purfleet) and the most complete sites, where the most clear and intelligible sense of the development of ordnance yards from storage to complex handling and inspection systems can still be gained. The most complete remaining sites, despite differing degrees of alteration and loss, comprise the great inland depot at Weedon, Marchwood on the Hampshire coast, and three sites relating to each of the major dockyards: Priddy's Hard (opposite Portsmouth Dockyard), Upnor (opposite Chatham Dockyard) and Bull Point (upriver from Devonport Dockyard). Each of these display clear evidence in their fabric for the transition from their role as storage complexes into sites for the preparation and inspection of new types of propellants and projectiles, developments which took place against the background of the arms race of the second half of the 19th century, first against France and then against Germany. Thus the construction of an armour-clad and steam-powered fleet, followed by the introduction of rifled guns and rotating turrets, was accompanied by the development of ordnance, which rendered the forts of the Palmerston government, initiated in 1859 in reaction to a perceived threat from the French, obsolete only 20 years after their construction.

Priddy's Hard retains the best-preserved range of structures that relate to the navy's transition from the age of sail, powder and solid shot to the Dreadnought class of the early 1900s; it encompasses the period of Britain's dominance as a sea power on a global scale. Bull Point, under development from 1856, was from the outset provided with a set of buildings planned and dedicated to the various functions which were now coming into demand, in particular those relating to the filling and manipulation of shells; it comprises a remarkable example of integrated factory planning of the period.

Also important to the evaluation of these sites has been their international context. The value and importance of the ordnance yards is indeed closely linked to the development of British naval power, as no other great power of continental Europe weighted the strategic benefit so heavily toward naval rather than military strength. As we have seen, the major Ordnance Depots were concentrated around the naval dockyards at Plymouth, Portsmouth and Chatham, in contrast to those arsenals located in the cities or forts of other European powers which were sited in response to landward threats. The Zeughaus in Graz, Austria, built in 1642 and retaining a full complement of armour and ordnance, stands out as a uniquely complete example. Little is known to have survived from ordnance sites developed in conjunction with the naval bases of other European powers, and even the better-preserved dockyard sites – such as the Venice Arsenale, the Drassanes in Barcelona, the Real Caranero Arsenal at Cadiz, Rochefort on France's Atlantic coast and Karlskrona in Sweden – do not have Ordnance Yards displaying the coherence and time-depth of what remains at Priddy's Hard. The Prussian navy was serviced from Danzig, until a new building yard was started at Wilhelmshafen in 1860. Kiel, a German port after the annexation of Schleswig-Holstein in 1865, was developed as the main German dockyard following the establishment of the Imperial Navy in 1867. As such it has a much briefer history than all the British examples. In other parts of Europe, however, such as in the Trubia area of Asturias in Spain[2], entire landscapes were shaped by the nationalisation of ordnance production on a scale not seen in Britain. This is rich ground for future students of the subject to explore – the extent, for example, to which traveller cranes (as used at Purfleet) were utilised for magazines and manufactories of ordnance elsewhere in Europe.[3]

Arsenals and military heritage sites throughout Europe face significant financial challenges with respect to their long-term use. The viable long-term conservation of these sites is heavily reliant on co-operation and joint-working between a wide variety of interests and disciplines, as the mixed-use redevelopment of Woolwich Arsenal and other sites in Europe has made clear.[4] These are, however, some of the most challenging historic sites to conserve for future generations, and a fine balance has had to be met between the needs for recording and in-situ conservation. This is due firstly to practical considerations: their extent, complexity and the problems of decontamination. Many are also located in some of the most economically and socially disadvantaged areas of the country. Inevitably, the focus of discussion is on the extent to which the most important fabric can be adaptively reused without compromising its historic importance, or even allowed to be demolished. The decision to build in permanent or temporary materials is fundamental to the long-term ability of these buildings to survive and find new uses. At Priddy's Hard, for example, there is a marked contrast between the solid structures of the historic core of the site around the magazine complex, the 1880s shell-filling complex built just outside the ramparts and the fragile timber structures built for the laboratory complex of the 1890s, built within the mid-18th-century ramparts. These buildings are highly vulnerable to decay and vandalism. The decision was eventually taken to focus on the retention of a small but representative grouping of the laboratory huts, and then provide for the long-term management of the remainder as footprints, within the physical constraints of the ramparts, which had been extended around them and which convey a sense of the scale and dangerous nature of the inspection, repair and processing of ordnance that was carried out within the laboratory complex.

The depots built from the 1870s are either incomplete or present even more limited opportunities for the preservation of fabric. Chattenden's overall layout has survived intact within its woodland setting, although the magazines – subject to subsidence within a decade of their construction in the 1870s – have been heavily adapted. Very little of the built infrastructure has survived at nearby Lodge Hill, which like Chattenden now awaits redevelopment for housing. The options for such a redevelopment will need to include the retention of the grid-like template of the site, and most certainly the anti-aircraft positions on the ridge to the north of the site; these latter include the earliest sites associated with anti-aircraft measures in Britain, installed in 1912–13. Lodge Hill provided the model for developments at Bedenham, begun in 1908 as an extension to Priddy's Hard and which remains in full use as a Defence Munitions site. The shell stores have all been demolished and the magazines reclad and upgraded for modern usage. Also in continuing use are Frater, which opened in 1918 as a mine depot and after 1959 became the main centre in the Portsmouth area for the repair and maintenance of torpedoes, and Elson, where magazines were built from the 1920s around the 1859 Fort Elson and which expanded as a missile repair facility in the 1960s.

The depots developed after 1914 await a comprehensive programme of survey and analysis. Some such as RNAD Crombie, Ernesettle and Beith are still in active military use. They occupy dispersed sites, typically spread over several square miles of land, and clearly present limited opportunities for more than careful recording and integration into landscape and regeneration schemes. Broughton Moor in Cumbria, opened in 1937 and closed in 1992, is a case in point. Plans are now afoot by Allerdale District Council to purchase the site from the Ministry of Defence and, through interpretation of its industrial and military history,

enhance the amenity and wildlife potential of the site. Dean Hill, on the Wiltshire/Hampshire border, is another example of a site where options for development or otherwise were, in spring 2006, still being considered by the relevant local authorities. Dean Hill is a very extensive site that still retains its laboratory complex where munitions were checked and then reconditioned: brick examination buildings, each served by rail and set within concrete traverses, and then more substantial earth-covered buildings for the more dangerous job of restoration.

Notes

1   Cocroft 2000, pp. 263–273; Evans 2004
2   Roberto Suarez Menendez, *Fabrica de Trubia, 1794–1987*, Centro de Escultura de Cadas, Carreno, 1993
3   As for example its use in a Barcelona gun foundry in 1766 (Utrilla, Antonio de Lizaur y de (2004) 'Las Reales Atarazanas y la Maestrana de Artilleria' in Corbalan, Juan Miguel Munoz (ed) *La Academia de Matematicas de Barcelona*, Ministerio de Defensa, Barcelona.
4   For more information on this redevelopment, see www.interreg3c.net.

Select Gazetteer of Key Sites

RNAD BULL POINT
Devon

There is no public access to this site, which remains in use by the Ministry of Defence.

Bull Point, located just to the north of the Royal Navy's new steam yard at Keyham, was the last great project of the Board of Ordnance, which was abolished in 1856. It provided storage for 40,000 barrels of powder in an integrated complex, which included a floating magazine where powder was unloaded and the 1805 St Budeax laboratory where it was first checked and processed. There is a stylistic coherence between

the buildings – mostly in ashlar with rock-faced dressings and fronting an avenue to the south of the magazines – and the magazines themselves; with Weedon Bec, they comprise the most coherent architectural ensemble in any of the Ordnance Yards. Bull Point also constitutes a remarkable set-piece example of integrated factory planning of the period, from the outset being provided with a set of buildings planned and dedicated to the various functions for the processing, as well as the storage, of those new types of ordnance that had a revolutionary impact on the design of naval ships and fortifications. A further building campaign of 1893–1906 left Bull Point prepared for the First World War. The cordite and dry

A.1 The south side of the main axial route, looking south-east, showing the fuze store, examining room and case store (14, 15 and 18 on plan). *(Jeremy Lake)*

A.2 Above: A 1947 view of workers at Bull Point using a traveller crane to shift ammunition. (Plymouth Naval Base Museum)

A.3 Below: The view looking south-east along the main axial route, showing in the foreground the hydraulic press house, for pressing flannel cartridges, and the offices with the flat roof of c.1940. (Jeremy Lake)

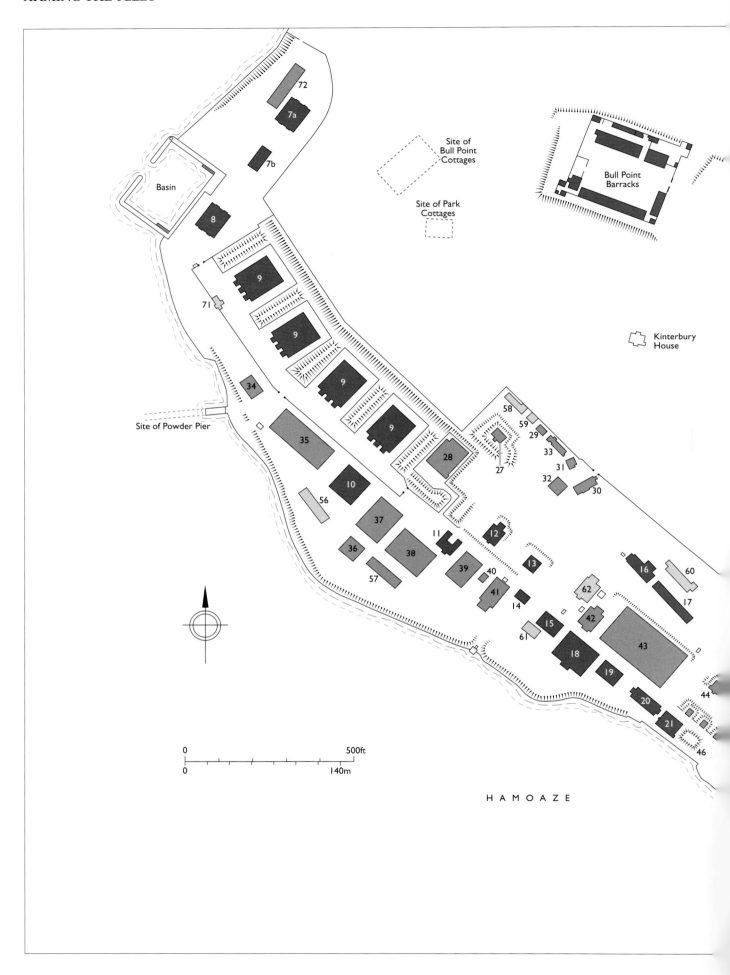

Bull Point – phased plan of site

Based on information from Wessex Archaeology 1999 report 'The Royal Dockyards at Plymouth Archaeological Assessment' and *Bull Point; the Development of the Buildings* by David Evans (English Heritage, 2000). *(Stephen Dent)*

Key
No. Date/building

■ 1775 – 1830
1 Receiving House (demolished)
2 No.1 Stoving House (demolished)
3 Boiler House (demolished)
4 No.2 Stoving House (demolished)
5 Dusting House (demolished)
6 Mixing House

■ 1851 – 1857
  Basin
7a Shell Magazine (demolished)
7b Flannel Cartridge Store (demolished)
8 Receipt & Issue Magazine
9 Magazines
10 Empty Barrel & Case Store
11 Store for planks, Flannel Cartridges, Foreman's Office & Printers
12 Storekeeper's Office
13 Hydraulic Press House
14 Store for Percussion Caps, Fuzes & Percussion Tubes
15 Examining Room (?)
16 Pattern & Class Rooms (1862–3)
17 Cottages (demolished)
18 Empty Barrel and Case Store
19 Filling and Packing House
20 Breaking-up House (?)
21 Painters Shop
22 Smithery
23 Shell Filling Room
24 Laboratory Expense Magazine (demolished)
25 Filling Room (demolished)
26 Flannel Cartridge Filling Room (demolished)

■ 1893 – 1906
27 Dry Guncotton Magazine
28 Cordite Magazine
29 Departmental Works Carpenters' Shop
30 Police Offices
31 House for Crews of Steamers
32 Search Room (demolished)
33 Filled Shell Store
34 Empty Powder Case Store
35 Covering for Shell Base
36 No. 3 QF Magazine

37 QF Ammunition Store
38 New QF Ammunition Store
39 Wet Guncotton Store
40 New Mine Shop
41 Mine & Countermine Store
42 Shifting Room
43 Shell Store
44 Munitions Store (later Timber Store)
45 Cartridge Filling Rooms (demolished)
46 Boiler House for Cartridge Filling Rooms (demolished)
47 Shell Filling Rooms
48 Weighing Room
49 Shell Painting Room
50 Proving Room for Fuzes
51 Electrical Generating Station
52 Soldering Shop (demolished)
53 Workshop for cleaning Cartridges (demolished)
54 Tinmen's Shop & Cleaning Room
55 Charging Shed (incorporating Acid Store)

□ 1916 – 1939
56 Storage Hut (1939)
57 Storage Hut (1939)
58 Store (1947)
59 Store (1947)
60 First Aid Station (1939, demolished)
61 Receipt & Issue Store (1956)
62 Unknown (1920s?)
63 New Proof House (1934)
64 Trotyl and Shellite Shifting Room
65 Paravane Sub-Depot (1917)
66 First Aid Station (1939)
67 Charging Room for Electric Trolleys (1924)
68 New Workshops (1935)
69 Transfer Shed (1916)
70 Storage Shed (1940)
71 Observation Post – post 1950
72 Munitions Store, later Timber Store (c.1900)

Notes:
For reasons of clarity, various Second World War era air raid shelters, together with some other minor modern structures have been omitted.

The coastline at the extreme south-eastern corner of the site has been extended by reclamation in recent years – this plan shows it as it was for most of the site's history.

Bull Point House

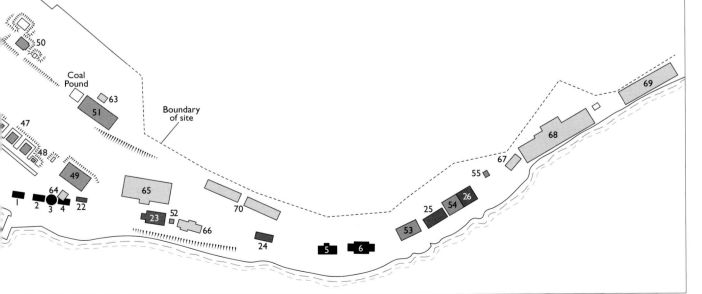

guncotton magazines, enclosed within earthwork extensions of the 1850s magazine earthworks, and the wet guncotton store are now the best surviving group representative of the development of these new explosives at the end of the 19th century. There is also the finest example – maintaining the high architectural standards established in the 1850s – of a store (37 on plan) for the

A.6 The fine pedimented entrance to Bull Point Barracks. *(Stephen Dent)*

A.4 Bull Point House (1851–7); residence of the Superintendent of the site, in 1947. *(Plymouth Naval Base Museum)*

A.5 A 1947 view of the interior of the new building for empty powder cases (1895–6), which by 1913 had become a receipt store for non-combustibles. *(Plymouth Naval Base Museum)*

ammunition of the quick-firing guns being increasingly fitted onto warships. Also part of the site, although some distance to the north, are the barracks built in 1855–8 for the garrison guarding Bull Point, and the most complete defensible barracks of the period outside Pembroke in Wales. The complex comprises soldiers' and officers' quarters, a magazine and other ancillary buildings. It is surrounded by a tall defensible wall, projecting at the corners to form bastions covering alternate sides, with rifle slits.

A.7 The cordite store of 1899–1905, which originally had a raised roof and front parapet, and a pair of traveller cranes. *(Jeremy Lake)*

A.8 The shifting room of 1901–2. *(Jeremy Lake)*

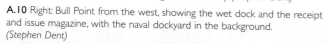

A.9 Above: the classically styled receipt and issue magazine, with (right) a detail of the ventilation and the fine granite masonry. *(Stephen Dent)*

A.10 Right: Bull Point from the west, showing the wet dock and the receipt and issue magazine, with the naval dockyard in the background. *(Stephen Dent)*

A.11 The Camber, the wet dock of 1851–4 with, in the foreground, a bollard created from an old cannon. *(Stephen Dent)*

TIPNER POINT
Hampshire

By the 1780s, war with France, and the invasion scare of 1779, led to concerns about the vulnerability of the arsenals and had exposed an alarming situation concerning the state of the nation's gunpowder. The former was foremost in the mind of the new (appointed 1782) Master-General of the Board of Ordnance, George Lennox, the Third Duke of Richmond. Although his plan to enhance the landward fortifications of Portsmouth and Plymouth was defeated in the House of Commons in 1786, his other strategy – to divide and separate the magazines – was implemented at Portsmouth with the acquisition of land at Tipner Point between 1789 and 1791. The original design for a pair of circular vaulted magazines was superseded by the present one for a magazine with groined arches and a copper-clad wooden roof. From 1805 until the mid 1820s Tipner acted as deposit magazine for the restoving of old gunpowder at nearby Stamshaw (which has been demolished). The magazine accommodation at Tipner, Marchwood and Upnor was increased following appraisal by Lord Panmure, the Secretary of State for War, of the Committee on Magazines report of March 1856. The southern extension to the magazine was built with parabolic arches, as used at Weedon Bec and Upnor. On the division of the ordnance depots between the two services in 1890, the site passed to the army, and on conversion of the magazines into general ordnance storage the present iron doors were inserted.

The powder magazines (structurally complete by 1798, extended in 1856–7 and internally

A.12 Tipner today, looking north east, showing surviving buildings amidst the scrap yard. From left to right; the cooperage, a store and the magazines. *(Geoffrey Dennison)*

A.13 The small arms store, with old torpedoes and guns lying on the roof. *(Stephen Dent)*

remodelled after the Second World War), the cooperage, shifting room and perimeter walls of 1800 are all listed at grade II. Four other buildings survive from the third phase of 1891–1910. The site was sold by the Ministry of Defence in the early 1970s and is now a scrap-metal yard.

A.14 The magazines from the north-east, showing in the foreground that of 1798 with the 1856–7 extension projecting to the rear. (Geoffrey Dennison)

A.15 Cooperage, interior showing stairs and wooden panelling. (Stephen Dent)

A.16 The cooperage, completed in 1800, from the south-west. (Geoffrey Dennison)

A.17 The shifting house, completed in 1800, from the east. It was converted into a magazine in 1827, and still used for housing explosives in the Second World War. (Stephen Dent)

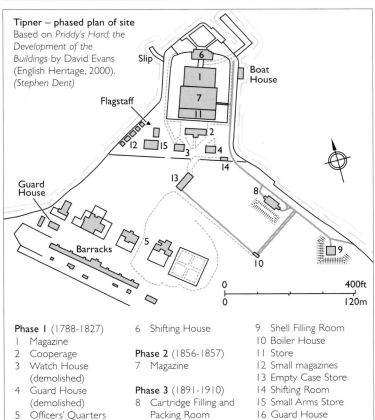

Tipner – phased plan of site
Based on Priddy's Hard; the Development of the Buildings by David Evans (English Heritage, 2000). (Stephen Dent)

Slip

Boat House

Flagstaff

Guard House

Barracks

0 _____ 400ft
0 _____ 120m

Phase 1 (1788-1827)
1 Magazine
2 Cooperage
3 Watch House (demolished)
4 Guard House (demolished)
5 Officers' Quarters

6 Shifting House

Phase 2 (1856-1857)
7 Magazine

Phase 3 (1891-1910)
8 Cartridge Filling and Packing Room

9 Shell Filling Room
10 Boiler House
11 Store
12 Small magazines
13 Empty Case Store
14 Shifting Room
15 Small Arms Store
16 Guard House

PRIDDY'S HARD
Gosport, Hampshire

Explosion! Museum of Naval Firepower
Priddy's Hard, Gosport, Hampshire. PO12 4LE
02392 505600 / 023 9250 5678 24hr line
www.explosion.org.uk
April – October and School Holidays:
   open every day (except 24, 25, 26 Dec)
November – March:
   Thursday, Saturday and Sundays only
April – Oct: 10am–5.30pm
November – March: 10am–4.30pm
Last admission one hour before closing

Before development from the early 1990s the site covered over 25 acres. Most of this has now been built on. The first gunpowder magazine and its surrounding buildings now houses the Explosion! Museum of Naval Firepower, which combines the history of the Priddy's Hard Armaments Depot with the history of naval weaponry. Other elements of the site are found along the waterside and amongst the recently built housing.[1]

1770–1776

The boundary of the first phase of the site – drafted in 1769 and finished by the end of September 1777 – is the northern end of the Gosport Lines, earthwork defences for the protection of the naval dockyard that date back to the late 17th century and were extended around Priddy's Hard from 1757. It comprised a basin or camber for powder vessels, a powder magazine, a cooperage for the repair of powder barrels, a rolling way (for moving powder in barrows or trollies), labourers' cottages, officers' houses and a shifting room (for the examination of powder). Offices were added in 1811–12, the other remaining pre-1840s alteration being the remodelling of the cooperage and shifting room (4 on plan) as a two-storey range in the early 19th century, and its

A.18 Priddy's Hard looking south, prior to its closure in 1989, showing the vast extent of the post-1880s development away from the 18th-century ramparts. In the foreground are warehouses of the New Gunwharf, built for the repair of guns and their loading mechanisms in 1918, and accessed by a broad-gauge railway which continued to supply the transfer shed for landing shells next to the shell store. At the top is the 18th century Royal Clarence Victualling Yard, and the naval fuel depot. See also the plan overleaf. (NMR 15770-04)

A.19 The offices were built following complaints in 1811 by the officers about the lack of facilities. Officers' accommodation was usually on the first floor, with activities including accounts, ledger rooms, registry and messengers on the ground floor. The design is typical of naval dockyard buildings of the late 18th century. The original building was extended by sixteen bays, to the left, in 1920. (NMR BB94-10332)

Priddy's Hard – phased plan of site

Based on information from Wessex Archaeology 1999 report 'The Royal Dockyards at Portsmouth, Archaeological
Assessment'; *Priddy's Hard; the Development of the Buildings* by David Evans (English Heritage, 2000) *(Plan by Stephen Dent)*

Key

No. Dates/buildings

■ 1774 – 1815

Camber Basin
Ramparts (1776–7)
1 Offices and Storehouse
(1811, includes 1920s extension)
2 Coach House and Engine House
(1780s, includes later extension/rebuilding)
3 A Magazine (1770–76)
4 B Magazine (1775, Cooperage and shifting
room remodelled early 1799)

■ 1847 – 1849

5 North range of Laboratory (with later infill)
6 Cottages for Laboratory Workers, later
converted into Tube and Rocket Store
7 Laboratory Boat House
8 Remaining buildings from east range of
Laboratory (remainder of Laboratory
demolished)
9 Foreman's Office, Shoe House and
Rolling Way and Wash House
10 Shifting Room

■ 1859 – 1881

11 Case Store of c.1881–2 with Rolling Way
originally connected to 16 to rear
12 Fire Engine Shed (c.1860–74)
13 Part of the Small Arms Cartridge Factory
(c.1860); by 1874 Accommodation &
Artificers' Shop (now demolished)
14 Part of the Small Arms Cartridge Factory
(c.1860); by 1880 Cook House & Proof House
15 Shell Store (1879)
16 Covered Rolling Way (c.1879)
17 Shed for empty powder cases & barrels
(c.1859, rebuilt in brick 1865)
18 Store, including link to 17 (c.1860)
19 C Powder Magazine (1860–61)
20 E Powder Magazine (1878–9)

■ 1886 – 1906

21 Shell Filling Rooms and Shell Fuzing Room
(1886–87 and later)
22 QF Shell Filling Room (1887-89)
23 Expense Magazine for Shell Filling Rooms
(1886)
24 Boiler House (1895)
25 Unheading Shed (c.1890s)
26 Shell Emptying Room (1903)
27 Shell Painting Room (1900–01)
28 Five rooms for examining filled powder cases
(1897, two to north demolished)
29 Room for securing, labelling and stencilling
boxes and cases (1897)
30 Latrines (1899, demolished)
31 Room for filling cordite cartridges (1897)
32 Two rooms for filling cordite cartridges (1897)
33 Room for labelling and stencilling boxes (1897)
34 Two rooms for filling cartridges (1897)
35 Room for unheading powder barrels (1897)
36 Shifting Room (1897)
37 Proof House (1889, converted 1897 into
Drying Room for cartridges)
38 Two stores (1895)
39 Shifting Room (1886–99)
40 Proof House (1896–7)
41 Search Shed and Telephone Room (c.1900)
42 Shell Store (1896–7)
43 Filled Shell Store (1899)

44 Mine & Countermining Store, with attached
Examining Room (1899–1900)
45 6pdr and 3pdr QF Ammunition Store (1889)
46 Empty Package Store (1896–7)
47 Empty Powder Case Store (1891)
48 Case Store (1901)
49 Shifting Room (1898–9)
50 Waiting Room and Electrical Switch Room
(1902–06, demolished)
51 Shelter Shed and Search House including
smoke hut (1902–03, demolished)
52 Women's Search Room
(1886, rebuilt 1916, demolished)
53 Case Store (1890s rebuilding of earlier
structure, remodelled 1938)
54 Carpenters' Shop (1903, with later extension)
55 6pdr and 3pdr QF Ammunition Store (1896–7)
56 Shed for examining warheads (1902-03, demolished)
57 Buildings for repairing 6pdr and 3pdr QF ammunition
(1901, demolished)
58 Cordite Magazine (1905–06, demolished)
59 Cordite Magazine (1898–9)
60 Laboratory Boiler House (c.1900, demolished)
61 Two Wet Guncotton Stores (1898–9, demolished)
62 Dry Guncotton Magazine (1898–9, demolished)

■ 1914 – 1954

63 Building for cutting Cordite, and building for fuzing
ammunition (1915, central block 1943, demolished)
64 Buildings for packing cartridges (1915, demolished)
65 21 Cartridge Filling Rooms (1915, demolished)
66 Five Fuze and Tube Filling Rooms (1915, demolished)
67 Office and Fuze Filling Section (1915, demolished)
68 Packing Room and store (demolished)
69 Inspector's Office for HE Shells (c.1914)
70 Pay Office and Fire Engine House (c.1915–20)
71 Women's Search Room and smoke hut (c.1916)
72 Shell Store Transfer Shed (1917–18)
73 Tinsmiths' and Painters' Shops (1916)
74 Empty Case Stores (1915)
75 Four Cartridge Filling Rooms (1915, demolished)
76 Trotyl Melting Room No.1 (1915)
77 Trotyl Melting Room No.3 (1915, demolished)
78 Amatol Store (1915, demolished)
79 Mine Store (1916, demolished)
80 Depth Charge Store and Bomb Store
(1916, rebuilt by 1937 as Fuze Filling Stores, demolished)
81 Women's Shifting Room (1916, demolished)
82 Fuze Room, Packing Room and Fuze and Tube Room
(1915, demolished)
83 Paravane Repair Shop (1916, extended 1938, demolished)
84 Two Cutting and Packing Rooms (1917, demolished)
85 QF Examining Room (1917, reconstructed 1941,
demolished)
86 Building for pressing Tetryl pellets (1915, demolished)
87 Medical Buildings (1915, extended 1917, demolished)
88 Empty Case Stores (1916, demolished)
89 Tube and Fuze Store (1917, demolished)
90 Paravane Store and Examining Room (1916, demolished)
91 Switchboard House (c.1918)
92 Store for Detonators for Fuze and Tube Stores (1917)
93 Cartridge Transfer Shed (1917/18, extended 1940,
demolished)
94 Central Sub-Station (1918)
95 Latrine for Cartridge Filling Rooms (1915, demolished)
96 Surface Shelters (c. 1940, demolished)
97 Underground Shelter (c. 1940, demolished)
98 Latrines (1940, demolished)
99 Part of Proof House Group (c.1940)
100 Latrines (c.1940, demolished)
101 Oil Store / Inflamables (1917)

Notes:

For reasons of clarity various Second
World War era air raid shelters, together
with some other minor modern structures,
have been omitted.

The numbering used on this map does not
relate to the official MoD building numbers, still
evident on parts of the site, and in the report
Priddy's Hard; the Development of the Buildings.

Ongoing development of the site means
that some buildings may have been recently
demolished.

The dating of some buildings
is tentative only.

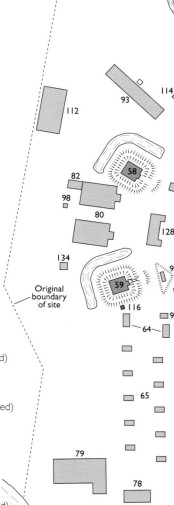

102 Underground air raid shelter (1940)
103 Surface Shelter (1940)
104 Two Police Posts (1940)
105 Electrical Sub-station (c. 1919)
106 Humphrey Hut (c.1919, demolished)
107 Offices (1940s, demolished) Store for
    inflammables (1917)
108 Pump House (1940, demolished)
109 Gas Decontamination Building
    (1939, demolished)
110 Store and Office (c.1940, demolished)

111 Muster Station (1940, demolished)
112 Non-Explosive Store (1953-4, demolished)
113 Laboratory Expense Magazine (c.1928,
    demolished)
114 Laboratory Room (1920s, demolished)
115 First Aid Station (1939, demolished)
116 Trailer Pump Houses (c.1939)
117 New Laboratory Shifting Room (1939,
    demolished)
118 Articles in Use Store (1939, demolished)
119 New Wash House (1938)
120 Shifting Room (c.1916–19, demolished)
121 Ferry Gate Canteen (1943, demolished)
122 Officers' Mess (1940s)

123 South Sub-station (1940, demolished)
124 Temporary Hutting (1939, demolished)
125 Tailor's Workshop (c.1940, demolished)
126 Examining Rooms (c.1919)
127 Workshop (after 1932, demolished)
128 Laboratory Component Store and Office
    (1940, demolished)
129 Air Compressor Building
    (c.1920s, demolished)
130 Pyrotechnic Room (1940, demolished)
131 Igniter Press House and Pump Room
    (1938, demolished)
132 Small Press Room for filling Igniters and
    Igniter Room (1940–42, demolished)
133 Printers' Shop (1941, demolished)
134 Guncotton Drying Rooms (1940)
135 Stores (?) (c.1940s, demolished)
136 Store for Magazine Components
    (1940, demolished)
137 Latrines (1920s)
138 Shelter, later store and workshop (c.1940)

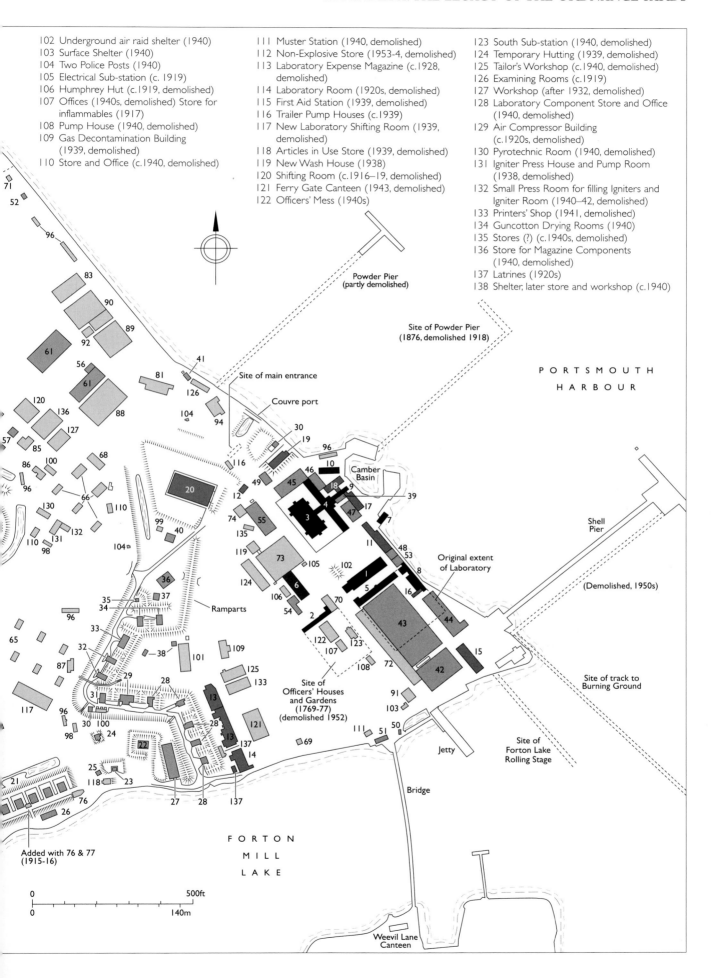

239

refronting in *c*.1847. Two additional magazines were projected (and designed) in 1776 and, though never built, had a permanent effect on the shape of the site; the Commanding Royal Engineer of the Portsmouth district, Captain Archer, was ordered to strengthen the line of fortifications – which until 1779 comprised temporary pallisades and fascines – to allow for them. The earthwork defences, which remain as a massive boundary to the core part of the site, comprise a rampart with demi-bastions. In 1844 it was decided to restore and improve them, making the dry ditch a wet ditch and adding a drawbridge and defensible wall (couvreport) which protected the main entrance. The camber, originally of timber and from early in the 19th century subject to successive remodelling and facing in stone, needed continual dredging in order to ensure its continued use.

1847–1849

In 1847–8 a laboratory complex was built at Priddy's Hard, following a decision to move it out of the Portsea area of Portsmouth onto a more secure site. What survives, although only one and a half sides of a quadrangle, comprises – along with the Royal Laboratory at Woolwich Arsenal – the most complete of all the laboratories. It was also of great historical significance, marking a key stage in the development of the 19th-century navy and explosives technology. The principal function of the laboratories had been the production of small arms ammunition, but this situation was to change, and with it the role of Priddy's Hard. The development of artillery meant a great increase in the

use of filled shells and the fuzes required to detonate them, and so facilities were needed to fill and empty shells, and prepare fuzes. From 1845 shells were being introduced into naval service on an unprecedented scale (a shell store at the gunwharf in Portsmouth was begun in 1853), and in the Crimean War preparations were made for shell filling at Priddy's Hard. Apart from the operational buildings, a small expense magazine (demolished) was built in order to hold the explosives needed for the daily work in the laboratory, linked by a tramway to the magazine.

1859–1881

The further redevelopment of Priddy's Hard began in 1859 with the construction of the small arms factory (13 on plan) and in the following year C Magazine (19 on plan). This was originally intended for the receipt of ammunition from ships, and formed the terminus of a transport system, linked to the laboratory, that was to play a key role in the development of a shell-filling complex in the 1860s. This eventually necessitated the demolition of the east ranges of the laboratory, partly converted for shell-filling purposes in the 1860s but without the capacity to meet demand when shells replaced solid shot as the standard naval ordnance. Tramways connected the powder pier and new E Magazine (20 on plan) – built in 1878–9 as a replacement for A Magazine, henceforth used for small arms ammunition and filled shells and rockets – to the shell filling room (demolished) and finally the shell store of 1879.

The covered rolling way and buildings around the camber (all wooden) were rebuilt in brick from the 1860s. The first of the shifting houses to have been moved out of the main magazine enclosure from 1843 (10 on plan) was not rebuilt until 1877–83. An increasing number of buildings (sited around the camber) were also required to house the store of empty cases in which shells were individually packed and supplied to the ships: there are seven of these stores, ranging in date from 1859 to the 1890s. The vital job of repairing these boxes was carried out in the carpenters' shop.

1886–1906

The development of complex shell-filling systems at once differentiated Priddy's Hard from the other depots. After an explosion at the shell filling room in 1883 it was decided to move this activity to outside the historic fortified boundaries of Priddy's Hard, and to distribute the activity among several smaller buildings. In 1886–7, therefore, a set of shell filling rooms and a fuzing room, later joined by a shell filling room for quick-firing shells, an expense magazine (now a unique surviving example) and unheading room (rebuilt in the

A.23 The boat house, prominently located next to the camber, was built in 1847 for the new laboratory complex, and later rebuilt in brick. This is the only example of this building type to have survived in any of the ordnance yards. *(Jeremy Lake)*

1890s), were built outside the ramparts along the edge of Forton Creek. They comprise the first and – despite the loss of one or two units – most complete suite of purpose-built rooms for filling and fuzing shells in an ordnance yard. All the filling rooms were heated by hot-water pipes supplied from a boiler house. Priddy's Hard was to develop the most complex internal communications system of any of the yards until the rails for the powder line (1 foot 6 inch gauge) and the shell tramway (2 foot 6 inch gauge) were replaced by small self-propelled vehicles. The size of the complex bears witness to the vast quantities of powder needed as propellant and explosive filling for shells of the 110-ton monster guns of the 1880s, much more powerful than the smooth-bore 68-pounder which had been the largest gun in service at the time of the Crimean War. The 1880s was a decade in which more effective breech-loading systems and the emergence of the 12-inch gun became the standard naval armament. Shells for the new QF guns were stored in a new building (45 on plan), which was built c.1889 to the north of the 18th-century magazine enclosure wall and survives together with its traveller crane.

Drastic changes in the administration of the yards were made following the decision in 1890 to divide their control between the two services. Spurred on by the arms race with Germany, the Admiralty at once began a great expansion

A.24 The area of the shell filling complex, shell painting room and small arms cartridge factory, photographed just prior to the redevelopment of the area for housing. *(Stephen Dent)*

A.25 The traverses that surround the 1886-1906 shell filling rooms are pierced by a continuous row of arches. *(Explosion! Museum of Naval Firepower)*
A.26 Inset, upper: A pill box on the outer ramparts. *(Stephen Dent)*
A.27 Inset, lower: A later laboratory building, showing heating and lighting arrangements. *(Stephen Dent)*

programme which affected Priddy's Hard, Bull Point and Upnor. A great change in the construction of magazine buildings was also caused by the introduction in the 1890s of the new explosives cordite and guncotton (58–62 on plan), which were stored – under different conditions from gunpowder – to the north and north west of the ramparts. This part of the site has lost its former layout and most of its buildings; two of the magazines and their ramparts are the only survivals. Bull Point (Plymouth) now has the best-retained buildings representative of the new technology.

In 1896–7 a new laboratory (28–35 on plan) was constructed for filling cartridges (mainly with cordite), comprising frangible wooden buildings protected by massive traverses, within the southern section of the 18th-century defences. These, although not intended as durable buildings, are of great significance in being both the first examples of this type to be built and – as a result of clearances at Bull Point and Lodge Hill – the only examples of these fragile structures to survive. The rampart ditch was filled in and given a wooden tramway system, and the traverses were built out at right angles to the banks of the ramparts to separate each building from the next. The ends where they met the tramway were finished in concrete as additional protection against explosion. Their imprint on the landscape is thus clearly marked. Massive shell stores were added to store the finished articles,

together with a mine store, though in that period the naval use of mines was very limited.

The site had 240 employees in 1895, and larger shifting rooms were required to accommodate the expanded workforce. The development of Priddy's Hard after 1900 was affected by the traumatic event of an explosion in the new shell store in November 1902. It was decided that the site was far too close to the naval dockyard for bulk storage of explosives, and after the opening of Bedenham it was now largely turned over to shell and cartridge filling and many non-explosive activities, such as the examination and repair of rockets, powder cartridges and other munitions. The new laboratory complex thus assumed increasing importance in the inspection, repair and processing of shells, cartridges, bullets, fuzes, primers, igniters and detonators. This role would increase still further in the First World War.

1914–1918

The First World War brought about a great expansion of Priddy's Hard. This was partly due to an extension of the laboratory to meet the increased need for filled cartridges and partly because of the introduction of new explosives and weapons systems. TNT, known in the services as trotyl, could be melted on a water bath and poured into shells. In 1915 the shell filling buildings of 1886 outside the ramparts were converted to work as TNT shell filling rooms and two trotyl rooms were added. Amatol was an explosive comprising ammonium nitrate and trotyl, and stores were required for this. A new mine store (79 on plan) was built in close proximity to the amatol store, and the shell emptying rooms were adapted as mine filling rooms. A whole group of buildings dedicated to cartridge filling and fuze filling was required (65 and 66 on plan). New weapons requiring storage, filling and maintenance were depth charges, bombs for aerial use, and the anti-submarine device of the towed explosive paravane. Similar additions, but to a lesser degree, were made at Bull Point, which retains the

only surviving example of a building used for the storage and maintenance of paravanes. A transfer shed (72 on plan) linked the mine and shell stores to the main rail system.

1918–1989

The mine store – rendered redundant by the opening of the mine depot at Frater – was adapted as a transfer shed, in connection with the remodelling of the 1890s laboratory buildings as shell examining rooms. The painters' and tinsmiths' shop (73 on plan) was adapted with tall doors and a tram road into a workshop for handling torpedoes. The Second World War witnessed the construction of more buildings, including air raid shelters, and the adaptation of fabric on others – such as the small arms factory of 1859 – with flat roofs offering some protection against incendiary bombs. Some of the old magazines were also used as refuges. Most fabric was temporary in nature, and very little was built after 1945. By the late 1960s, when the new laboratory closed, the site was already scaling down, and this was followed by the closure in the 1970s of the shell filling rooms outside the ramparts (21 on plan), known to workers as The Straight, and the transfer of its functions to Bedenham, Elson and Frater. There was a brief resurgence of activity during the Falklands War, but in 1986 the rail link was terminated and in 1989 the site was closed.

A.28 Destruction of one of the laboratory buildings of 1897 has left upstanding the steel gantry for hauling up shells, inserted – together with the 1-ton railway – in 1923. The same building before destruction is shown in figure 7.21). *(Stephen Dent)*

A.29 The gunwharf at Priddy's Hard, during or just after the Second World War. The guns (5.25, 4.7, 4.5 or 4-inch breech and barrel combinations) are either awaiting issue, awaiting repair, repaired awaiting reissue, or in for scrapping. The big house is just outside the gunwharf fence and was the home of the Nisbet family who had owned the land upon which the gunwharf was built until the First World War. The heavily fenced area on the left is the north-western edge of the Priddy's Hard laboratory. In the background between the depot fence and the houses are the Reserve Fleet Playing Fields. *(Priddy's Hard Archive 1998.4.203)*

A.30 The Camber was continually subject to encroachment from the sea, until at last it began to be revetted in stone from 1830. This view, at low tide, shows one of the surviving hand-operated cranes, on the southern arm. While the cabin has been removed, the rest of the crane is original. Beyond can be seen the Shell Pier. *(Stephen Dent)*

A.31 Above, right: A 'thunder bell' outside the shell emptying room. Consisting of the body of an obsolete anti-submarine projectile hung up with a clapper fitted inside, it was rung to give warning of a fire should one happen. This led to it also being used to warn of thunder, the precursor of lightning, hence its name. When the bell was rung during a storm all those working in the laboratory were supposed to go to the shifting rooms for lectures. In practice they generally drank tea and read the paper on these occasions. Since clocks were not allowed in the laboratory buildings, the bell was also rung by the foreman five minutes before the official knocking off time, allowing the workers five minutes to lock up the rooms and get to the shifting room to change. In this role it became known as the 'five minute bell'. *(Stephen Dent)*

After 1989

The area of Priddy's Hard within the ramparts was acquired by Gosport Borough Council, and designated a conservation area. Hampshire County Council provided invaluable technical advice on the preservation of fabric on the site. In 1990, A Magazine and the structures attached to it were listed at grade I, and other structures – E magazine, C magazine, the office building and the ready use magazine (23 on plan) – at grade II. The thematic survey of ordnance yards by English Heritage has, apart from underpinning the extension of listing designation to cover other key buildings on the site, played a key role in informing the sustainable management and development of the site as a whole.

In the mid 1990s a three-year Conservation Area Partnership Scheme was entered into by the county, Gosport Borough and English Heritage (the latter replaced by the Heritage Lottery Fund in year three) and a range of repair and restoration works were carried out on the site, including the reconstruction of the collapsed north wing of the camber, and extensive repairs to the A Magazine complex. This impetus led to further substantial investment from the South East England Development Agency and other partners to help provide critical infrastructure within the site. The Millennium Project saw further works undertaken, including the museum within the magazine complex – opened in 2001 with Heritage Lottery funding – and the new Forton Lake Bridge, which links Priddy's Hard to the Millennium Promenade along Gosport Waterfront. A new bypass was constructed from the A32 to provide direct access to the site and to new housing to the north.

The Explosion! Museum of Naval Firepower is situated in the oldest part of the site of Priddy's Hard naval armaments depot, based around the late 18th-century gunpowder magazine. The collection of weapons and ammunition, including many instructional versions, was instigated on the site in the late 1960s. The weapons include small arms, guns, torpedoes, mines, depth charges and missiles.

The current plan is to develop a mixed scheme around the museum complex, to include offices and a pub/restaurant towards the south-east corner, public open space to include a heritage walk in the ramparts, and carefully considered residential development in the centre of the area between the ramparts and museum buildings. Crest Homes purchased the latter with permission to develop 198 residential units. The form of this development was subject to careful negotiation with English Heritage and Borough officers, resulting in a scheme that respects the historic texture of existing buildings on the site and their setting. One particular benefit has been the construction of a building on the site of the original officers' quarters that replicates the scale and in some key respects the design of the original building that was demolished in the 1950s. Its principal façade is constructed in Flemish bond with a mixture of red brick and blue brick headers. The ramparts, a concern for some time due to continuous vandalism, have been made more secure and a scheme is currently being prepared to turn this area into a heritage trail and nature conservation area. Funding for the repair and restoration of some of the laboratory buildings has been secured through the redevelopment by Crest Homes. Further plans are under way to secure the long-term future of the grade II★ listed E Magazine within the ramparts, by looking to re-open some historic tunnels that linked the building to the remainder of the site, the building currently having very poor access. Various appropriate commercial or community uses are being considered.

Notes
1   Thanks to Rob Harper, Conservation Officer at Gosport Borough Council, and Jo Lawler, Director of Explosion! Museum, for contributions to the post-1945 section of this summary history of the site.

MARCHWOOD
Hampshire

Marchwood was conceived in 1811 as a store depot like Tipner (Porstmouth) and like Tipner it was a satellite to the main depot at Priddy's Hard. Three magazines were built, each with a 6,800 barrel capacity, a small internal L-shaped channel for moving barrels by barge and a centrally placed shifting room. The shortcomings revealed through the Crimean War brought about the decision to increase storage capability at Marchwood, Tipner and Upnor. This was marked

A.32 Exterior of C magazine today. Compare with figure A.33, below. *(Stephen Dent)*

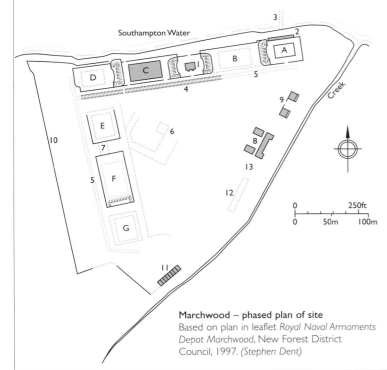

Marchwood – phased plan of site
Based on plan in leaflet *Royal Naval Armaments Depot Marchwood*, New Forest District Council, 1997. *(Stephen Dent)*

Key

A Magazine A (1814–16 – now ruined)
B Site of Magazine B (1856–7)
C Magazine C (1856–7 – now converted to apartments)
D Site of Magazine D (1814–16)
E Site of Magazine E (1856–7)
F Site of Magazine F (1856–7)
G Site of Magazine G (1814–16)

1 Examining Rooms (1814 – now converted to apartments)
2 Receiving Rooms (1856–7 and later)
3 Site of jetty
4 Remains of canal
5 Site of canal
6 Site of Controller's House (1814–16)
7 Site of Cooperage and Stores (1814–16)
8 Barracks (1816 – now Frobisher Court)
9 Office and Guardhouse (now Marchwood Yacht Club)
10 Surviving boundary wall
11 Workers' cottages (c.1891)
12 Site of workers' cottages
13 Site of Parade and Drying Ground

Note: Thick lines denote surviving walls, dotted lines are demolished.

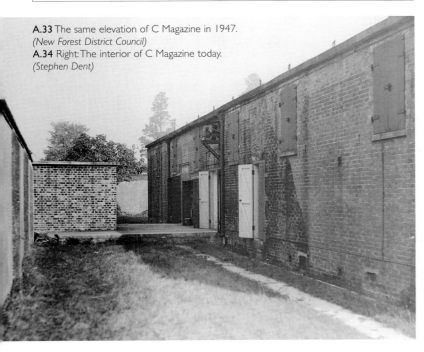

A.33 The same elevation of C Magazine in 1947. *(New Forest District Council)*
A.34 Right: The interior of C Magazine today. *(Stephen Dent)*

A.35 Right: The colonnaded front of the former depot office and guardhouse, built in 1814. (See also figure 2.43.) *(Stephen Dent)*

A.36 Below, left: Part of the perimeter wall and traverse. *(Stephen Dent)*

A.37 Below, right: Only one arm of the L-shaped canal of 1814–15 survives. *(Stephen Dent)*

at Marchwood by a vast increase in its storage, four new magazines, three of 14,400 and one of 9,600 barrels capacity being built in 1856–7. The establishment began to be wound down soon after; there were forty-five employees in 1898. B, E, F and G magazines were destroyed by the Luftwaffe in June 1940, and the Admiralty's use of the depot declined steeply after 1945; it was closed in 1961. The principal surviving buildings have been listed at grade II. These include the barracks and flanking officers' quarters, now renamed Frobisher Court and divided into several houses. The Marchwood Yacht Club occupies the former offices and guardhouse, now the club house, and also the magazine, the shoe room for changing into magazine clothing, and the examining room for unheading barrels and examining their contents. One of the Crimean War magazines survives, with some of its barrel racks. The whole site was also designated as a

conservation area in 1997, which provides additional protection to the walls marking the extent of the demolished magazines, the sea wall, perimeter wall and the walls to the former canal of 1814–15. One of the magazines and the two laboratory buildings have been converted into houses.

UPNOR
Kent

Upnor Castle, Medway, Kent. ME2 4XG
01634 402276 / 01634 718742
visitor.centre@medway.gov.uk
25 March – 30 September, 10am-6pm
1 – 31 October, 10am-4pm
Last admission 45 minutes before closing

Upnor Castle is an English Heritage property open to the public for most of the year. The remainder of the ordnance yard was sold by the Ministry of Defence in 2004.

The castle at Upnor on the Medway, built between 1559 and 1567 to the designs of the military engineer Sir Richard Lee, has after the Tower of London a longer history of association with the storage of explosives than any other site. Built in order to protect naval shipping anchored in the Medway, its importance as a fort declined after the Dutch raid of 1667 and the recasting of the nation's defences. It was then converted for use as a magazine and store, a function it continued to serve until

1913. The castle was adapted for this role, some laboratory facilities being provided in the south tower, while other areas were made to serve as cooperage and shifting room. After 1827 buildings in the water bastion were lowered to form a new laboratory building, the magazine in the castle being converted into a laboratory storehouse.

Plans were drawn up to replace Upnor Castle by a modern magazine by 1806, and in 1808 the construction of one of 10,000 barrels capacity was decided upon. The site was quarried out of a rocky hillside to provide natural traverses. The CRE, Colonel D'Arcy, settled on catenary instead of rounded vaults, to give greater height within: these had already been used within the casemates at Dover Castle. Despite the new magazine, 3,500 barrels continued to be stored in the castle, but this was proposed to be discontinued. Restoving on this site was out of the question and that operation was performed at Faversham. The Crimean War brought the inadequacies of storage provision on the site to a head, a situation compounded by the fact that filled shells could not be kept in the same magazine as gunpowder: shells were carried

through the laboratory, where gunpowder was being examined and filled into cartridges, and then hoisted 20 feet into an adjacent chamber. In 1856 the decision was made to build a new shell store and magazine, the latter with a capacity of 23,000 barrels. These were completed in 1857. The former B Magazine of 1856-7 survives. It is internally distinguished by its catenary arches, previously employed by the Royal Engineers in the Drop Redoubt and the Napoleonic tunnels at Dover. The gabled facades and use of Tudor gothic detail has resulted in a strongly 'architectural' 19th-century magazine, possibly in response to its prominent location on the Medway and close to the castle. The stretch of brick wall in front is pierced by four blocked openings for the former powder piers which stretched into the Medway. An additional shell store was built in 1860-1. In 1877,

space for expansion on the site for bulk store magazines being non-existent, a new site was acquired inland for five such magazines at Chattenden: this served as a deposit magazine to serve Upnor, to which it was linked by railway. The Upnor site, however, continued to expand eastwards along the Medway in the late 19th century, with storage for wet and dry guncotton in 1895-6 – the main explosive in mines and torpedo warheads - and shell filling facilities in 1906-7: the latter (demolished, only the traverses remaining) were built much later than at Priddy's Hard and Bull Point, this function having been previously carried out at Woolwich. The site is now a conservation area, and the B Magazine building is listed at grade II★. The site is currently the subject of development proposals, this being a prime area for housing overlooking the Medway.

A.38 Upnor today, showing the castle with its bastioned defences projecting into the Medway, the early 18th-century barracks to its left, and the ordnance yard, served by the former railway which curves out of the top of the photograph. To the right is the former B Magazine of 1856–7 and buildings associated with the eastward expansion along the Medway. *(NMR 23184-22)*

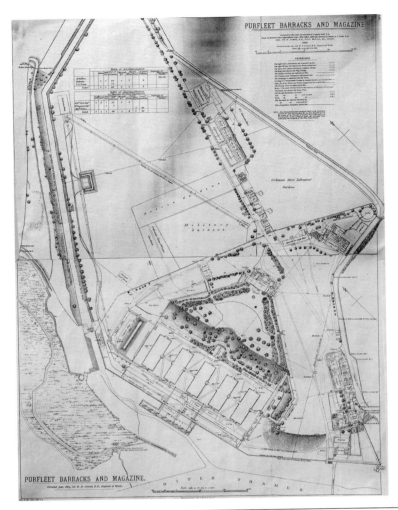

PURFLEET BARRACKS AND MAGAZINE.

PURFLEET
Essex

Purfleet Heritage Centre
Thurrock Museum & Heritage
Communities, Libraries & Cultural Services
No.5 Magazine, Centurian Way, Purfleet, Essex
01708 866764 / 01708 523409
thurrock.museum@thurrock.gov.uk

Purfleet became the Ordnance Board's centre of gunpowder storage as a result of an Act of Parliament passed in 1760, surpassing in size both the Tower of London and Upnor Castle on the Medway. It stored powder, transported after 1787 from the Royal Gunpowder Factory at Waltham Abbey, and supplied both the army and the navy. The depot comprised a group of five magazines (each with a capacity of 5000 barrels) built in 1763–5 by James Gabriel Montresor of the Royal Engineers for the Board of Ordnance. The site also included barracks for officers and men, a proof house for the testing of powder and a clock tower over the entrance archway to the compound, attached to the boundary wall. The proof house, part of the boundary wall and War Office markers, and one of the magazines, now housing a museum managed by Thurrock District Council, survived the demolition that followed its closure in 1973.

A.39 Plan of the original layout of the site, with the row of magazines and the projecting landing stage, the walled enclosure, proof house and storekeeper's house.

WEEDON BEC
Northamptonshire

Weedon's location next to the Grand Union Canal made it the ideal choice in 1802 for a central ammunition depot, as it was close to the small arms factories and workshops of Birmingham and also far away from the more vulnerable defended coastal areas and the other ordnance yards mainly sited close to the Royal Navy Dockyards. The original plans to build a small arms factory were abandoned, and instead Weedon became the first inland depot of the Board of Ordnance – as early as 1807 it supplied armaments for the expeditionary force bound for the Netherlands. From 1837 the storehouses were used as barracks and as a prison (Nos 5 and 7 being converted for this purpose), and from 1855 as a clothing store. In the 1870s it was converted into one of the depots created under the army reforms of Edward Cardwell, the Secretary of State for War, and from 1885 as a weapons and equipment store. A large clothing store was built during the Boer War of 1899–1902, from which date the site retained an important role in taking small arms and clothes prior to dispatch by rail. After closure in 1965, it was used as a government supply store.

Four functionally separate sites marked the planning of Weedon Bec's major first phase of 1804–16. These were the storehouse enclosure, the magazine compound, the barracks (demolished) and housing (known as the Pavilion) for the depot's principal officials (demolished), such as the Storekeeper and the Clerk of Cheque. The latter groups were built on high ground to the north, close to the Daventry–London road, and were clearly designed to both complement and enhance the effect of the storehouse and magazine groups set on lower ground to the south, especially as viewed from Weedon Bec. What survives comprises a unique planned military-industrial complex, complete with its own defensible transport system and defensible perimeter walls. The canal widens into a large central basin, flanked by pedestrian bridges, in the centre of the storehouse enclosure. The gatehouses at its west and east ends were provided with winding gear for operating portcullis gates that provided further defensive measures. Casemates were formed in the angles of the walls, which were surmounted by bomb-proof layers of sand and gravel capped by a layer of bricks and finally a stone-flag walkway, which was accessed by ramps with stone-paved stairs and runways for the deployment of small artillery pieces. The magazine

Related sites

Portsmouth – Square Tower

The Square Tower, situated at the end of the High Street in Old Portsmouth, is administered by Portsmouth Museums and Records Service. The exterior can be viewed at any time, while the interior is open to the public on certain days, and can also be booked for special occasions. Further information can be obtained from Portsmouth Museum (02392 827261) or from Portsmouth Tourist Information Centre, The Hard, Portsmouth (02392 826722).

Portsmouth – Gunwharf

This site was substantially redeveloped after 1997 for retail and residential purposes, and few buildings that survived the bombing

of the Second World War can be viewed by the public. The principal surviving buildings are The Grand Storehouse (also known as the Vulcan Block) and the Customs House, both dating from 1811, and The Old Infirmary of 1835. The main entrance to the site, Nelson's Gate, was built in 1803. Parts of the boundary wall also survive.

Gosport – Fort Blockhouse

Although the submarine base HMS *Dolphin* was closed in 1999, Fort Blockhouse remains MoD property, and is currently part of a medical facility. It has occasionally been open for guided, pre-booked parties during Heritage Weekends. Contact Gosport Borough Council on 02392 522944 for details.

Medway – Chatham gunwharf

The site of the original gunwharf at Chatham has been totally redeveloped, although two buildings remain: the early 18th-century storekeeper's house and offices (now The Command House public house) and a former ordnance store, built in 1805 and decommissioned in the 1950s.

Plymouth – Morice Yard

The buildings of Morice Yard are within the perimeter of HM Naval Base. There is no public access.

Plymouth – Mount Wise

The area of the laboratory at Mount Wise has been redeveloped for housing and flats. Part of the perimeter wall and gateway can be seen from James Street.

Felixstowe – Landguard Fort

This site is managed by English Heritage. The Ravelin Block was restored from 1979 by the Felixstowe History and Museum Society, and is now their headquarters and museum.

Beer Quarry

There are guided tours of the caves as well as a museum, all dealing with the site's history of quarrying since Roman times. Open from Easter to September, see www.beerquarrycaves.fsnet.uk

A.40 The Vulcan Block and Customs House at Portsmouth Gunwharf as they are today, surrounded by the modern development of the site. See also figure 9.30. *(Stephen Dent)*

compound was separated by an open area of over 200 metres, as protection against the effects of possible explosion, and was extended westwards by an additional magazine and earthen traverse in about 1857. The storehouses (which principally housed muskets, guns and their carriages) are comparable as a planned group to those found in late 18th-century naval dockyards, most notably at Portsmouth and Chatham, and the finest set-pieces of early 19th-century civil dock warehousing, such as John Foster's Goree warehouses of 1810 in Liverpool's George's Dock and Telford and Hardwick's work for the St Katherine Docks Company in London. This quality treatment, especially marked on the south elevations with their rusticated basements, is repeated internally, where even the heavy axial beams have had their supporting posts chamfered with scrolled stops. Although the magazines (built to the distinctive British double-vaulted plan) are smaller in terms of their

individual scale than other contemporary examples, as a group they had no rival until the suite of traversed magazines were built at Bull Point, Plymouth, in the 1850s. Catenary arches as used here were first used at Tipner in the 1790s and then for Colonel D'Arcy's magazine at Upnor. The use of traverses makes the group highly innovatory in terms of its planning, blast walls of earth (sometimes faced in brick) being henceforth a characteristic feature of magazine complexes. These traverses have also uniquely assumed an architectural form.

The closure of Weedon Bec in 1965 was followed by the demolition of the upper barracks site for an industrial estate and the Pavilion and gardens as a housing estate. The remainder of the site was sold by the Ministry of Defence in 1984. The magazines have long been used for an antiques and furniture restoration business, and the storehouse area is shortly to be developed for a mixed residential, leisure and retail use.

Appendix B
The Royal Engineers

During the 18th and early 19th centuries, the career structure of Engineer officers constantly changed. A brief chronological account will help to explain the roles of all those who had a hand in the development of ordnance storage. In 1717 this was the establishment for Great Britain, excluding Minorca and Gibraltar.

1 Chief Engineer
2 Directors
2 Sub-Directors
6 Engineers in Ordinary
6 Engineers Extraordinary
6 Sub-Engineers
6 Practitioner Engineers

When the Chief Engineer, Thomas Lascelles, retired in 1750, the position was not filled, as there were three Directors – in Ireland, Minorca and the West Coast of Africa. In 1755 eight additional Practitioner Engineers were added to the establishment, additional stations abroad being Virginia, Newfoundland and Nova Scotia. In 1757 the office of Chief Engineer was refilled and the officers received military ranks, the equivalents being listed below:

Chief Engineer	Colonel of Foot
Directors	Lieutenant-Colonels
Sub-Directors	Majors
Engineers in Ordinary	Captains
Engineers Extraordinary	Captain-Lieutenants
Sub-Engineers	Lieutenants
Practitioner Engineers	Ensigns

In 1759 the establishment was increased again:

1 Chief Engineer
2 Directors
4 Sub-Directors
12 Engineers in Ordinary
12 Engineers Extraordinary
14 Sub-Engineers
16 Practitioner Engineers

The foreign stations were now Gibraltar, Annapolis, St John's, Halifax and Placentia (Minorca having been lost). The American War of Independence necessitated the addition of fourteen more practitioners, and one of the first acts of the Duke of Richmond as Master-General of the Ordnance was to reorganise the Corps of Engineers in 1782. The Engineer grades, with the exception of Chief Engineer, were abolished, and Army titles alone used, though the rank of Major was dropped. The officers could hold an Army rank (such as Major General) quite apart from that held in the Corps. The establishment thus became:

1 Chief Engineer and Colonel
6 Colonels Commandant
6 Lieutenant Colonels
9 Captains
9 Captain-Lieutenants
22 First Lieutenants
22 Second Lieutenants

The same warrant that promulgated this reorganisation established a committee of five officers, including the Chief Engineer, who were to meet at the ordnance office in the Tower at least two days a week to consider all plans and estimates for new works and repairs. In 1784, Richmond decided to reduce the Corps to peacetime proportions:

1 Engineer-in-Chief
5 Colonels
5 Lieutenant Colonels
10 Captains
10 Captain-Lieutenants
20 First Lieutenants
10 Second Lieutenants

In addition, a small Corps of Invalid Engineers was created of those in semi-retirement and liable to be recalled to service in case of emergency. The officers were to be formed into ten companies, each of five officers, to be distributed to: the West Indies; Quebec and Jamaica; Nova Scotia and Newfoundland; Gibraltar; Plymouth Division; Portsmouth Division; Chatham Division; Scotland and Newcastle; Jersey and Guernsey; Surveying and ready for Field Service.

In 1787 the title of the corps was altered to Royal Engineers, and the Revolutionary and Napoleonic Wars brought about successive augmentations to the establishment. In 1802 the title of Chief Engineer became Inspector General of Fortifications; he was to be selected by the Master General from the two Colonels Commandant. The Tower Committee was abolished, with all plans and estimates being referred to the Inspector-General. In 1804 the rank of Captain-Lieutenant was abolished, becoming Second Captain. By the end of the war the establishment had swollen:

5 Colonels Commandant
9 Colonels
22 Lieutenant-Colonels
45 Captains
45 Second Captains
90 First Lieutenants
45 Second Lieutenants
1 Brigade Major

Drastic reductions were made after the conclusion of the war, but after 1825 more officers were required to perform the

Ordnance Survey of Ireland. In 1826, architecture was placed on the syllabus of the Engineer Establishment at Chatham, and the corps was to justify its peacetime existence through the wholesale secondment of officers to work in civil departments of the Government. Their work in designing and superintending the massive redevelopment of the Royal Dockyards in order to support the newly created steam navy is by now well known, but engineers also worked on the Great Exhibition, the Albert Hall and the Opera House at Valletta, formed the senior management of the prison service (designing many of the buildings), officered the Railway Inspectorate, settled international boundary disputes, and were responsible for huge civil engineering schemes in Canada and India. After the abolition of the Master General and the Board of Ordnance in 1855 the Inspector General of Fortifications served directly under the Commander-in-Chief, and the Royal Engineers and Royal Artillery worked under the same administration as the rest of the army. In 1856 the long-standing separation of the officers and other ranks into different organisations was terminated when the Corps of Royal Sappers and Miners was absorbed into the Corps of Royal Engineers, a former Private in the Royal Sappers and Miners becoming a Sapper in the Royal Engineers.

Principal Figures in the Board of Ordnance and after

John Archer

Sub-Engineer in 1748; Engineer Extraordinary at Minorca in 1755, there during the siege; Captain-Lieutenant in 1757; Captain Engineer in Ordinary in 1759; at the siege of Belleisle in 1761. Captain at Gibraltar in 1762; Commanding Engineer at Portsmouth in 1769; in post till promoted to Lieutenant Colonel in 1777, but by 1784 an unemployed Colonel.

Edward Boxer (1822–1898)

Assistant to Professor of Fortification at Royal Military Academy in 1850; Captain and Assistant Instructor in Practical Artillery in 1852; and in 1855, Firemaster at Royal Laboratory, where chain of command was Director, two Firemasters, Assistant Firemaster at Priddy's Hard. In 1856, appointed Superintendent at Royal Laboratory (titles of Director and Firemaster were dropped, with Boxer in charge of a Captain Inspector and a Captain Tester and the Assistant Firemaster at Priddy's Hard). In 1857 the post of Captain Tester was abolished, and Priddy's Hard placed in charge of a Storekeeper, no longer directly under Boxer. His immediate subordinates in 1858 were a Captain Inspector and Captain Instructor. In 1860 Boxer was promoted Major and then Lieutenant-Colonel. In 1863 Captain Majendie (the future Chief Inspector of Explosives) was Captain Instructor. In 1864 the post of Captain Inspector was dropped, replaced by an Assistant Superintendent, Captain Fraser. In 1867 Majendie was Assistant Superintendent, Captain Orde Browne (subsequently a well-known writer on ordnance matters) was

Captain Instructor. Promoted Colonel in 1868 and Major-General in 1869, Boxer resigned at the end of the latter year and left Woolwich.

James Bramham (d. 1786)

Draughtsman at Gibraltar for four years; Practitioner Engineer in 1744. In 1747 engaged in the defence of Bergen-op-Zoom, promoted Engineer Extraordinary in 1748, skipping the grade of Sub-Engineer. Surveyed the area around Breda, before being sent to West Africa in 1755 to survey military stations. Engineer in Ordinary in 1756, and engaged in a project for the defence of Jersey. Captain-Lieutenant in 1757, working on fortifications at Milford Haven between 1758 and 1761. Chief Engineer at the siege of Belleisle in 1761. In 1762, promoted Lieutenant Colonel; became Director in 1766; in 1777 became Colonel and Lieutenant Governor of the Royal Military Academy, Woolwich; and after Skinner's death became Chief Engineer and Major-General in 1781, holding the office until his own death.

John Brewse

Second Engineer at Newfoundland in 1745; Sub-Engineer at Nova Scotia in 1755; Captain-Lieutenant at second siege of Louisbourg in 1758; Captain and Engineer in Ordinary in 1759. Lieutenant Colonel in 1777; Chief Engineer during the siege of (British held) Minorca, 1781; Member of the Tower Committee of Engineers in 1784.

Sir William Congreve (1741–1814)

Joined the Royal Artillery. In 1783 became Deputy Comptroller of the Royal Laboratory, Woolwich. In 1785 invented a new and more efficient press for extracting saltpetre from old or defective gunpowder, and in 1789 became Comptroller of the Royal Laboratory and Inspector of Gunpowder Manufactories at Faversham and Waltham Abbey. Improved the manufacture and methods of proof of gunpowder. Colonel Commandant of the Corps. Created baronet in 1812; succeeded as Comptroller by his son William (1772–1828) who held the office until his death.

Robert D'Arcy

Lieutenant at the siege of Minorca in 1781; at Barbados in 1784; Commanding Engineer at Chatham in 1806; Commanding Engineer at the assault on Copenhagen in 1807; at Walcheren in 1809.

Matthew Dixon (d. 1793)

Sub-Engineer in 1744; engineer attached to Admiral Boscawen's expedition to the East Indies in 1747; Engineer Extraordinary at Nova Scotia by 1755; Captain at the siege of Louisbourg in 1758; Engineer in Ordinary and Captain in 1759; senior Engineer at the siege of Havannah in 1762. Commanding Engineer at Portsmouth by 1766; Commanding Engineer at Plymouth in 1769; Colonel by 1784. Resigned through ill health in 1787.

Sir William Jervois (1821–1897)

Second Captain on survey work through the Kaffir War of 1846–7; in 1856 appointed Assistant Inspector-General of Fortifications; Secretary to the Royal Commission on the National Defences in 1859; Deputy Director of Works with responsibility for fortifications and in general charge of the programme of defensive works in 1862. Knighted in 1874. Then in 1875 made Governor of Straits Settlements, Governor of South Australia in 1877, finally Governor of New Zealand from 1882 to 1888.

Charles Lennox, the third Duke of Richmond and Lennox (1735–1806)

Succeeded his father to the title in 1750. Captain in the 20th Regiment of Foot in 1753; Lieutenant-Colonel in the 33rd Regiment of Foot in 1756; Colonel of the 72nd Regiment of Foot in 1758. Engaged in political activities, opposing Pitt's policy in America. In 1782 made Master General of the Ordnance in Rockingham's second administration, resigned in April 1783, succeeded by Townshend, but resumed office in December on Pitt's return to office. Developed extensive plans for the fortification of Portsmouth and Plymouth, defeated by the casting vote of the Speaker in 1786, some minor elements of the scheme being executed. Satirised in *The Rolliad*. Dismissed in 1795.

Griffith Lewis (1784–1859)

Gazetted Second Lieutenant in the Royal Engineers in 1803 and Lieutenant later in the same year. Served in the Mediterranean until 1811, then employed in constructing the Torres Vedras lines. Under Wellington he took part in the siege of San Sebastian, losing a leg; promoted to Captain in 1813, he was invalided home. He was in Newfoundland between 1819 and 1827, being made Lieutenant-Colonel in 1825. Commanding Engineer at Jersey from 1830 to 1836, at the Cape of Good Hope from 1836 to 1842, in Ireland from 1843 to 1847, and at Portsmouth from 1847 to 1851, he finished his career as Governor of the Royal Military Academy from 1851 to 1856. Promoted Major-General in 1851 and Lieutenant-General in 1858, when he was also made Colonel Commandant.

Gother Mann (1747–1830)

Commissioned as Practitioner Engineer in 1763. Employed on the defences of Sheerness and the Medway until 1775, being made Sub-Engineer and Lieutenant in 1771. He was then sent to Dominica and was there, as Engineer Extraordinary and Captain Lieutenant, when the French captured the island in 1778. Returning to England, he reported on coastal defences, and in 1775 was sent to Canada as Commanding Engineer, then Captain. Returning in 1791, he was present at the sieges of Valenciennes and Dunkirk in 1793, becoming Lieutenant-Colonel. He returned to Canada in his former capacity until 1804, becoming Major-General in 1803. From 1805 to 1811 he served in Ireland and on various committees in London, becoming Colonel-Commandant in 1805 and Lieutenant-General in 1810. In 1811 he succeeded Morse as Inspector-General of Fortifications, holding the office until his death.

Robert Morse (1743–1818)

Ensign volunteer for Engineer duties at siege of St Malo in 1758, involved in the attempt on Martinique in 1759 and, having been made Lieutenant and Sub-Engineer, the siege of Belleisle in 1761. Captain-Lieutenant in 1763 and from that date to 1773 was Assistant Quartermaster-General at headquarters, combining that post for much of the time with the command of the Medway and Tilbury engineers. In 1773 he went to the West Indies as Commanding Engineer of the recently acquired islands of Dominica, St Vincent, Grenada and Tobago. Returning to England in 1779, he worked at Plymouth and Falmouth, moving to New York in 1782 as Chief Engineer in North America, becoming Lieutenant-Colonel in 1783. In 1788 he became Colonel and in 1791 went to Gibraltar as Commanding Engineer. Major-General in 1793, he returned home in 1796; in 1799 he was promoted to Lieutenant-General and in 1802 became the first Inspector-General of Fortifications. He resigned through ill health in 1811.

Henry Morshead (d. 1831)

Commissioned as second Lieutenant in Royal Artillery in 1792, transferred to Royal Engineers in 1794. Took part in the sieges of Landrecies and Nijmeguen. Returned in 1795, going to Plymouth. Made first Lieutenant in 1796 and sent the next year to San Domingo, transferring to Gravesend when that island was evacuated in 1798. Captain-Lieutenant in 1801, he was successively at Portsmouth and Plymouth, being made Captain in 1805. In 1808 he was part of the expeditionary force that took Madeira, and he remained on the island until 1812. Lieutenant-Colonel in 1813, he became Commanding Engineer of the Western district, and made Colonel in 1825. In 1829 he went to Malta as Commanding Engineer, dying there as acting Governor.

John Oldfield (1789–1863)

Cadet in 1803, he joined the Trigonometrical Survey at Bodmin in 1805, was commissioned as Second Lieutenant in 1806 and promoted Lieutenant in the same year. Served in Nova Scotia from 1807 to 1809, subsequently at Dorchester and Fort George, becoming Second Captain in 1811. He went to Holland in 1814; promoted Captain in 1815, he inundated the country around Ypres and was present at Waterloo. After being placed on half-pay in 1819, he spent many years posted to Ireland, and in 1830 was appointed Commanding Engineer in Newfoundland, and promoted to Lieutenant-Colonel in 1831. From 1835 to 1839 he was Commanding Engineer at Jersey, serving in Canada in the same capacity from 1839 to 1843. Returning home, he commanded the Western District till 1848, when he was Commanding Engineer in Ireland. In 1854 he was promoted Major-General, subsequently becoming Lieutenant-General and Colonel-Commandant in 1859, and General in 1862.

Sir Charles Pasley (1780–1861)

Commissioned in the Royal Artillery in 1798, but transferred to the Royal Engineers the following year. He served in the Mediterranean between 1799 and 1807, becoming Second Captain in 1805, and was an aide-de-camp to Sir John Moore till his death at Corunna. During the Walcheren expedition in 1809 he was severely wounded at the capture of Flushing, preventing him from further active service. He commanded a company of Military Artificers at Plymouth in 1811, and began to develop his system of instruction in fieldworks. In 1812 he was appointed the first Director of the Engineering Establishment at Chatham, and in 1814 became Lieutenant-Colonel. He remained in charge of this till 1841, writing a standard textbook on military engineering and developing, among many other things, the art of underwater demolition (*Mary Rose* was one of the objects of his attention). He left Chatham to become Inspector-General of Railways, retiring in 1846 and being made a KCB.

Robert Pilkington (1765 –1834)

Commissioned as Second Lieutenant in the Artillery in 1787, he transferred to the Engineers in 1789 and went to Quebec, where he was successively promoted First Lieutenant (1793), Captain-Lieutenant (1797) and Captain (1801). Returning to England in 1803 he was briefly appointed Commanding Engineer at the Faversham gunpowder factory, before being placed in charge of the construction of the Weedon Depot. As Lieutenant-Colonel, he was part of the expedition to Walcheren, and was in charge of the destruction of the basin and defences of Flushing. Returning to England, he was sent to Weedon again, before being appointed Commanding Engineer of the North-Western District. In 1818 he became Commanding Engineer at Gibraltar, staying there till 1830 and promoted to Major-General in 1825. On his return to England he became Colonel-Commandant, and Inspector-General of Fortifications in 1832.

William Roy (1726–1790)

Appointed as an assistant to the Deputy Quartermaster General in 1746, engaged in opening up communications through the Highlands, and in 1755 was made a Practitioner-Engineer. A French invasion scare removed him from Scotland to survey the parts of the country thought to be most at risk, and in 1757 he took part in the expedition against Rochefort. By 1765 he was Engineer-in-Ordinary and Deputy Quartermaster-General, and in addition was appointed to the new post of Surveyor-General. He reported on various fortifications, including Gibraltar and the Channel Islands, and was promoted Colonel in the army in 1777 and Major-General in 1781. In 1783 he set out the base line for the triangulation between London and Dover, the foundation of all subsequent surveys, and in the same year was appointed Lieutenant-Colonel, Colonel and Director, and served on the Duke of Richmond's Fortification Board. In 1785 he was awarded the Copley Medal of the Royal Society for his scientific surveys.

Henry Savage

Gazetted Second Lieutenant 1809 and First Lieutenant 1811, he served in the Peninsula from 1813 to the end of the war. Promoted Captain in 1815 and Lieutenant-Colonel in 1846 (one of the victims of extremely slow promotion in the Corps following the post-war economies), he was Commanding Engineer at Nova Scotia in 1850, Colonel in 1854 and later Commanding Engineer at Chatham from 1855 till 1857.

William Skinner (d. 1780)

Practitioner Engineer in 1719, assisted on the fortifications of Minorca in 1722, assisted on the survey of Gibraltar in 1725 and served during the siege, staying there for 18 years, becoming Chief Engineer at Gibraltar in 1741. Sub-Director in 1743; Director in 1746. Recalled to England in 1746 to fortify the Highlands. Colonel and Chief Engineer of Great Britain in 1757; Major-General in 1761; Lieutenant-General in 1770. Died at the age of 81, still in office.

Sir Henry Storks (1811–1874)

Commissioned as an Ensign in the 61st of Foot in 1828, exchanging regiments twice before going on half-pay as a Major of the 38th of Foot. He was then Assistant Adjutant-General during the Kaffir War of 1846–7, and Assistant Military Secretary at Mauritius between 1849 and 1854, having become a Colonel in the latter year. He was in charge of the British establishments in Turkey during the Crimean campaign, and on returning was Secretary for Military Correspondence at the War Office. He was awarded the KCB in 1857 and in 1859 was appointed as the last High Commissioner for the Ionian Islands. Storks became Major-General in 1862 and, after the resignation of the British Protectorate in the following year, became Governor of Malta in 1864. However, he was soon sent to Jamaica to inquire into the recent disturbances and their repression, replacing the Governor responsible until returning to England in 1866; rewarded for his work by being made a Privy Counsellor. In 1867 he was appointed Controller-in-Chief of the eponymous Department. On the decision in 1870 to give charge of warlike stores to the revived position of Surveyor-General of the Ordnance Storks assumed this new office, holding it until his death in 1874.

George, Viscount Townshend (1723–1807)

Served under Cumberland at Culloden, Lieutenant-Colonel in 1st Regiment of Foot Guards; retired from the service in 1750 after differences with Cumberland. A strong advocate of the militia system, he was responsible for the Bill establishing it on a national basis. In 1759 he was appointed Brigadier-General under Wolfe in the Quebec operation, taking command after Wolfe's death. Lieutenant-General of the Ordnance from 1763 to 1767, when he was appointed Lord-Lieutenant of Ireland. Not considered to have been a success in this role, he was recalled in 1772. Master General of the Ordnance from 1772 to 1782, he briefly again became Master General of the Ordnance in 1783.

Appendix C

Instructions for Running Ordnance Magazines at Marchwood, 1814

Instructions for the good Government of the Office of Ordnance at Marchwood Magazine, committed to the Care of R.B. Ady Esqr. Appointed Ordnance Storekeeper at that Station.

1st You are to keep a daily Register of all such Letters received from The Master General, the Principal Officers of the Board, or any of them or by Their Order to Minute down the day of their receipt, and to return Answers with all diligent dispatch, and you are also to make an arrangement from day to day, of the Business or Work that is to be done in the Cooperage or in the Magazine, appointing a sufficient number of Labourers to perform the same, and taking care that none of them be taken off such work until it shall be finished; You are not to employ any of the Foremen, Artificers or Labourers who are placed under your Superintendence upon any Services not connected with the Ordnance, yet if there should be any relaxation of Business and the Men can be spared without detriment to the Magazine Duty, you may then employ them in keeping in Repair the Kings Roads, and what may be necessary to be done to the Grounds round the House and Buildings belonging to the Magazine. All Office Books whatever, - whether kept by yourself or any Person under your direction are to remain in a Press in the Public Office for the free Inspection of every Person concerned.

2nd You are not to employ any Extra Coopers, Artificers or Labourers or incur any Expense without Orders from the Board, and when any Person in the Service of this Office misbehave, you are to represent the same to the Board, and you are not to suffer any Artificer, Cooper, Labourer or other Person belonging to the Office, to enter the Magazine or to come within the Outward Gates, that has the least appearance of Intoxication, but on finding such, you are to suspend them and report their misconduct to the Board, and if any Labourer is found drunk or intoxicated on Guard, you are immediately to relieve him, suspend him and report the same to the Board, and in order to preserve a due respect and Subordination from the several Artificers and Labourers, you may for Small Crimes and Misdemeaners too trifling to trouble the Board with, cheque them not exceeding one days Pay, Minute the Persons name, his Crime and your reasons for cheequing him, that the Board may have recourse thereto when they think proper. − With respect to the Working time of Artificers and Labourers, the Board refer you to the established regulation dated 30th June 1786, a Copy of which is herewith enclosed. No Labourer Cooper or others employed in or about the Magazine are to leave their Work on frivolous pretences, all the Outward Gates to be kept shut, and the Labourer's are not to let any one pass during the Working Hours, without leave from you.

3rd You are to give strict charge to the Labourers doing duty as Watchmen, that they permit no Persons to go into the Magazines, or Inclosures of them, but such as are employed in the Service of the Office, and that no Person whatsoever be permitted to Smoke near the Magazine, the several Persons whose duty obliges them to go into the Magazine, are constantly to change their Shoes, and to put on Magazine Pumps' and when the door is opened the Floor of the Magazine is to be swept and well watered, likewise the Passages leading thereto, you are to take great care that no Iron be used about the Tackles for Swivels, Canhooks or any other Tools or Instruments used in the Magazines, but only such are made of Wood or Copper.

4th You are to take care that of the Serviceable Powder that which has been longest in Store be always issued first except by special order from the Board to the contrary and that all new Barrels when properly seasoned, be exactly tared and the weight of the Tare marked on the Barrel.

5th You are to take care that no Barrels of Powder lay open in the Magazine, except during a Proof, and that all Remnants to be immediately headed up entering the quantity and quality of the same in a Book to be kept for that purpose; No Powder is to be shifted without being removed into the Shifting House and having a sufficient number of Tanned Hides under the Barrels, in order to keep the Powder as much as possible from the Floors, the loose Powder is to be carefully swept up and not suffered to remain. You are to take care that powder be properly and securely stacked in the several Bays, and in case any of the Heads of the Barrels fly or start, you are immediately to cause the same to be removed and the Powder shifted into a Serviceable Barrel.

6th On the Arrival of Powder from any Place, you are most carefully to examine every Barrel in order to discover if any of the Hoops are fastened with Iron Nails, and if there is any Iron on any part of the Barrels, and you make such discovery, you are on no account to receive any of the Barrels so circumstanced, but immediately to cause the same to be reembarked and make a report thereof to the Board, very fatal Accidents having happened in other Places from inattention to the above Circumstances, - this Regulation is never to be dispensed with, and you are to enter a Minute of the Examination made on every arrival of Powder for the satisfaction of the Board.

7th You are strictly to take care that all the Engines, Hose, Ladders, Firehooks etc. be kept in perfect repair, and so lodged that they may at all times be ready and fit for use. The Fire Engines and Hose are to be examined and played the first Monday in every Month, and if any Repairs are wanting the same to be immediately reported to the Board. – You are to take care that the several Pumps are kept in proper repair, and in case they should at anytime be defective you are immediately to write to the Board that directions may be given for the same being put into perfect repair.

8th You are upon the application of the Clerk of the Works, to cause such of the Labourers as are not necessarily employed upon His Majesty's Service to Work under his direction in performing such Works as are ordered by the Board, and the Clerk of Works is to deliver to you every night a report of their attendance, agreeable to which report you are to include them in the Pay Lists, inserting the Cheeques made by him.

9th You are upon observing Water to issue from Barrels of returned Powder to order the same to be unheaded, and the Water gently poured off and the Barrels to be reheaded and properly stowed. – You are to be particularly careful not to suffer Powder to be put into wet or damp Barrels, but to reject such as have the least appearance of Moisture till properly seasoned; you are to send a Monthly state of all Powder in the Magazines to the Board, and to the Controller of the Royal Laboratory.

10th The Boat belonging to the Office is not to be employed on any pretence whatever; except upon His Majesty's Service, without an Order from the Board, so that no unnecessary Expense may be brought on the Office.

11th You are not to suffer any Merchandise or Goods – belonging to any Private Person to be lodged in the Magazine.

12th You are to take care that the Cisterns be kept constantly full of Water for the Security of the Magazines, employing the Labourers upon such Service.

13th You are to make up your Accounts of such Sum of Money as you have paid for Service of the Office Quarterly transmitting the name at the Expiration of each Quarter, and when you find it necessary to demand a further Imprest, you will make out and transmit with it, a State of your cash, showing the Expenditure of former Imprest, and the Balance remaining in your hands.

14th You are to keep a Minute Book wherein you are to enter Minutes of everything that is ordered or Transacted at the Magazine a fair Copy of which is to be sent to the Secretary's Office Annually. You are also to keep a day Book of all Receipts and Issues of Powder and other Stores, that proper Vouchers may be drawn up fair and entered in the respective Journals, and from thence transferred into the Ledger, which the Storekeeper is Annually to transmit to the Board, accompanied with the proper Vouchers.

15th You are to see that the several Persons borne on your Cheeque Books, do their Duty and perform what may be required of them in their several Stations, you are to Superintend them whether Artificers or Labourers at the different Places at which they are employed (excepting such are employed by the Clerk of the Works for whom he is responsible) to see they do their Duty with care and diligence, that they do not misspend or waste their time by loitering or otherwise, and if any are found Idle, negligent or disorderly in performing their Business, you are to cheeque them. The Superintending the Men is considered to be your Duty and you are not on any account to leave it to the direction of the Foreman, except in case of Illness or Multiplicity of Business. You are to see that the several Artificers and Labourers are called three times a day, that is to say at going to Work in the morning, returning to Work after Dinner and leaving Work at Night, and to cheeque such as are absent from Call.

You are likewise strictly to take care that no Artificers or Labourers waste or Embezzle any of the Kings Stores, and if any such waste or Embezzlement is discovered, you are immediately to signify the same to the Board. You are to make out Monthly Pay Lists for such Artificers as have actually worked or Watched, which List must be properly certified before you pay the same.

Lastly you are to cause these Instructions to be entered fair in a Book to be kept in the Office for that purpose, that no one may plead Ignorance of the same, and you are also to enter in the said Book, all such additional Orders as the Board shall in future think necessary to give for the Government of the Department at Marchwood.

Given at the Office of His Majesty's Ordnance, under the Seal of the said Office this Fifteenth Day of February 1815. By Order of the Board

Signed R. W. Crews
Secretary

(Hants CRO, 109 M91/COL 17)

Endnotes

Introduction

1 Jonathan Coad, *The Royal Dockyards 1690–1850*, Scolar Press, Aldershot, 1989; David Evans, *Building the Steam Navy*, Conway Maritime Press, London, 2004

2 James Douet, *British Barracks 1600–1914*, Stationary Office, London, 1998

3 Wayne Cocroft, *Dangerous Energy. The archaeology of gunpowder and military explosives manufacture*, English Heritage, London, 2000. Sources for the other depots are: for Marchwood, a 1997 report by Roger Bowdler of English Heritage; for Purfleet, a 1994 report by Paul Pattison and Peter Guillery for RCHME, supplemented by the same authors as 'The Powder Magazines at Purfleet', in *Georgian Group Journal*, VI, 1996, pp.37–52; and for Weedon, an interim report of 1998 by Adam Menuge and Andrew Williams for RCHME. The Marchwood and Weedon reports are held at the National Monuments Record, Swindon.

Chapter 1

1 Oxford Archaeology, Chatham Gun Wharf Archaeological Desk-based Assessment, Report for Medway Council, 2003

2 Major-General Whitworth Porter, *History of the Corps of Royal Engineers*, vol. 1, London, 1889: p.154

3 A. D. Saunders, *Fortress Britain: Artillery Fortification in the British Isles and Ireland*, Liphook, Beaufort Press, 1989: p.120

4 Liet, Edwards Simpson, *A Treatise on Ordnance and naval Gunnery*, New York, 1862: p.204

5 L. Lochée, *Elements of Fortification*, London, 1780; Lieut. Colonel C. W. Pasley, *Course of Military Instruction*, originally composed for the use of the Royal Engineer Department. vol. 3, London, 1817; A. D. Saunders, *Upnor Castle*, London, 1967; H. W. Semark, *The Royal Naval Armament Depots of Priddy's Hard, Elson, Frater and Bedenham*, Winchester, 1997; J. G. Coad, *The Royal Dockyards, 1690–1850*, Aldershot, 1989

6 WO 55/2272; Adam Menuge and Andrew Williams, *Royal Ordnance Depot, Weedon Bec*, RCHME Report, NMR 97080; Peter Guillery and Paul Pattison, RCHME Report, 1994, NMR Swindon: NBR Index No. 93577; P. Guillery and P. Pattison, 'The Powder Magazines at Purfleet' in *The Georgian Group Journal*, VI, 1996: pp.37–52; SUPP 5/64; Lieut. Colonel C. W. Pasley, *Course of Military Instruction*, originally composed for the use of the Royal Engineer Department. Vol.3, London, 1817: pp. 372–4. For a detailed discussion of the Board of Ordnance in this early period, see N. P. Baker, *The Architecture of the English Board of Ordnance, 1660–1750* (unpublished PhD thesis, University of Reading, 1985); also, Nigel Baker, *The Building Practice of the Board of Ordnance, 1680–1720*

7 WO 55/2005, WO 55/2142, WO 55/2142, WO 47/68, WO 47/72, PC 1/9/24, WO 47/73, WO 47/74, WO 55/2143, WO 47/76, WO 55/2006, WO 47/80, WO 47/82, POR/IO/1/1, WO 47/86

8 WO 47/88, WO 55/2147, WO 47/89, POR/IO/1/1, WO 55/2010

9 WO 30/115B, WO 47/84, WO 55/2269, WO 47/86, WO 47/87, WO 47/89, PLY/O/12, PLY/I/26

10 WO 30/115D, WO 46/17; D. C. Evans, 'The Duke of Richmond, James Glenie, Maker, and the Fortifications Bill', in *Fort*, XVI, 1988; D. C. Evans, 'The Redoubts on Maker Heights, Cornwall', in *The Georgian Group Journal*, IX, 1999; SUPP 5/868

Chapter 2

1 This probably refers to mealed powder, which was ordinary gunpowder reduced to a fine dust that ignited readily, burned rapidly, and so was very suitable for use in fuzes.

2 WO 55/2007, WO 55/2005, WO 55/2105, WO 55/2009, WO 55/2010, WO 55/2022, WO 55/2158

3 WO 55/2158, WO 55/786, WO 55/786, WO 55/2105, WO 55/2163, WO 55/2024, WO 55/2025, WO 55/2030, WO 55/2164

4 Sir William Congreve, *A Statement of Facts, relative to the savings which have arisen from manufacturing Gunpowder at the Royal Powder Mills; and of the Improvements which have been made in its strength & durability since the year 1783*, London, 1811; on the manufacture of gunpowder and the building types evolved, see W. D. Cocroft, *Dangerous Energy*, London,

2000; WA/I/1, SUPP 5/866, WO 55/2161

5 WO 55/786, WO 47/2398, WO 44/307, WO 55/805

6 WO 55/797, SUPP 5/869, WO 55/2032

7 The Waltham Abbey buildings are dealt with in Cocroft, 2000; WO 55/1887, WO 55/767, WO 55/786, SUPP 5/867

8 Brian Lavery, *The Arming and Fitting of English Ships of War 1600–1815*, London, Conway Maritime Press, 1989, p.144; R Wilkinson-Latham, *British Artillery on Land and Sea, 1790–1820*, London, 1973, p.21

9 WO 55/2189, WO 55/2115, WO 44/142

10 WO 55/2024, WO 55/2029, WO 47/90, POR/I/2/41, WO 44/142

11 Alan Faulkner, *The Grand Junction Canal*, Rickmansworth (W. H. Walker & Brothers), 1993, pp.64–6; A. Menuge, *The Royal Military Depot Weedon Bec*, RCHME, 1999; B. Williams, *Captain Pilkington's Project: The Great Works at Weedon 1804 to 1816*, Norton, privately published, 2003; Adam Menuge and Andrew Williams, *Royal Ordnance Depot, Weedon Bec*, RCHME Report, NMR 97080; Peter Guillery and Paul Pattison, RCHME Report, 1994, NMR Swindon: NBR Index No. 93577; P. Guillery and P. Pattison, 'The Powder Magazines at Purfleet' in *The Georgian Group Journal*, VI, 1996: pp.37–52; WO 55/719, WEE/IO/1/2, WO 44/192. For magazines at Weedon Bec, see drawings of 1816 in Royal Engineers' Library, W140 (D38).

12 B. Lavery, *The Arming and Fitting of English Ships of War, 1600–1815*, London, 1987; POR/IO/1/8, POR/IO/1/10, POR/IO/1/11, POR/IO/1/17, POR/IO/1/18, WO 55/2025

13 T. 1/426, SUPP 5/868, WO 55/2350, WO 55/767, WO 55/719, WO 54/516; E. Paget-Tomlinson, *The Illustrated History of Canal & River Navigations*, Sheffield, 1994; WO 55/2065, POR/O/3/64; A. C. Benson and Viscount Esher, ed. *The Letters of Queen Victoria*, vol. 1, London, 1907, pp. 26–7

14 R. Bowdler, *Former Board of Ordnance Gunpowder Magazines, Magazine Lane, Marchwood, Hampshire*, English Heritage Report, London, 1997; WO 55/787, WO 44/243, E. Paget-Tomlinson, *The Illustrated History of Canal & River Navigations*, Sheffield, 1994; POR/I/2/38, POR/O/3/37, POR/O/3/36, WO 47/2631, POR/O/3/37, POR/I/2/40, POR/I/2/41, WO 44/241, POR/O/3/39

15 WO 44/62, WO 44/64, WO 44/681a; W. D. Cocroft, *Dangerous Energy*, London, 2000; WO 55/786; A. Menuge and A. Williams, *The Royal Ordnance Store, Southtown and Gorleston, Great Yarmouth, Norfolk*, RCHME, Cambridge, 1999; Parliamentary Papers (1817) IV, 131f, quoted in Roger Bowdler, *Report on Marchwood Magazines*, English Heritage, 1997, note 4

Chapter 3

1 WO 55/2170, WO 49/144, WO 55/2257, WO 44/681b, WO 44/681a; P. A. Magrath, *Fort Cumberland, 1747–1850, Key to an Island's Defence*, Portsmouth, 1992; WO 55/2654, WO 55/790; G. H. Williams, *The Western defences of Portsmouth Harbour, 1400–1800*, Portsmouth, 1979; WO 44/62, WO 44/64

2 WO 49/144, WO 55/1887, WO 44/122, WORK 41/88, WO 55/2064, WO 49/146, WO 44/643

3 The Assistant Firemaster of the Laboratory, who would take charge of the processes, described the finalised plans for the proposed operations of the restored St Budeaux powder works. Each Stoving House was calculated to dry 43 barrels at a time, which constituted a Lot. Under the old system, it required half a day to prepare and set each Lot in the stove, half a day to draw each Lot and one whole intervening day to dry. The drying of a single Lot of powder therefore took up three days at the stoves. But by continuing the operation through a number of Lots, turning the steam alternately into each of the two stoving houses, the drawing of one Lot and the setting of another would occupy one day, during which a third Lot was drying – so that three Lots would be processing on the same day, as in the following table:

	1	2	3	4	5
Lot 1	set	drying	drawn		
Lot 2		set	drying	drawn	
Lot 3			set	drying	drawn

One Lot would therefore occupy 3 days in stoving, three Lots 5 days, 15 Lots 17 days. On the stopping of the stoves the personnel would transfer to the Dusting House, there not being enough staff to carry on both operations together. Each Lot required one day for dusting, with the proofing of 15 Lots, and the mixing of 3 Lots occupying one day each. The Assistant Firemaster calculated that the optimal use of the plant would be to work 15 Lots together, which would necessitate magazine space for 645 barrels, but allowance should be made for 800.

4 WO 44/643, WO 55/800, WO 44/307

5 A tender for the work was received from Thomas Burton (of Lambeth) of £7,680, which was accepted, but by the end of September no notification had been received of eligible securities. Even so, it was expected that the work would be completed in July 1848. Satisfactory securities could not be obtained and in February 1848 the contract was transferred to Messrs Locke & Newham, with two months additional time being allowed. WO 44/502, WO 55/806, POR/O/3/53, WO 55/2100, WO 44/502, MR 1/1911(5), WO 55/2103, WO 55/794/1, WO 55/794/2

6 WO 55/2103, WO 795/2, WO 55/2104

7 WO 55/2104, WO 55/794/2, WO 55/2105, WO 55/2106, WO 55/2109, WO 44/128, WO 55/806

8 WO 44/309, WO 44/313, WO 55/806, WO 55/805

9 WO 44/313, WO 55/806

10 WO 44/14

11 WO 44/314, WO 55/806, WO 55/807

Chapter 4

1 WO 55/807, WO 46/99, WO 55/2104, WO 55/2106, WO 55/2109, WO 55/2105, WO 55/795/2

2 WO 55/2105, WO 55/2106, WO 55/2107, WO 49/176

3 WO 55/2108, WO 55/2109, WO 46/102, WO 46/101, WO 55/807, ADM 160/36

4 WO 55/2109, WO 55/2110, ADM 160/101, WO 55/2111, POR/I/2/unnumbered, ADM 160/37, WO 55/2112

5 The lead-up to the abolition of the Board of Ordnance is most recently described in J. Sweetman, *War and Administration*, Edinburgh, 1984. The deliberations of the Magazine Committee have not been located; *The Panmure Papers*, ed. Douglas & Ramsay, 2 vols, London, 1908, contains no relevant material and none is catalogued in the Dalhousie papers. The sole reference found is in the Royal Engineers' Letterbooks, CHA/I/3/42.

6 CHA/I/3/42, ADM 160/38, ADM 160/105, ADM 160/38, ADM 160/107

7 POR/I/2/unnumbered, WO 55/2114, WO 55/2996, WO 55/2120, WO 55/2112, POR/I/2/unnumbered

8 WO 44/573, WO 46/104, WO 33/18

9 WO 46/103, SUPP 6/528, ADM 1/7549/B, WO 33/15

10 WO 55/2113, WO 55/2114, WO 55/2115

11 WO 33/8, POR/O/3/71, WO 55/2117

12 Herbert of Lea Papers 5A/38

13 WO 46/96, POR/O/3/73, WO 55/2117, Herbert of Lea Papers 5A/38, 5B/35; Lord Stanmore, *Sidney Herbert, Lord Herbert of Lea, A Memoir*, 2 vols, London, 1906; *Report of the Commissioners appointed to consider the Defences of the United Kingdom*, London, 1860; WO 55/2117, POR/O/3/73

Guarding the Magazines

1 POR/IO/1/1, WO 47/90; J. Douet, British Barracks, 1600-1914, London, 1998; WO 55/2015, POR/I/2/41, WO 55/787

2 WO 44/573, ADM 224/41, ADM 224/42, WO 55/2180, WO 55/2189, WO 55/2219

3 WO 55/2224, WO 78/610, ADM 179/12, T 1/8858A/5157-8

4 C. Dobinson, *AA Command*, London, 2001: pp.13–14

5 ADM 116/4049, ADM 116/3492; The Royal Marine Police were themselves replaced by the Admiralty Constabulary in 1949, to be succeeded by the MOD Police in 1971: A. R. Salter, *The protection of Chatham Dockyard through the ages*, Gillingham, 1983

6 Calling up Royal Marine pensioners would enable sufficient personnel to be found for providing new guards and for augmenting existing guards at the following places:
• The ammunition depots at Bandeath, Lodge Hill, Marchwood, Holton Heath and Errnesettle
• The water supply at Holton Heath
• The railway at Priddy's Hard and the railway bridge between Upnor and Lodge Hill
• The Dockyards at Sheerness, Chatham, Portsmouth, Plymouth, Rosyth

The above were all that were considered necessary during the emergency. Wrabness and Copperas Wood, though particularly isolated, were not to be protected by retired Marines, but by newly recruited civilians. Close liaison was to be arranged between the Civil police and the service guards at Upnor, Bedenham, Frater, Priddy's Hard, Bull Point and Crombie. ADM 116/3492

Chapter 5

1 WO 55/2118, WO 55/2119, ADM 160/112

2 WO 55/2177, PTM/1846, PTM/1800, WO 33/15, WO 78/3101, WO 33/18. For James Nasmyth's involvement in the development of the steam navy and its yards, see David Evans, *Building the Steam Navy. Dockyards, Technology and the Creation of the Victorian Battle Fleet, 1830-1906*, London, 2004.

3 COL 20/5; *The Times*, November 3 1864; WO 55/2181, WO 55/2177

4 WO 55/2181, WO 33/15

5 WO 55/2182, WO 55/2204, WO 55/2185, WO 55/2189, WO 33/18; The gunnery ship HMS *Excellent* was land-based from 1866 when it was established on Whale Island, Portsmouth.

6 *Parliamentary Paper*, June 30 1868, *Copy of Correspondence between the Treasury and the War Office respecting the Formation of the Department of Control*; Major General A. Forbes, *A History of the Army Ordnance Services*, vol.2., London, 1929, describes the antagonisms; a recent account of Cardwell's reforms and a brief account of the Control Department can be found in E. M. Spiers, *The Late Victorian Army, 1868–1902*, Manchester, 1992; WO 33/27/600, PRO 30/48/18 (The Cardwell Papers)

7 WO 55/2191, WO 33/21a/419, WO 55/2192, WO 55/2193

8 ADM 116/655, WO 55/2192, WO 55/2193; the anecdote from the Crimea is from Captain C. Orde Browne, 'Our Rifled Projectiles and Fuzes', in *Proceedings of the Royal Artillery Institute*, vol.VII, 1871; *Parliamentary Paper*, February 18, 1870, *Copy of papers relating to the dismissal of Colonel Boxer from the Office of Superintendent of the Royal Laboratory*; WO 55/2194, WO 55/2196

9 On Storks, see *Dictionary of National Biography*; WO 33/27/600; M. Roper, *The Records of the War Office and related Departments*, London, 1998

10 WO 33/18, WO 55/2196, WO 55/2197, ADM 116/182, WO 33/22, WO 33/24

11 The Director of Artillery, given the responsibility for ordnance storage after the 1870 reorganisation, proposed to take another officer away, but the Deputy Controller in charge of the gunwharf turned this proposal down. There had never been less than two officers there, and because of the increase in work a third was added in 1867. (That post was reduced in 1870, the officer being replaced by a clerk from the Army Service Corps.) In the laboratory department the posts of Firemaster and Clerk had merged when the Royal Ordnance Factory was set up, but the duties had greatly increased since that time. Two officers had also been withdrawn from the gunwharf and Young stated that '… although the Department has hitherto been able to steer clear of failure, the Establishment is inadequate to the efficient performance of the duties.'

12 WO 55/2206, PTM/1783, PTM/1788, PTM/1789, PTM/1795, PTM/1845, WO 55/2201, WO 55/2200, WO 55/2202, WO 55/2204, WO 55/2205, WO 55/2206

13 SUPP 6/528

14 WO 78/610, WO 78/2643/5

15 SUPP 6/528, WO 55/2219

16 WO 55/2210, WO 55/2224, PTM/2622, PTM/2623, PTM/2625, PTM/2626, PTM/2627, PTM/2631, PTM/2632, PTM/2633, PTM/2634, PTM/2635, PTM/2803, WO 78/2315, WO 55/2214

17 PTM/3132, WO 55/2213, WO 55/2219, PTM/2943, PTM/3055, PTM/3056, PTM/3057

18 PTM/1830, WO 55/2199, WO 55/2211, WO 55/2213, PTM/3056, WO 55/2219

19 WO 55/2205, WO 55/2214, WO 55/2219; Lieut. Col. W. Baker Brown, *History of Submarine Mining in the British Army*, Chatham, 1910; PTM/2758, PTM/3042

20 PTM/2536, PTM/2537, PTM/2538, PTM/2688, PTM/2689, PTM/2758, PTM/2766, WO 55/2224

Chapter 6

1 LAB 59/2, WO 55/2224, WO 55/2226

2 WO 55/2226, WO 55/2227, WO 55/2225

3 WO 55/2226

4 WO 55/2226, ADM 189/4, WO 55/2229. *Inflexible* was a battleship, which mounted the largest guns in use by the Royal Navy at the time (four 16-inch rifled muzzle loaders) and the thickest armour ever carried by a RN ship (two feet at the thickest). Her first Captain was none other than Jacky Fisher.

5 When considering vessels to hold the powder for filling at Tipner, the Chief Constructor at the dockyard stated that the only vessels available for conversion to floating magazines were *Carnatic* (in fairly good condition), which would cost £5,000, *Lord Warden* and *Repulse* (also in fairly good condition), would cost £4,000 not including the costs of removing the engines. *Victoria* was not suitable without extensive repairs; *Melampus*, needing a new upper deck and extensive repairs to topsides, would cost £5,000. The Admiral Superintendent cut this list down to *Carnatic* as a magazine and *Melampus* for mines, their conversion costs being £5,000 and £2,000 respectively. Such decisions as had been made were thrown into confusion by the Admiralty announcing in the spring of 1886 that it would be unable to carry out the dredging necessary to make the previously agreed improvements to the usability of Tipner (though a new pier had been provided), as the dockyard extension work was taking up all their resources. WO 55/2229, WO 55/2230

6 WO 55/2230, PTM/2967, WO 33/46/?, ADM 256/21; Ovey's approximate estimate for the scheme was: Shell filling & Fuze rooms, including Traverses, Latrines &c – £2,680; Railings round site – £472; Magazine – £161; Tramways – £871; Total – £4,364. PTM/2958, PTM/2959

7 At the time the QF Shell Store was designed for Priddy's Hard, the magazines were being used as follows: A – Machine gun & small arms ammunition; B – half for Land and half for Naval small arms & Machine gun ammunition; C – Gunpowder for making up cartridges; D – Powder removed from shells; E – Deposit Magazine for ships in harbour. No filled shells were held at Priddy's Hard; they were all kept at the gunwharf, where an additional (and this time final) filled shell magazine was provided for in the 1890–91 Estimates, when the Quadrangle there was also roofed over. An additional Empty Powder Case Store was added to the complex of buildings around the Camber at Priddy's Hard. PTM/2958, PTM/2959, PTM/2967, ADM 151/54, ADM 151/55; Chesneau & Kolesnik, eds., *Conway's All the World's Fighting Ships, 1860–1905*, London, 1979; ADM 256/26, WO 55/2231, ADM 256/26, ADM 256/22; MOD (N) Library, *Report of the Committee to Inquire into the Purchase, Custody, and Accounts of Naval Warlike Stores*; ADM 256/24, PTM/1818, PTM/3024

8 In February 1889 two sites were selected, the preferred one being on the Upnor side of the Chattenden Magazines, outside the boundary wall, and directly connected to the railway from Upnor to Chattenden. The local CRE was asked to prepare a design and estimate. The new buildings at Priddy's Hard were be taken as a model for shell filling, and for cartridge filling those at Bull Point (presumably the old wooden buildings at St Budeaux recommended for that purpose in 1875) could serve as a guide. The Ordnance Store Officers at Portsmouth were consulted about the suitability of the Priddy's Hard buildings as exemplars. All ordinary requirements of cartridge filling, shell filling, examinations or repacking were being met there, and all examinations, filling and packing of cartridges, and repacking of fuzes or other perishable stores were carried out in air-dried rooms. Although the shell filling rooms were new and well arranged, the portion of the station arranged for the other Laboratory operations was patch work, arranged as an expedient, and could not therefore in any way be taken as a pattern by which to design premises at Upnor. As at Priddy's Hard, floating magazines were required for the storage of bulk powder, guncotton and mines on the Medway. To provide the necessary improved communications with these hulks – *Forte* and *Leonidas* were the original choices – over £3,000 had been allotted for the financial year 1888–9 for a new landing stage with connecting gangways. By August 1890 designs had been drawn up for a Laboratory, costing £9,000, at Upnor. ADM 256/21, ADM 256/24

9 ADM 256/22; It was decided in 1887 that E.X.E. powder was to supersede black prism powder for RML and 6-inch BL guns. By December 1888 Priddy's Hard was issued with 420,000 lbs, Bull Point with 537,800. In store were 793,600 at Purfleet and 422,000 at Marchwood. Due from manufacturers were 55,800 from Chilworth and 700,000 from Waltham Abbey; ADM 256/21

10 WO 32/7068; ADM 151/55, Ruddock Mackay, in *Fisher of Kilverstone*, Oxford, 1973, pp.190–2, pointed out Fisher's position at this time; ADM 116/266, ADM 116/283

11 ADM 1/6987

12 ADM 256/22, ADM 1/7397B; MOD (N) Library, *Report of the Committee to Inquire into the Purchase, Custody, and Accounts of Naval Warlike Stores*; the committee examined the current proposals for conversion and found the costs were:

Ship	Location	£
Newcastle	Devonport	8,500
Thalia	Portsmouth	6,500
Valorous	Portsmouth	6,500
Forte	Chatham	6,000
Bellerophon	Portsmouth QF Depot	3,000
Kent	Devonport QF Depot	3,000
Grampus	Portsmouth. Alterations for mine stowage	250

WO 32/7031, ADM 256/24

13 MOD (N) Library, *Report of the Committee to Inquire into the Purchase, Custody, and Accounts of Naval Warlike Stores*; ADM 131/31, ADM 1/7397B

14 ADM 116/868, ADM 179/12, ADM 179/13, ADM 256/26, ADM 167/23, PTM/1797, ADM 179/13, ADM 179/16, 038146, 038147, 038164, 038161, 038179, 038197, 038198

15 *The Times*, 8 March, 1889; ADM 116/583; ADM 116/459, ADM 216/6

16 ADM 116/655, LAB 59/4, ADM 116/551

17 ADM 116/868, ADM 116/126

18 ADM 116/882, WO 78/4263, WO 78/3280, WO 78/4755; *Manual of Submarine Mining*, vol.1, 1901; plates CXXII and CXXVIII; ADM 256/24

19 ADM 1/7278

Developments in Ordnance and Armament

1 WO 55/2118, WO 55/2119; Captain F. S. Stoney, 'A Brief Historical Sketch of our Rifled Ordnance, from 1858 to 1868', in *Minutes of Proceedings of the Royal Artillery Institution*, VI, 1870; the tale of the inaccuracy of the Armstrongs at Kagoshima appears in O. Parkes, *British Battleships*, London, 1966 (but written between 1925 and 1956) and has been subsequently repeated; H. A. Baker, Woolwich and the Heavy RML's, Worthing, 1989; for details of the development of powders see Cocroft, op.cit.; Lieut.Col. F. G. Baylay, 'Modern Types of Guns,' in *Professional Papers of the Corps of Royal Engineers*, 1883; In the 1880s, controversy raged over the design of BL guns, as it had in the 1850s between the supporters of the Armstrong and Whitworth systems. A representative example is J. A. Longridge, *Is England to be caught napping?*, London, 1885

2 WO 55/2110

3 In December 1872, twenty-eight 12-inch Palliser shells were returned from *Monarch* to Priddy's Hard. They had been filled on board. One had no bag at all, five had bags partly filled, then pushed into the shell and filled up with loose powder. All the charges were deficient in varying degrees. WO 55/2199.

4 WO 55/2110, WO 55/2109, WO 55/2117 WO 55/2119; 1873 *Manual of Gunnery for HM Fleet*; October 1872 *Regulations for Gunpowder Magazines; Handbook for the 9"12 ton RML; Handbook for the 12.5"38 ton RML*; 1880 *Manual of Gunnery for HM Fleet*

5 LAB 59/3, ADM 256/35. By the end of March 1891, 123,234 lbs of the new E.X.E. powder had been used for cartridge filling, and the following prism powder was on hand:

Priddy's Hard	Lbs.
6" cartridge	5,671
12.5 and 12" cartridge	33,830
Loose	75,931
Bull Point	
6" cartridge	8,694
12.5 and 12" cartridge	3,535
Loose	73,855

711,165 lbs. were in store abroad. These explosives were soon to lose their predominance. ADM 256/25, ADM 256/26.

For the large calibres, the outfit and present reserve for 13.5-inch and 16.25-inch guns was more than could be fired by all the guns (including reserves) without the barrels being worn out, and they were consequently reduced. The reductions per calibre were:

Calibre in inches	Present outfit	Future outfit
16.25	246	196
13.5	246	196

12	282	262
9.5	282	262

ADM 256/29, ADM 151/64.
The projected needs of the navy were

	Tons
1894/5	700
1895/6	1,070
1896/7	640
Total	2,410

Half of this was to be supplied by Waltham Abbey and half by the trade. ADM 256/30, WO 33/55/327, ADM 256/31, ADM 151/66

6   In 1867 the Superintendent of the Royal Laboratory suggested that the cracking of shells could be prevented by casting the shot with a cavity of 1¼ to 1½ inches in the cylindrical part of the shell, the base being closed by a wrought-iron plug. As not many shot had proved defective so far, it was decided not to go to the expense of changing the pattern. However, when later that year a change had to be made anyway, because of the introduction of a new form of studding the shot to engage the rifling, the opportunity was taken to alter the casting. In November 1867 the first examples were tested at HMS *Excellent* and found to give superior penetration to the existing pattern. After March 1870 the manufacturing process was improved by only casting the head in the chill mould, the body being cast in sand. This gave superior penetrative powers and made the body of the shell less liable to break up, but the metallurgical problems persisted. On investigation, a large number were broken up at Woolwich in the course of manufacture, and in every case fissures were found extending from the rear end of the cavity towards the outside of the projectile. It was thought that there were two causes: the unnecessary thickness of the shot towards the rear end and the stresses within the metal caused by the differential cooling between the nose and the body. It was proposed to mitigate the former by enlarging the cavity to approach that of the shell; this was done, and the problem seemed to be over. However, in 1880, the *Manual of Gunnery for Her Majesty's Fleet* discussed this: 'The manner in which the head is cast being the opposite extreme to annealing, which renders metal uniform and even throughout its mass, it is not surprising that its particles should be in an unnatural and constrained condition, and that on slight provocation such molecular action should take place as would cause the projectile to split'. The manufacture of Palliser shot and shell for RML guns was discontinued in 1883, and production switched over to studless versions for BL guns. In these a reversion was made to the small cavity as proposed in 1867, though now with a diameter of 2¼ inches. *Manual of Gunnery for Her Majesty's Fleet*, London, 1873; *Extracts from the Reports and Proceedings of the Ordnance Select Committee*, V, 1867; *Treatise on Ammunition*, London, 1887; *Treatise on Ammunition*, London, 1892; *Manual of Gunnery for Her Majesty's Fleet*, London, 1880; ADM 151/55, ADM 151/70

7   ADM 256/35, ADM 151/68, SUPP 5/148, TH 29

8   In December 1853 the following proportions of filled cartridges were supplied to screw ships (WO 55/2109):

		Per gun
Bow & stern pivots		180
8" 65 & 60 cwt	Distant	40
	Full	20
	Reduced	20
32-pdr 56 cwt	Distant	40
	Full	20
	Reduced	20
Filled 6" shell	Bow & stern pivots	60
	Side guns & carronades	10
32-pdr round shot	Bow & stern pivots	120
	Side guns & carronades	70

9   Cartridges for the 13.5-inch BL were assembled in fifteen layers, fourteen of 108 prisms each, and one of such a number, not less than 81, as would bring the total weight of powder up to 157½ lbs; should the top layer consist of less than 81, one or more prisms had to be removed from each layer to make up the requisite number. As with the 16-inch RML, seven prisms of black powder were inserted in the centre of the top and bottom layers to facilitate ignition. WO 55/2206; *Handbook for the 12.5" 38 ton RML*; WO 55/2226; 1887 *Treatise on Ammunition*; 1892 *Manual of Gunnery for HM Fleet*; WO 33/55.

10   *Brassey's Naval Annual*, 1887; ADM 151/55, ADM 151/64; *Treatise on Ammunition*, 5th. ed., London, 1892; PTM/2961, GO/2, ADM 256/21; *Treatise on Ammunition*, 10th. ed., London, 1915

11   The following applied to QF 6-inch Mk.I cartridge (WO 33/55):

1. Before filling, the cartridge case is to be carefully examined and wiped out before the electric primer and igniter are secured in the base, and if the case is lacquered inside, a paper liner is to be inserted.

2. The cordite is to be brought to the building or compartment in a case, cordite, wood, containing 100 lb. The operator will carefully weigh the cordite charge, 13 lb. 4 oz., size ³⁰⁄₄, and the cordite is to be carefully inserted in small handfuls into the cartridge case, so as not to disturb the igniter; a millboard disc, a felt wad, and a paper cylinder are to be placed over the cordite, the edge of the lid is to be coated with fuze cement. The lid is then inserted in the top of the case, and set down by using a hollow metal drift, the projecting clips on the mouth of the case turned over by means of a small metal hammer, the joint is to be further secured with cement. The cartridges are then removed to the building or compartment for packing.

3. Cordite limit. Not more than 150 lb. of loose cordite, six unfinished and four finished cartridges, are to be in the building or compartment at one time.

4. No implements or tools, other than those undermentioned, are to be used in this work.
    Brushes, camel-hair
    Drifts, metal, for setting down lids
    Hammers, metal
    Key, metal, for screwing in primers
    Mallets, wood
    Pots, copper, for cement
    Scissors, metal
    Shovels, copper
    Stools, wood, with hole for primer to pass through
    Trays, wood
    Weights and scales, metal

5. The tables and floors are to be covered with wadmiltilts, and kept free from loose cordite. Not less than three buckets filled with water are to be kept in the building or compartment.
    Gauging and Packing the Cartridges
    No other work is to be done in this building or compartment.

6. The cartridges, when gauged, are packed three in a box, which is to be wiped out before packing. A label is to be attached to the inside of the lid of each package, bearing the date of packing, also the number and name of the examiner and gauger. When closed, each package is to have the descriptive, explosive, group, class, and "This end up" labels attached.

12   1892 *Manual of Gunnery for HM Fleet*; WO 33/55.

13   ADM 151/55, ADM 116/266, Capt. H. Garbett, RN, *Naval Gunnery*, London, 1897; WO 55/2108, WO 55/2109; General Sir Howard Douglas, *A Treatise on Naval Gunnery*, 4th .ed., London, 1855; WO 55/2116; J. Scoffern, *Projectile Weapons of War*, 3rd .ed., London, 1858; Sir William Armstrong, contribution to 'The National Defences', in *Proceedings of the Institution of Civil Engineers*, vol.20, 1861; WO 55/2118, WO 55/2181, WO 55/2192, WO 55/2193; Captain J. Orde Browne, 'Our Rifled Projectiles and Fuzes', in *Minutes of Proceedings of the Royal Artillery Institution*, VII, 1871; *Treatise on Ammunition*, 4th ed., London, 1887; Cocroft, *op.cit.*; *Treatise on Ammunition*, 10th ed. London, 1915

14   A return of February 1889 of the percentage of damaged but repairable powder cases returned:

	Harbour vessels	Channel Squadron	Foreign service
Portsmouth	50%	70%	70%
Devonport	30%	70%	100%

The cost of the repairs was £300 at Portsmouth, £170 at Devonport and £1,800 at Chatham (including transport costs to Woolwich). As an incentive it was decided that if eighty per cent of cases returned after having been issued for over twelve months were found to be serviceable the gunner was to get 1/- per case, if between sixty and eighty per cent 6d a case. However, the Department of Naval Ordnance did not think it was in the power of gunners to control damage to powder cases, and the allowances were never made. Matters did not get better, and in 1898, after trials of the ammunition supply arrangements on the new protected cruiser *Diadem*, Priddy's Hard reported the following damage:

6" QF	1,024 with loose & damaged lids
	32 serviceable
12-pdr 12-cw QF	1,564 with loose & damaged lids
	220 serviceable
12-pdr 8-cwt QF	190 with loose & damaged lids
	10 serviceable

Measures were taken at the Ordnance Depots to ensure on the serviceability of the cases, and in November 1896 it was decided that air pumps were to be used for testing air-tightness of powder cases, while at Priddy's Hard a lean-to by the Cook House was added as a shop for testing powder cases with hot water. A more substantial building was provided the next year for labelling, stencilling and testing filled powder cases; this formed part of the New Laboratory complex.

By 1900 shells were painted in the following colours:

Tips		
Shot (except case)		White
Shell	Common & Palliser	Black
	Shrapnel	Red
Bands		
Steel projectiles (except shrapnel)		White band round head
Armour piercing shells		2 white bands round head
All filled shells		Red band round head
Practice shells		Yellow band round body
Bodies – HE yellow, all others black.		

Lyddite shells were yellow, filled ones with a red band. WO 33/15, WO 55/2101, SUPP 5/764; WO 55/2103; 1875 *Notes on Naval Guns*; WO 55/2120, WO 55/2220, ADM 256/21, ADM 256/22, ADM 256/35, ADM 256/32, PTM 2953, PTM 2941, ADM 256/23; 1892 *Manual of Gunnery for HM Fleet*; 1900 *Notes on Naval Guns and Torpedoes*; WO 55/2114, WO 55/2115

[15] Though so simple, the test was very delicate, the standard tint being produced by the release of 0·000135 milligrams of the gas. The time for the colour change to be effected denoted the condition of the cordite. Any cordite M.D. that passed a 12-minute heat test was to be issued, then to be heat tested every two years. By the 1930s, new cordite had to take a minimum of 30 minutes in order to be accepted; once issued the standard was reduced, being no less than 10 minutes at 71·1°C. By the 1950s, with further improvements to the explosive, this had been reduced to 5 minutes.

[16] For the early development of proving and proof houses, see Cocroft, *op. cit*; *Handbook of the Manufacture and Proof of Gunpowder*, 1870 ed.; *The Cyclopaedia; or Universal Dictionary of Arts, Sciences and Literature*, A. Rees, 1811; SUPP 5/840, ADM 256/44, *Treatise on Ammunition*, 1915 ed.; ADM 116/1370; *Text Book of Explosives used in the Services*, 1938 ed.; *Services Textbook of Explosives*, 1954 ed.

Chapter 7

[1] Sir Charles Petrie, *The Life and Letters of the Right Honourable Sir Austen Chamberlain*, 2 vols, London, 1939; for Richards see DNB; ADM 1/7278, CAB 37/41/7, CAB 37/41/6

[2] Officer training began on the site of Dartmouth Naval College in 1863. The present buildings, all to the designs of Sir Aston Webb, date from 1899–1905.

[3] ADM 1/7278, ADM 1/7318, ADM 1/7572, ADM 1/7319

[4] ADM 116/868. The DNO stated that the space needed was for the following stores:

• Cannon cartridges	322,000 cu ft	
Available at Marchwood,	168,000	
Leaving	154,000	
• 6 & 3 pdr. QF	79,300 cu ft	
Available at Priddy's Hard	38,400	
Leaving	40,900	
• Small arms & MG	38,000 cu ft	
Accommodation available at Priddy's Hard		
• Dry guncotton	2,500 cu ft	
None available		
• Wet guncotton	40,400 cu ft	
None available		
• Filled shells	28,300 sq ft	
Available at Gunwharf	6,600	
Leaving	21,700	

Raban's original estimate, on the supposition that Horsea would be used, included Police accommodation at Frater Point (to guard guncotton magazines) at £550 and the following for Priddy's Hard and Horsea magazines:

Priddy's Hard	£
3- & 6-pdr QF	4,510
Filled Shells	15,400
Dry guncotton	275

	20,185
Add 10% for roads	2,000
	22,185
Add 10% for extra cost of work at Priddy's Hard	2,200
	24,385 say 25,000
Horsea	£
Cannon cartridges	17,600
Wet guncotton and mines	4,400
	22,000
25% for roads	5,500
	27,500
25% for extra cost of work at Horsea	6,875
	34,375 say 35,000

[5] ADM 1/7549/B; 248,500 cubic feet were required, 198,500 for cannon cartridges and 50,000 for QF. QF ammunition was stowed in No.3 powder Magazine. *Newcastle* offered 125,800 cubic feet with the three magazines offering 40,000 each, so there was only a deficiency of 2,700; however, a recent redistribution of the proportion of the reserves had increased the requirements for cannon cartridges and QF to 269,000 and 65,000 respectively. With the disposal of *Newcastle* 149,000 and 65,000 cubic feet would have to be provided.

[6] ADM 116/655. The accommodation required was: Cannon cartridges – 264,000 cubic feet; 6- & 3-pdr QF – 79,000. The available space was: Upnor A Magazine – 45,000; Upnor B Magazine – 88,000. This meant that 210,000 cubic feet needed to be provided.

The possession of the Chattenden magazines was vital because:
• Immediate additional magazine accommodation was required urgently at Chatham for the navy, the existing accommodation being utterly inadequate to store the ammunition that should be in the Station at that time.
• There was ample land at Chattenden on which the further magazine accommodation required for the navy could be erected. If this depot were not transferred to the Admiralty a site elsewhere would be required, which would be exceedingly difficult and costly to obtain. The advantages, both in point of time and cost, of securing a ready-made Establishment were very great.
• The Chattenden magazines were already connected to the Naval Depot at Upnor by rail.
• The Chattenden depot ws situated on a hill, and was exceptionally safe as regards the effect of an explosion on the dockyard or neighbourhood. Its position was also satisfactory strategically.
• The magazines were within easy distance of the South-Eastern Railway.
ADM 151/67

[7] At £6,794, No.1 Magazine was a major building project for ordnance storage; though built from naval funds, the building appears to have been originally shared with the army, as its Shifting Room, which was added in 1891 (presumably when it was ready for use), was used by both Services. An ammunition store for 3-pounder QF was also added in 1891; this was a lighter version of the 6-pounder building, the walls being of corrugated iron with cast iron stanchions. The complex was finally completed in 1901–2, with a store for QF ammunition (ranging from 12-pounder to 6-inch) and an iron-framed building with 9-inch brick infill and an iron-trussed roof covered with slates on boarding. In 1903 a barge pier was constructed to supplement the jetty of the original powder magazine. All the buildings save the original magazine were allotted to the navy by the Forwood Committee, and were known at first as No.1 Group at the Plumstead Marshes, and later as the Tripcock Magazines. SUPP 5/1031

[8] WO 33/15, SUPP 5/1031, ADM 116/868. (Differing dates for the first cordite magazine are given in the two preceding sources; that in ADM 116/868 has been followed as originating nearer to the magazine's construction.) SUPP 6/90, SUPP 6/91, WO 33/56, T1/10764B/1497

[9] WO 32/7127, WO 32/7129, ADM 116/868

[10] WO 32/7128, PTM/2938, PTM/2940, PTM/2941, PTM/2942, PTM/2943, ADM 116/868.

Magazine accommodation before the great transformation of 1897–8

	Contents	Working capacity (in cubic feet)	Quantity stored (in cubic feet)
Carnatic	Filled cartridges & loose powder	69,000	55,000
E Magazine	Filled cartridges & loose powder	25,800	19,600
C Magazine	Loose powder & cordite	3,500	2,600
G Magazine	QF	31,500	16,500

[11] In March 1898 the third report of the Portsmouth Committee showed that its members were still undecided about this point. Since the second report the store for 3-pounder and 6-pounder QF and part of the filled shell store had been completed, and some conditions had changed. Marchwood was to be utilised to its full capacity, and powder and cordite could be stored in the same storage magazine, though as has been seen, not in the same compartment. Cordite in brass cartridge cases could be kept in an ordinary explosive storehouse. The amount of storage space required had increased to: Powder – 105,000 cubic feet; Cordite – 36,000; QF – 127,000; a total of 268,000 cubic feet. Marchwood could offer 258,000 cubic feet, with Priddy's Hard offering 25,800. A surplus of 15,800 cubic feet was therefore available. Although sufficient accommodation theoretically existed, the Commander-in-Chief felt very strongly that the ammunition should be kept inside Portsmouth Harbour for outfits of the Fleet Reserve, outfits of the Dockyard Reserve, outfits of tenders to gunnery ships and special service vessels, and part of the outfits for ships under construction. These required 25,000 cubic feet for powder, which were available at Priddy's Hard, 18,000 for cordite cartridges above 6-inch calibre, and 63,000 for QF filled with cordite. If it were decided not to utilise Marchwood then additional accommodation should be provided, to the extent of 25,000 cubic feet in the shape of a cordite magazine and 50,000 cubic feet in the form of an explosive storehouse.

[12] ADM 116/868

[13] PTM/2469; *Parliamentary Paper*, March 28 1905, *Account of Naval Works Acts*; ADM 116/126; *Parliamentary Paper*, March 1900, *Statement of estimated cost & expenditure on Naval Works*; ADM 1/7549B

[14] CAB/37/52/41, T 1/9548B/12295, CAB 37/57/63, ADM 1/7490B, ADM 1/7572, ADM 1/7573, ADM 1/7633

[15] ADM 131/43, COL 18/2

Chapter 8

[1] ADM 256/27, ADM 256/31, ADM 256/32, ADM 151/68, ADM 256/33

[2] ADM 256/34, LAB 59/5, ADM 131/41

[3] *Diadem* trials reported:
6-in QF – 1,024 with loose & damaged lids; 32 serviceable
12-pdr 12 cwt QF – 1,564 with loose & damaged lids; 220 serviceable
12-pdr 8 cwt QF – 190 with loose & damaged lids; 10 serviceable
ADM 151/70, ADM 256/34, ADM 256/35, ADM 256/33, ADM 116/1025, ADM 1/7599, ADM 256/37, LAB 59/5, ADM 256/39, GO/1

[4] ADM 131/44, ADM 1/7397B, Rear-Admiral Sir Sydney Eardley-Wilmot, *An Admiral's Memories. Sixty-five years afloat and ashore*, London, n.d. [1927]

[5] The committee members noted that the total capacity of the cordite magazine was about 500 tons, and had held on occasion as much as 400 tons. This magazine was within 183 yards of the powder magazine (E), which also had a capacity of 500 tons. In addition, there were the stores containing QF cartridges and ammunition, though these were not considered to be a great source of danger, as the charges were in brass cases packed in tin- or zinc-lined boxes. According to Home Office regulations, the danger zone for 500 tons stored in one building without traverses was calculated at 8,000 yards, or with traverses 4,000 yards. When the same quantity was stored in 10 separate buildings at 200 yards distance untraversed, or 100 yards traversed, the danger zone was then reduced to 850 yards, little more than one tenth of the above distance. With this in mind, the committee had to decide whether the storage magazines at Priddy's Hard constituted a danger to the dockyard. Three questions led to their conclusion that it did:
1. What were the probabilities of an ignition taking place?
2. If an ignition of cordite took place, would it develop into an explosion?
3. If either or both the existing magazines exploded, to what extent would the dockyard and shipping suffer?
Although the committee's terms of reference were mainly concerned with the final point, the first was also very important. With regard to point one, although the precautions taken against ordinary magazine risks appeared to be thoroughly complete, there were certain eventualities (which included, though never mentioned, the tendency of AP shells to spontaneously explode) that could not be provided for by any known methods, in addition to the risk from the shell-filling rooms in the laboratory, about 250 yards away. Even though only 200 lbs of explosive were allowed to be present in each, the shell rooms were more dangerous than the cartridge making buildings in which 1,000 lbs could be stored, since the distance of 250 yards, though quite sufficient to prevent a communicated explosion, was insufficient to entirely eliminate the possibility of a piece of a large shell finding its way through the roof of the cordite magazine. E Magazine was bombproof, but some risks could never be prevented:
• Lightning – A good system of conductors could greatly diminish this risk, but even when protected by the most modern method, lightning had blown up buildings containing explosives.
• Spontaneous decomposition of inferior or defective nitro-compound – This risk could be greatly minimised by frequent examinations and the non-admission of damaged explosive, but could not be entirely disregarded.
• Wilful Act - either of a lunatic (as had happened as recently as 1900 at Brean Down Fort, part of the Severn Defences, where a demented sentry exploded a magazine by firing a rifle into it), or of an enemy in time of war.
With regard to the liability of ignited cordite to explode, extensive experiments had been carried out with quantities of cordite amounting to as much as 2,500 lbs in bulk. The general result of these experiments did appear to indicate that when ignited it did not explode unless strongly confined (as in the chamber of a gun) but it was questionable whether the mere ignition of a quantity so great as was contained in the Priddy's Hard Magazine would not generate sufficient heat and pressure to develop an explosion. With guncotton, dynamite, picric acid and even saltpetre, it had been shown that the question of ignition developing into explosion was simply dependent on the quantity. Moreover, on one occasion when a quantity of small-arm cordite not exceeding 1,600 lbs had been packed at a very high density in R cylinders, a very violent explosion resulted. Experts disagreed on the manner of such an explosion, whether it was a true detonation or merely very rapid combustion such as takes place inside a gun, but the fact remained that the crater formed was as large as would have been made by an equal charge of blasting gelatine. Furthermore, there was no certainty that cordite would always be the Service propellant, and calculations based on cordite only might have no relevance in the future. Also, in addition to the cordite magazine, E Magazine had to be reckoned with, and any ignition there would undoubtedly cause an explosion. However, the gradual but continual substitution of cordite for gunpowder would enable the Admiralty before long to dispense with any considerable storage of powder. In short, it was not possible, even by the most elaborate precautions, to entirely eliminate the chances of an ignition taking place in either of these magazines; that if such ignition were to take place it was highly probable that, even if cordite were the only explosive involved, it would develop into an explosion; and that in the event of an explosion the buildings in the dockyard would either be destroyed or so seriously shaken as to disable the machinery they contained. COL 20/5, ADM 256/40

[6] COL 18/2, ADM 1/7961, T 1/11188/3579

[7] The Chatham Magazine Committee decided that a standard gauge line from Chattenden to Sharnal Street might be dispensed with, transfer arrangements between the two gauges being made instead at Sharnal Street. A public enquiry was held on the proposed Teapot Hard line, and in September it was decided that no further steps be taken, but the line between Chattenden and Sharnal Street was to be proceeded with at a later date. However, by December things looked different again. Land was required for a tramway running to a proposed torpedo range by Teapot Hard (a canal in partly reclaimed land as at Horsea Island), a plan to be finally sanctioned in February 1905. Teapot Hard was also restored to the agenda by the decision, in 1903, to provide a laboratory for cartridge filling at Lodge Hill and another at Teapot Hard for shell filling, in order to avoid sending shell from there to Lodge Hill for filling and return to the jetty. An entrance at the east gate was also necessary and shifting and searching rooms were required.

[8] T 1/10565B/22914, ADM 1/7549, COL 18/2, T 1/10764B/1497

[9] COL 18/2

[10] COL 18/2, ADM 151/79, SUPP 5/151

[11] T 1/10565B/22914, ADM 256/41, ADM 151/77, ADM 151/78

[12] ADM 256/44, COL 18/1; MOD(N) Library, Whitehall, *Office Memoranda*; GO/7; the cartridges sent from Lodge Hill were:
• 2,000 x 13.5-in
• 3,500 x 12-in
• 9,200 x 6-in
• 10,000 x 12-pdr

Bull Point sent the following cartridges:
- 500 x 12-in
- 14,000 x 6-in
- 5,000 x 6-in QF
- 15,000 x 6-pdr

13 ADM 116/1025, GO/3, COL/20

14 Initially the scheme for Bedenham comprised five magazines, a railway pier, and subsidiary buildings, the provisional estimate being £67,000. The design – and the site – allowed for great expansion in the future at comparatively small expense. This had not been provided for in the estimate of £1,158,048 for magazines under the Naval Works Act of 1905, and the Admiralty asked that the regular Navy Estimates provide for the costs. The Treasury did not agree to this.
ADM 116/1025, GO/3, COL/20;

The cordite that required storage was for:

	Tons
Ready supply of filled cartridges for replacement of ships in Commission	200
Ready supply of filled cartridges for Gunnery School	50
Filled cartridges requiring examination or repair at Priddy's Hard	100
Filled cartridges for Ships building and repairing	150
Loose cordite for filling cartridges	100
First replenishment of the fleet on outbreak of war	300
Second replenishment of the fleet	300
TOTAL	1200

The only available depot for the remaining cordite in the Portsmouth District was Marchwood, and it was proposed that filled cartridges should be stored there for the following purposes: 550 tons for Reserves for Effective Ships other than those required for first and second replenishments of the fleet on outbreak of war; 70 tons for Merchant Cruiser outfits; 150 tons for Special Service Vessels. In addition, it would hold surplus cartridges not likely to be required for immediate issue, the quantities of which would be unpredictable. Despite the provision of £6,000 in the 1905 Works Loan, mostly for an anti-climb fence and improvements to the pier, the facilities for the rapid issue of ammunition at Marchwood were still of a very inferior nature and it was not thought that more than 70 tons of cordite could be embarked in lighters in 24 hours in case of a national emergency. Because of its proximity to Southampton, the committee did not think it politic to undertake any large alterations at Marchwood to transform it into a shipping centre, or to increase the amount of ammunition stored there.
ADM 256/41, COL 18/1, COL 18/2, T 1/11188/3579, PTM/3674, PTM/3677; MOD(N) Library, Whitehall, *Important Questions dealt with by the Director of Naval Ordnance*, 1912; PTM/3639

15 In 1903 it was ordered that all 6- and 3-pounder QF cases made before 1895 be scrapped. Some batches of ammunition gave more concern than others, and in December 1904 all 4.7-inch QF made by Kynoch were withdrawn. By the summer of 1908 there was a surplus of 6-inch and 4.7-inch lyddite shells, and all those pre-1898 were taken out of service, to be boiled out and weighted with salt for use as practice shells. After March 1911, all 6- and 3-pounder QF dating from 1898 and earlier was converted to practice ammunition, throwing an additional load on the depots. Woolwich was to convert 59,748 rounds, Priddy's Hard 16,849, Bull Point 11,320 and Upnor 16,118.
GO/1, GO/4, GO/6, ADM 116/1370; March 28, 1905, *Account of Naval Works Acts*

16 8369 Parliamentary Paper, March 28, 1905, *Account of Naval Works Acts*; ADM 179/28

17 At Bull Point, the old Filled Shell Store held:

BL 13.5-in	440
12-in	1,500
9.2-in	2,300
7.5-in	2,800
6-in	9,000
QF 4.7-in	4,600
BL & QF 4-in	6,900
TOTAL	27,540

The new Filled Shell Store held:

BL 13.5-in	600
12-in	5,400
9.2-in	800
7.5-in	600
6-in	27,540
QF 4.7-in	7,600
BL & QF 4-in	24,000

12-pdr	77,200
TOTAL	143,740

The Fuze Store held 6,650 various fuzes, 202,500 electric tubes and 75,200 percussion tubes; the Wet Guncotton Store held 2,800 charges of 16 1/4 lb, and 480 torpedo warheads.

Chapter 9

1 Brigadier-General Sir James Edmonds, *Official History of the Great War: Military Operations*, vol. 1, 3rd ed, 1933: pp. 6–7, 453

2 *History of the Ministry of Munitions*, 12 vols, HMSO, London, 1920–1924

3 For the development of explosives and the building types developed for their manufacture, see W. D. Cocroft, *Dangerous Energy*, London, 2000. The wartime depots in France are described in: *The Work of the Royal Engineers in the European War, 1914–1919*; *Work under the Director of Works (France)*, Chatham, 1924; and Major-General A. Forbes, *A History of the Army Ordnance Services*, vol. III, London, 1929.

4 Information on the transport arrangements is in: RM 15, MUN 4/4977; E. A. Pratt, *British Railways and the Great War*, 2 vols, London, 1921; J. A. B. Hamilton, *Britain's Railways in World War 1*, London, 1967; A. Earnshaw, *Britain's Railways at War*, Penryn, 1995; C. F. Dendy Marshall, *A History of the Southern Railway*, London, 1936

5 T 1/11519, SD1

6 ADM 186/174, TH 29, ADM 137/4052, ADM 1/22864, 038053, 038092, 038159, 038186, 038258, ADM 137/1889

7 PTM/1841, PTM 1844, RM3, *Handbook on Ammunition*, 1915

8 RM3, PTM/2927, PTM/3016, PTM/3018, PTM/3019, PTM/3098, PTM/3099, PTM/3119,

9 ADM 179/31, ADM 179/36, ADM 179/38

10 ADM 179/38

11 The new buildings at Priddy's Hard were to be:
- New Tinsmiths' Shop
- Carpenters' Shop, to be provided by reappropriating an Empty Case Store and Empty Package Store adjoining
- Painters' Shop for use in conjunction with these
- New Empty Package Store to replace above
- Extension of Latrine and a Timber Store

The Priddy's Hard work was estimated at £10,680, the gunwharf work at £18,240; the time scale was:

Tinsmiths' & Painters' Shops	£5,075	6 months
Carpenters' Shop conversion	£3,515	3 months
New Empty Package Store	£1,690	3 months
Latrine & Timber Store	£400	3 months

RM3, PTM/3270

12 RM3, T1/12533/16220, MP/66, PTM/2476

13 There were roughly three categories of emergency magazine, the first two being improvisations: below ground, in quarries, salt mines or caves; brick kilns (the majority); and a few special magazines built on peace lines. Extreme pressure of accommodation led to the building of purpose-built magazines during 1918. On July 18, 1917, the following accommodation was available at propellant magazines (MUN 7/45).

Magazine		in tons	
	Normal capacity working	Approved maximum	Nominal maximum capacity
Crowhurst	1,000	800	1,155
Derby	1,100	850	1,200
Edwalton	1,200	1,000	1,400
Exeter	750	600	1,000
Glenfield	1,700	1,400	1,750
Gloucester	3,300	2,200	4,680
Hamworthy	900	750	1,000
Liverpool (Herculaneum)	To be abandoned		
Longtown	2,300	1,800	5,200
Extra accommodation required	5,000	4,000	6,000
Madeley	1,400	1,120	1,650
Measham (Coronet)	1,400	1,000	1,120
(Red Bank)	800	1,650	1,000
Middleton	1,800	1,440	2,250
Pinhoe	500	400	525
Reigate (Caves)	1,800	1,440	2,500
Rishton	800	640	1,000
Shortwood	2,500	2,000	2,960
Shutfield	900	720	1,200

Skipton	4,000	3,200	5,250
Southwater	1,100	880	1,150
Trafford Park	1,500	1,200	1,750
Warnham	1,500	1,200	1,800
Ruabon	2,500	2,000	2,750
Eye Green	2,500	2,000	3,000
Dogsthorpe	1,100	880	1,200
Coalport	2,250	1,800	2,500
High Brooms	2,250	1,800	2,500
Milburgh	1,750	1,400	1,300
Moira	2,500	2,000	2,000
Pant	1,900	1,500	2,200
Heather	2,000	1,600	2,500
Binfield	1,150	1,000	1,350
Rowlands Castle	2,250	2,000	2,560
Verwood	1,000	900	1,200
Totals	60,600	48,440	72,980

Military Magazines

Portsmouth	1,000	800	1,000
Weymouth	200	160	200
Portland	300	240	300
Devonport	60	60	60
Totals	1,560	1,260	1,560

Accommodation at TNT Magazines

	Normal capacity working	Approved maximum	Nominal maximum capacity
Corsham (Quarry)	2,500	2,000	3,233
Dudley	650	520	655
Godstone	1,200	960	1,650
Northwich (Pool Mine)	2,500	2,000	3,000
Peterborough	2,500	2,000	3,000
Pingle	900	720	950
Rhos	1,000	800	1,030
Wrexham	800	640	1,100
Wheatsheaf	1,800	1,440	2,500
Whittlesea	1,100	880	1,400
Baynards	1,200	960	1,200
Hicks	1,750	1,400	2,000
Warboys	1,120	900	1,346
Total short tons	19,020	15,220	25,379

Accommodation at miscellaneous magazines

Gunpowder

Barking	450	360	450
Woods Hulks	400	320	401
Gloucester	1,700	1,200	
Total	2,051		

Picric Acid

Westbury	550	440	550
Northwich (Crystal Mine)	2,000	3,416	
Corsham (Quarry)		400	
Holwell	600	500	760
Total	5,126		

Sabulite

Thurmaston	850	680	848

Composition Exploding

Buttington	220	200	220

Amatol, Thermite, etc.

Fletton	2,000	1,600	2,000

Phenol

High Carr	1,400	1,020	1,400

Ammonal, etc.

Northwich (Fletcher Mine)	2,000	5,000	

Perchlorate of Ammonia, etc.

Monk & Newells	1,300	1,040	1,800

[14] MUN 7/45, MUN 4/6294, MUN 7/46, MUN 7/43; extensive information on the work of Pickett et Fils is in: MUN 4/7003

Chapter 10

[1] For notes on the Admiralty Cordite Factory see W. D. Cocroft, *Dangerous Energy*, London, 2000

[2] ADM 1/22864, T 161/285; for Holton Heath, see M. R. Bowditch and L. Hayward, *A Pictorial Record of the Royal Naval Cordite Factory, Holton Heath*, Wareham, 1996; Cocroft, *op. cit.*; for the Ten Year Rule, see N. H. Gibbs, *Grand Strategy*, vol. 1, *Rearmament Policy*, London, 1976

[3] DSIR 4/2329

[4] The depletion was in the order of: 80 per cent for 4-inch HE for HA guns; 60 per cent for 15-inch; 22 per cent for 4.7-inch.

[5] T 161/1073, T 161/285; For Bridgeman, see S. Roskill, *Naval Policy between the Wars*, vol. 1, London, 1968, pp. 35–36

[6] T 161/778; S. Roskill, *Naval Policy between the Wars*, vol. 2, London, 1976, *passim*; T 161/1073

[7] The cost of accommodation at Dean Hill would be £70–£83 per ton, while the War Office and Air Ministry figures for converting quarries were £15–£25 per ton.

[8] T 161/1073, DSIR 4/2329, DSIR 4/2330, DSIR 4/2331

[9] CAB 24/276; Duff Cooper, *Old Men Forget*, London, 1953, p.215; T 161/1073

[10] T 161/1073

[11] On July 18, 1940, the future of Trecwn was decided. The depot was to be completed with 18 double magazines. The available storage expected by June 1941 was as follows:

Underground

	Number of magazines	Tons of ammunition
Ernesettle	4 (old type)	1,500
Crombie	22	13,200
Trecwn	52	31,200
Dean Hill	30	18,000
Milford Haven	7	4,500
Colwall Tunnel		6,000
Hawthorns Tunnel		2,000

Pre-war above ground magazines, operating under reduced wartime limits.

	Tons of ammunition
Chatham District	11,000
Portsmouth District	22,000
Plymouth District	4,000
Dutch Barges (Plymouth)	5,000
Copperas Wood	800
Crombie & Bandeath	18,000

Other magazines

	Tons of ammunition
Dolphinton	13,000
Pickwick Quarry	10,000
Goblins Quarry	5,000
Broughton Moor	45,000
Hulks	16,000
Ernesettle (above ground)	300
Trecwn (above ground)	3,400
Milford Haven (above ground)	400

It was projected that by June 1941, 274,000 tons would have to be accommodated, and only room for 240,000 tons would be available. T 161/1073

[12] N. J. McCamley, *Secret Underground Cities*, Barnsley, 1998; Brigadier A. H. Fernyhough, *History of the Royal Army Ordnance Corps, 1920–1945*, n.d., n.p.

[13] T 161/1073, COL 20; P. Clark, *The Chichester and Midhurst Railway*, Sheffield, 1979; W. Smith and K. Beddoes, *The Cleobury Mortimer and Ditton Priors Light Railway*, Oxford, 1980; ADM 1/28109; N. J. McCamley, *op.cit.*; ADM 1/28299

[14] COL 20, HO 198/131; for Fauld and Llanberis see AIR 2/6966, AIR 2/9162, AIR 17/14, AIR 19/523, MFQ 1003, MFQ 1004

[15] PHS 604H, Report on Operation Overlord by C-in-C Portsmouth, 1 August 1944; Explosion! Archive, Report on Operation Overlord by (8d) G. Algar Day, 14 July 1944; Martin Doughty (ed), *Hampshire and D-Day*, Hampshire Books, 1994

Glossary

Adams revolver A British revolver, one of many which followed the US made Colt, the chambers were originally muzzle-loaded; the weapon was converted to breech-loading in 1868 for naval use.

Amatol An intimate mixture of ammonium nitrate and trotyl (q.v.); used as a filling for shells and mines.

AP shell Armour piercing shell.

Armstrong gun Gun designed by Sir William Armstrong, usually referring to his rifled breechloader, which entered service in 1861 and had a short and unsuccessful career after promising much.

Armoury Building where small arms, edged weapons and their accoutrements are kept.

Arsenal (as opposed to magazine) Factory where all types of ordnance are made on a large scale and stored.

Artificers Skilled workmen employed on the maintenance and modification of ordnance.

Ball cartridge Cartridge with bullet (which was originally ball-shaped), as opposed to Blank cartridge (q.v.).

Bastion A projection from a fortification which enables flanking fire to be given, usually four-sided.

Black powder A very rapidly burning form of gunpowder. The term is often used generically for all gunpowder used as a propellant giving off clouds of smoke when fired, as opposed to smokeless powder.

Blank cartridge Cartridge without bullet, used for saluting, practice etc.

Blockships Sailing warships converted to steam, originally intended for harbour defence, but successfully operated in the Baltic during the Russian War.

Boiler House These were required to heat all the new Shell Filling Establishments with a circuit of hot water pipes.

Breech-loading (BL) guns Guns loaded at the breech, which was sealed by various gas-tight mechanisms.

Bursters Gunpowder charges intended to explode shells, contained in paper or linen bags. Obsolete by the end of the 19th century.

Camber A small dock, used for loading and unloading stores.

Caoutchouc Naturally produced Indiarubber.

Caponiers Parts of a fortification intended to provide flanking fire along a ditch.

Catenary vault Vault constructed to the profile formed by a rope hanging freely between two points at the same level

Collarmaker's Shop Workshop where horse collars and other forms of harness and tack were made and repaired - in the days before the internal combustion engine as essential as a garage is today.

Cocoa powder Form of gunpowder that burns more slowly and evenly than black powder, giving better propulsion.

Common shell For use against unarmoured ships and for bombarding.

Cooperage Workshop where wooden barrels are made and repaired.

Cordite Propellant based on a mixture of nitrocellulose and nitroglycerine, with the addition of a mineral jelly stabiliser, usually manufactured in the form of sticks or cords. Early cordite was found to be highly corrosive, and was replaced by Cordite MD with a much lower proportion of nitroglycerine, which was successful in increasing the life of barrels. The navy adopted Cordite SC (after the stabiliser, solventless carbamite), which was quicker to make and had a longer shelf-life. Cordite MC differed only in the nature of the stabiliser; Cordite RDB was introduced during the First World War as a result of a shortage of acetone, and used nitrocellulose containing a lower proportion of nitrogen. Cordite W, introduced after that war, resembled Cordite MD but used carbamite as the stabiliser; it materially reduced flash and smoke.

Cordite magazines These buildings needed to be temperature controlled, and were connected to the hot water pipe circuits.

Corticene A floor covering made of a mixture of ground cork and indiarubber, introduced around 1880 as a floor covering in danger buildings (q.v.) to replace animal hides.

CRE/CRA Commanding Royal Engineer/Commanding Royal Artillery [officer].

Cylinder charcoal Charcoal that has been distilled in iron cylinders, producing a superior charcoal for gunpowder manufacture.

Danger building Building in which potentially hazardous operations are carried out, subject to special regulations.

Depot (as opposed to yard or store) A headquarters establishment, where stores are held and distributed.

Densimeter An instrument used at Waltham Abbey in the later part of the 19th century for measuring the density of gunpowder.

Dusting House Building housing equipment to remove dust from gunpowder during its manufacture or restoration.

Empty Case Stores Shells, and many other articles, were held packed individually in wooden boxes. As each ship had a regulation outfit of shells assigned to it, together with those held in reserve, a large space was required to house the store of empty cases, which needed to be maintained.

éprouvette Device for proving the strength of gunpowder by using the gases formed in its explosion to raise a weight.

Examining Rooms (before 1875 officially known as Shifting Houses); these were for unheading barrels of powder and examining the contents.

E.X.E. powder Extra Experimental powder was introduced in 1887 to supersede previous powders for RML guns, and for 6-inch BL guns.

Expense Magazine for Shell Filling Rooms Barrels of powder sufficient for one day's work were stored here for immediate use.

Explosive shell Originally hollow metal spheres filled with gunpowder, the destructive effect being caused by the shell fragments after exploding.

Filled Shell Stores (after the Admiralty takeover) These were the largest buildings on ordnance yard sites, built from 1896.

Flannel cartridge Gunpowder used as a propellant was kept for immediate use in made-up cartridges; from the late 18th century flannel (which was entirely consumed on firing) was used to form the container instead of paper or parchment, which tended to leave ash residue.

Flashing Means of testing the degree of mixing of gunpowder by igniting a very small quantity on a plate, to see the residue.

Floating magazines (include working and deposit) Obsolete ships, dismasted and permanently moored, housing powder as in a land magazine.

Friction tube Tubes filled with detonating composition which ignites when subjected to friction by pulling a lanyard, used to fire guns. In the 19th century the army used copper tubes, the navy quills, to prevent injury to sailors' bare feet when the tubes were blown out of the gun on firing.

Fuze and Tube Stores In the 1850's fuzes were still very simple, but an essential part of the shell; they were normally stored separately, together with the firing tubes and percussion caps used to fire the guns.

Gaine Initiator for high explosive shell, involving a chain of detonations, for example, gunpowder, fulminate and Composition Explosive, which last exploded the shell filling.

Guncotton An explosive chiefly used for demolitions, and also in torpedo warheads; when wet it is very safe: military guncotton contained about 17% water.

Guncotton magazines

Wet: No special precautions were required for this safe explosive.

Dry: These resembled miniature versions of Cordite magazines.

Hale's war rocket A stickless war rocket first used by the British Army in the Crimean campaign; possibly last used in Sierra Leone in 1899, but still on the inventory at the beginning of the First World War.

Hang fires Failure of the propellant to detonate.

HE shells High explosive (i.e. producing a great disruptive effect) shells.

Laboratory Set of buildings and connecting paths in which all operations connected with the filling or emptying of shells or cartridges are carried out.

Laboratory Magazine Magazine which holds powder for filling shells in a Laboratory; usually held enough powder for one day's work.

Lighters Large open flat-bottomed boat, used in loading or unloading ships.

Lyddite High explosive shell filling made from picric acid; first used by British Army in the Boer War.

Magazine Building or buildings with connecting paths in which bulk powder and cordite and filled cannon cartridges are stored.

Martini-Henry rifle A falling-block action single-shot breech-loading rifle, in use by the British Army from 1874 until replaced by the Lee-Metford after 1891.

Matériel Military and naval hardware, from a ship to a bullet.

Millboard disk Protective wad formed from very thick paper.

Mine and Countermine Stores The majority of mines in use before 1905 were held by the Royal Engineers at their depots.

Mine Examining Rooms At Priddy's Hard and Upnor these are built as annexes to the Mine Stores.

Mixing House Building in gunpowder Factory, where the ingredients are weighed and mixed.

Moorsom fuzes Early type of shell fuze, operated by percussion, invented in 1850 and obsolete by 1867.

Naval Works Act Legislative measure by which the great expansion of naval shore facilities of the 1890s and early 1900s was financed.

Ordnance Plantation Plantation in which trees and shrubs useful for making gunstocks (e.g. walnut) or stabilising earth fortifications (e.g. quicksets) were grown.

Outfit the prescribed store of ammunition to be kept on a ship.

Palliser shell Shell with chilled cast point, used for attacking armour.

Paravane A torpedo-shaped float towed by a wire from a ship. Some had warheads to sink submarines, in others the cable was used to cut the cable of moored enemy mines to bring them to the surface to be sunk by rifle fire. The explosive paravane was not long in service and the buildings constructed to house and maintain them were soon put to other uses.

Pattern and Class Room Room in which instruction of ordnance staff was carried out. Approved 'sealed' patterns of matériel (q.v.) held for instructional purposes.

Pebble powder A type of gunpowder introduced in 1871, roughly cubical in form with rounded edges, and between ⅜ and ¾ inches across.

Pettman fuzes Type of percussion fuze adopted for naval use in 1862; performed very badly at the bombardment of Alexandria in 1882.

Picrates Salts formed by picric acid in combination with metals. Some are extremely sensitive and will cause the picric acid to detonate, lead picrate in particular; great care has to be taken if there is an extremely small amount of lead in any paints, metals or materials the picric acid is likely to come into contact with.

Picric acid A yellow crystalline solid used as a shell filling (q.v. lyddite) melted and poured into the shell, was very stable even at high temperatures, making shells filled with picric acid very suitable for tropical stations. A disadvantage was its propensity to form picrates.

Pitchmastic Bitumen based grit-free floor covering.

Portfires A brown paper tube, 16 inches long, filled with a combustible composition. When lit, it burned for 12 to 15 minutes, and was used for igniting purposes.

Powder Line Tramway reserved for the passage of gunpowder.

Powder mill Building housing millstones used for grinding freshly mixed powder moistened with distilled water to incorporate the ingredients thoroughly.

Powder pier Pier reserved for the loading and unloading of gunpowder.

Press House Building housing hydraulic press to compress powder that has been taken from the powder mill (q.v.) and broken down into small pieces.

Printing and model room Room in which labels for packaging are printed, also holding instructional models.

Priming tube See Friction tube.

Prismatic powder Gunpowder, each piece of which is moulded and pressed separately in a metal mould. The individual pieces were regular hexagonal prisms of varying dimensions. A piece of Prism2 powder, introduced in 1881, was about 2 inches high, just over 2⅕ inches in diameter, with an axial hole of rather more than ½ inch running through it, weighed just over half a pound.

Proof Houses Buildings used for testing gunpowder for quality and performance. (q.v. éprouvette, flashing).

Quick-firing (QF) guns Breech-loading guns of small calibre which fired fixed ammunition; i.e. the shot and cartridge case were in one piece, like a greatly enlarged rifle bullet. This enabled a rapid rate of fire to be maintained.

R cylinders A type of brass and gunmetal cylindrical powder case, in this instance used for containing one ½ or two ¼ cordite charges for the BL 12 inch Mark VIII gun.

Receipt & Issue magazines Also termed naval refitting magazines. These were intended to receive ammunition from ships coming in to refit or be paid off. Powder barrels that had been checked were held there for issue. The arrangements of Upnor and Tipner magazines, as a sequence of arches, meant that individual arches could be used for this purpose and a separate building was not required.

Redoubt Small self-contained fortification without bastions.

Restoving The process of restoring damaged gunpowder by drying it in rooms heated by hot water pipes, known as Stoving Houses.

RLG powder (Rifle Large Grain) A gunpowder of larger grain than previously made, introduced for use in the first RMLs (q.v.) Found unsuitable for calibres of 7 inches and upwards, was supplemented by P powder for that purpose.

RML Rifled muzzle loader. Constructed to ever-changing designs, these provided the bulk of the heavy weaponry of the army and navy from the supercession of the smooth-bore cannon until the mid-1880's.

Rolling stage A platform along which tumbrils of powder barrels were rolled. Note that the barrels themselves were never rolled. At Priddy's Hard it took the form of an earthen embankment running out 600 feet to low-water mark, for unloading vessels.

Royal Laboratory Established at Woolwich Arsenal in the late 17th century to supply fireworks for state ceremonials, by the late 18th century, under the Comptrollership of William Congreve, it became the centre for expertise on all matters to do with explosives.

Serge Serge was a woven twilled fabric, used as a cartridge envelope for the larger natures of guns, including all smooth-bore cannon.

Shalloon Shalloon was an entirely worsted fabric, used as an envelope for smaller cartridges, because of its thinner nature than serge.

Sheerlegs An A frame used for hoisting heavy weights, such as encountered in fitting out ships or lifting heavy guns.

Shell Emptying Rooms For emptying shells of their explosive charges prior to re-filling.

Shell Filling Rooms For filling shells with explosive.

Shell scraping Room For removing all markings from emptied shell prior to repainting.

Shifting Rooms Buildings where workers in Ordnance Depots changed from their civilian clothes into their specialist magazine clothing and shoes on arriving for work. The planning of these buildings became more elaborate than the old Shoe Rooms. Before 1875 the term was applied to Examining Rooms (q.v.).

Shoe Rooms These were the first spaces dedicated to changing into specialised magazine equipment. (q.v. Shifting Rooms).

Smoothbore (SB) A firearam or cannon without a rifled barrel, usually muzzle-loading.

Spithead mutiny One of the naval mutinies which occurred in 1797.

Store magazines These were solely intended for the bulk storage of gunpowder in the standard 100 lb barrels. Air vents were provided in the walls to prevent damp and all exposed metal surfaces were (or should have been) of copper. The classic British type was of two chambers with a massively thick bombproof vault, as opposed to the single chamber of the Vauban-type magazine (see page 14). The Keyham Point magazines, demolished in the early 1850's, were unique for their period in not being designed as bomb-proof (see pages 22–3); the next of this type (also demolished) was built in 1805 at Waltham Abbey. The Marchwood magazines followed this example, combined with the early use of traverses. The Upnor magazines took the form of a series of bombproof catenary arches.

Tailor's shop Building where flannel, serge or shalloon cartridges were sewn. The Master Tailor was responsible for examining and passing or condemning empty flannel cartridges.

Tetryl (or Composition Explosive – CE) An easily detonated nitro-compound, too sensitive for use as a shell filling, but very useful in building up an exploder system.

Thumbstalls When a muzzle-loading gun was being loaded the vent had to be closed up to prevent air being blown through it, and possibly reigniting any remaining materials; this was done by the gunner placing his thumb over it, and to protect his thumb he wore a leather thumbstall.

Time fuzes A device fitted to a shell to explode it after a predetermined time.

Toluol Obsolete name for Toluene, used in the manufacture of Trotyl (q.v.).

Transfer Sheds These marked the connection of the depots with the standard gauge railway network.

Traverse Barrier, usually of earth, to shield magazine or danger building in case of explosion and minimise the effect of blast.

Trotyl (TNT) A nitro-compound first used as a shell filling in Britain in 1914; very stable in storage, and requiring an initiator (such as Tetryl or CE, q.v.) to detonate it.

Trotyl Melting Rooms These were installed at the beginning of the First World War to deal with the new shell filling, which could be poured in a molten state into shells.

Trotyl and Shellite Shifting Rooms Shellite was a high explosive comprising a mixture of dinitrophenol and picric acid. Like Trotyl, it could be melted on a water bath. Special working costumes had to be provided, together with washing facilities, for all workers dealing with these substances.

Tumbril Four-wheeled cart, pushed by hand, used for the movement of powder barrels.

Unheading Room The barrels brought from the Expense Magazine were opened here before the powder was brought to the Shell Filling Rooms.

Vent In a muzzle-loading gun, a hole in the top of the gun connecting with the chamber, filled with powder and ignited to fire the gun.

Victualling Yard Major depots providing food and drink for the navy.

WD Vessels Vessels either owned or hired by the War Department for the carriage of ordnance materials.

Primary Sources

These are extremely rich and have been generated by a great range of bodies; not only obvious ones such as the three services and the Treasury that often struggled with them, but less likely candidates such as the Department of Scientific and Industrial Research all played their part. The work is largely based on these unpublished sources.

The National Archives
(formerly The Public Record Office)

ADM 1   Admiralty In-letters and Secretariat papers
ADM 7   Admiralty and Secretariat Miscellanea
ADM 116   Admiralty Cases
ADM 131   Correspondence of the Plymouth Station
ADM 137   Admiralty Historical Branch records
ADM 151   Correspondence of the Nore Station
ADM 160   Upnor Ordnance Depot records
ADM 179   Correspondence of the Portsmouth Station
ADM 189   Reports by Torpedo School
ADM 195   Photographs of Naval Works
ADM 214   Civil Engineer-in-Chief's papers
ADM 256   Naval Ordnance Department papers
AIR 2   Air Ministry Registered files
AIR 17   Maintenance Command files
AIR 19   Private Air Ministry office papers
CAB 24   Cabinet papers
CAB 37   Cabinet papers
DSIR 4   Building Materials Research Committee papers
LAB 59   Explosives Inspectorate Annual Reports
MUN 4   Records of the Central Registry of the Ministry of Munitions
MUN 7   Ministry of Munitions Files transferred to War Office
SUPP 5   Ordnance Establishments Records
SUPP 6   Ordnance Board Reports etc.
T 1   Treasury Board papers
T 5   Out-letters to Admiralty
T 161   Supply files

WO 32   Registered War Office files
WO 33   Confidential prints, etc.
WO 44   Ordnance Office In-letters
WO 45   Ordnance Office Reference Books
WO 46   Ordnance Office Out-letters
WO 47   Ordnance Office Minutes
WO 49   Ordnance Office Accounts
WO 54   Ordnance Office Registers
WO 55   Ordnance Office Miscellanea, including Engineer Papers
WO 78   Maps and plans

Maps and plans removed from documents
MPH   MPHH   MR   MFQ   MH
WORK 41   Maps and Plans

National Monuments Record (NMR)
PTM   Plans of buildings in the Portsmouth area

Hampshire Record Office (HRO)
The Priddy's Hard collection, 109M91, contains, among much else, the following pieces
CO   CH 26
COL 18, 20   GO 1, 3, 4, 6, 7
RM 3, 10, 15   SD 1
PH 34, 50, 67, 72, 79 (photographs)

Royal Engineers' Library
POR   Portsmouth Letter Books (In and Out)
PLY   Plymouth Letter Books (In and Out)
CHA   Chatham Letter Books (In and Out)
A   Plans
AE   Plans

Wiltshire Record Office
Herbert of Lea Papers

Devonport Management Limited
Fiches beginning 038

Select Bibliography

Compared with other aspects of military/industrial history, ordnance storage has attracted little attention in the past, and, as seen below, very few books have been specifically devoted to the subject.

Books and pamphlets

[Anonymous] *Instructions for the Management of Harvey's Sea Torpedo* (London, 1871)

[Anonymous] Ministry of Munitions, *Health of the Munition Worker* (London, 1917)

[Anonymous] *Technical History of the War. TH 29 – Ammunition for Naval Guns* (London, 1919)

[Anonymous] *The Work of the Royal Engineers in the European War, 1914-1919. Work under the Director of Works (France)* (Chatham, 1924)

Bacon, Admiral Sir R. H., *Lord Fisher, Admiral of the Fleet* 2 vols (London, 1929)

Baker, H. A., *Woolwich and the Heavy RML's* (Worthing, 1989)

Baker Brown, Lieut. Col. W., *History of Submarine Mining in the British Army* (Chatham, 1910)

Benson, A. C. and Brett, R. B., Viscount Esher, eds, *The Letters of Queen Victoria*, vol. 1 (London, 1907)

Bonnici, J. and Cassar, M., *The Malta Grand Harbour and its Dockyard* (Malta, 1994)

Bowditch, M. R. and Hayward, L., *A Pictorial Record of the Royal Naval Cordite Factory, Holton Heath* (Wareham, 1996)

Bowdler, R, *Former Board of Ordnance Gunpowder Magazines, Magazine Lane, Marchwood, Hampshire*, English Heritage Report (London, 1997)

Browne, Captain C. Orde, 'Gunnery' in *Brassey's Naval Annual* (Portsmouth, 1887)

Burkhalter, P., *Devonport Dockyard Railway* (Truro, 1996)

Chesneau & Kolesnik, eds, *Conway's All the World's Fighting Ships, 1860–1905* (London, 1979)

Clark, P., *The Chichester and Midhurst Railway* (Sheffield, 1979)

Coad, J. G., *Historic Architecture of the Royal Navy, an Introduction* (London, 1983)

Coad, J. G., *The Royal Dockyards, 1690–1850* (Aldershot, 1989)

Cocroft, W. D., *Dangerous Energy* (London, 2000)

Congreve, Sir William, *A Statement of Facts, relative to the savings which have arisen from manufacturing Gunpowder at the Royal Powder Mills; and of the Improvements which have been made in its strength & durability since the year 1783* (London, 1811)

Cooper, D., Viscount Norwich, *Old Men Forget* (London, 1953)

Marshall, C. F. Dendy, *A History of the Southern Railway* (London, 1936)

Dobinson, C., *AA Command* (London, 2001)

Douglas, General Sir Howard, *A Treatise on Naval Gunnery*, 4th ed (London, 1855)

Douet, J., *British Barracks, 1600–1914* (London, 1998)

Eardley-Wilmot, Rear-Admiral Sir Sydney, *An Admiral's Memories. Sixty-five years afloat and ashore* (London, n.d. [1927])

Earnshaw, A., *Britain's Railways at War* (Penryn, 1995)

Evans, D., *Building the Steam Navy* (London, 2004)

Fernyhough, A.H., *History of the Royal Army Ordnance Corps, 1920–1945* (n.p., n.d.)

Forbes, A., Major-General, *A History of the Army Ordnance Services*, 3 vols (London, 1929)

Garbett, H., Captain RN, *Naval Gunnery* (London, 1897)

Gibbs, N. H., *Grand Strategy*, vol. 1, *Rearmament Policy* (London, 1976)

Gordon, A. C. H., first Baron Stanmore, *Sidney Herbert, Lord Herbert of Lea, A Memoir*, 2 vols (London, 1906)

Hamilton, J. A. B., *Britain's Railways in World War 1* (London, 1967)

Hogg, O. F. G., *The Royal Arsenal*, 2 vols (Oxford, 1963)

Lake, J., *Historic Farm Buildings* (London, 1989)

Lavery, B., *The Arming and Fitting of English Ships of War, 1600–1815* (London, 1987)

Lochée, L., *Elements of Fortification* (London, 1780)

Longridge, J. A., *Is England to be caught napping?* (London, 1885)

MacIvor, I., *The Fortifications of Berwick-upon-Tweed* (London, 1972)

Mackay, R., *Fisher of Kilverstone* (Oxford, 1973)

Magrath, P. A., *Fort Cumberland, 1747–1850, Key to an Island's Defence* (Portsmouth, 1992)

Majendie, Captain V. and Boxer, Colonel E., *Descriptive Plates to Ammunition* (London, plates dated between 1863 and 1870)

McCamley, N. J., *Secret Underground Cities* (Barnsley, 1998)

Menuge, A. and Williams, A., *The Royal Ordnance Store, Southtown and Gorleston, Great Yarmouth, Norfolk*, RCHME (Cambridge, 1999)

Paget-Tomlinson, E., *The Illustrated History of Canal & River Navigations* (Sheffield, 1994)

Parkes, O., *British Battleships* (London, 1966)

Pasley, Lieut. Colonel C. W., *Course of Military Instruction, originally composed for the use of the Royal Engineer Department*. vol.3 (London, 1817)

Petrie, Sir Charles, *The Life and Letters of the Right Honourable Sir Austen Chamberlain*, 2 vols (London, 1939)

Porter, Major General W, *History of the Royal Corps of Engineers*, 2 vols (London, 1889)

Pratt, E. A., *British Railways and the Great War*, 2 vols (London, 1921)

Rees, A., *The Cyclopaedia; or Universal Dictionary of Arts, Sciences and Literature* (London, 1811)

Rigold, S. E., *Yarmouth Castle* (London, 1978)

Roper, M., *The Records of the War Office and related Departments* (London, 1998)

Roskill, S., *Naval Policy between the Wars*, vol. 1 (London, 1968)

Salter, A. R., *The protection of Chatham Dockyard through the ages* (Gillingham, 1983)

Saunders, A. D., *Upnor Castle* (London, 1967)

Scoffern, J., *Projectile Weapons of War*, 3rd ed. (London, 1858)

Semark, H. W., *The Royal Naval Armament Depots of Priddy's Hard, Elson, Frater and Bedenham* (Winchester, 1997)

Sigwart, E. E., *Royal Fleet Auxiliary* (London 1969)

Sleeman, C., *Torpedoes and Torpedo Warfare*, 2nd ed. (Portsmouth, 1889)

Smith, W. and Beddoes, K., *The Cleobury Mortimer and Ditton Priors Light Railway* (Oxford, 1980)

Spiers, E. M., *The Late Victorian Army, 1868–1902* (Manchester, 1992)

Sweetman, J., *War and Administration* (Edinburgh, 1984)

Tennent, Sir J. Emerson, *The Story of the Guns* (London, 1864)

Warlow, Lt. Cdr. B., *Shore Establishments of the Royal Navy* (Liskeard, 1992)

West, J., *Gunpowder, Government and War in the Mid-Eighteenth Century* (Woodbridge, 1991)

Williams, G. H., *The Western Defences of Portsmouth Harbour, 1400–1800* (Portsmouth, 1979)

Winter, F. H., *The First Golden Age of Rocketry* (Washington, 1990)

Wyatt, H. F. and Horton-Smith, L. G. H., *The Passing of the Great Fleet* (London, 1909)

Official Manuals

Handbook of the Manufacture and Proof of Gunpowder (London, 1870)

Treatise on Ammunition, 4th ed. (London, 1887)

Treatise on Ammunition, 5th ed. (London, 1892)

Treatise on Ammunition, 7th ed. (London, 1902)

Treatise on Ammunition, 10th ed. (London, 1915)

Treatise on Service Explosives (London, 1900)

Treatise on Service Explosives (London, 1907)

Treatise on Military Carriages, 6th ed. (London, 1902)

Text Book of Explosives used in the Services (London, 1938)

Services Textbook of Explosives (London, 1954)

Notes on Naval Guns (London, 1875)

Handbook for the 12.5" 38 ton RML (London, 1876)

Manual of Gunnery for Her Majesty's Fleet (London, 1873)

Manual of Gunnery for Her Majesty's Fleet (London, 1880)

Manual of Gunnery for Her Majesty's Fleet (London, 1892)

Notes on Naval Guns and Torpedoes (London, 1900)

Manual of Submarine Mining, vol.1 (plates), (n.p. but London, 1901 ed.)

Defensively Equipped Merchant Ships Pocket Book, (n.p. but London, 1942)

Official Reports

(where not found as enclosures in primary sources)

Report of the Commissioners appointed to consider the Defences of the United Kingdom..., London, 1860

Extracts from the Reports and Proceedings of the Ordnance Select Committee, V, 1867

Report on the Explosion of Gun-Cotton at Stowmarket on the 11th August 1871, 1872

Report of the Select Committee on Explosive Substances, 1874

Second Report of the Royal Commission appointed to inquire into the System under which Patterns of Warlike Stores are Adopted and the Stores Obtained and Passed for Her Majesty's Service, 1888

Report on the Circumstances attending an Explosion...during the emptying of some 3 pr. shells for Quick-firing Ammunition at Messrs. Kynoch & Co's...Ammunition Factory..., 1888

Report of the Committee to Inquire into the Purchase, Custody, and Accounts of Naval Warlike Stores, 1890

First Report of the Committee appointed to enquire into the Accident of the 13th December, 1893, at the Royal Gunpowder Factory, Waltham Abbey, 1894

Parliamentary Papers

Copy of Correspondence between the Treasury and the War Office respecting the Formation of the Department of Control, (June 30, 1868)

Copy of papers relating to the dismissal of Colonel Boxer from the Office of Superintendent of the Royal Laboratory, (February 18, 1870)

Statement of estimated cost & expenditure on Naval Works, (March 1900)

Account of Naval Works Acts, (March 28, 1905)

Articles

Armstrong, Sir William, contribution to 'The National Defences' in *Proceedings of the Institution of Civil Engineers*, vol. 20, 1861

Baylay, Lieut,Col. F. G., 'Modern Types of Guns' in *Professional Papers of the Corps of Royal Engineers*, 1883

Brown, D. K., 'The First Steam Battleships' in *Mariner's Mirror*, vol.63, 1977

Browne, Captain C. Orde, 'Our Rifled Projectiles and Fuzes' in *Minutes of Proceedings of the Royal Artillery Institute*, vol.VII, 1871

Encyclopaedia Britannica, 9th ed., 1880, article 'Gunnery'

Encyclopaedia Britannica, 12th ed., 1922 article 'Ammunition'

Evans, D. C., 'The Duke of Richmond, James Glenie, Maker, and the Fortifications Bill' in *Fort*, XVI, 1988

Evans, D. C., 'The Redoubts on Maker Heights, Cornwall' in *The Georgian Group Journal*, IX, 1999

Guillery, P. and P. Pattison, 'The Powder Magazines at Purfleet' in *The Georgian Group Journal*, VI, 1996

Savage, Major J. W., 'Diagrams of Service Ordnance etc.' in *Professional Papers of the Corps of Royal Engineers*, vol.XVI, 1890

Smith, Captain F., 'The Examination and Proof of Gunpowder as carried out at the Royal Gunpowder Factory, Waltham Abbey' in *Minutes of Proceedings of the Royal Artillery Institution*, vol.VII, 1871

Stoney, Captain F. S., 'A Brief Historical Sketch of our Rifled Ordnance, from 1858 to 1868' and 'The Construction of our Heavy Guns' in *Minutes of Proceedings of the Royal Artillery Institution*, VI, 1870

Thomas, L., 'The Action of Fired Gunpowder in Guns' in *The Illustrated Naval and Military Magazine*, vol.1, 1884

Index